Junior Cycle Maths

Text & Tests

First Year Maths

1

Paul Cooke • O.D. Morris • Deborah Crean

 The Celtic Press

First Published in April 2018 by
The Celtic Press
Ground Floor – Block B
Liffey Valley Office Campus
Dublin 22

This reprint April 2021

ISBN: 978-0-7144-2597-9

Page 88 234 10
Too page 11

Contents

Preface

This book is designed to accommodate the changes in the Maths syllabus as laid out in the new Junior Cycle specification.

It provides continuity with the learning methods that students experienced in Sixth Class of primary school and is suitable for the full range of ability in First Year. It encourages not only the development of the students' mathematical *knowledge* and *skills* but also the *understanding* needed to progress their learning of mathematics.

The book introduces the student to the full range of topics in the syllabus and is the first of two books that will comprehensively cover the Ordinary Level or the Higher Level course through the Junior Cycle. This approach avoids the difficulties associated with taking any topic all the way to examination standard in First Year.

An excellent range of imaginatively written and probing questions are provided on each topic, which help students to understand the mathematical concepts and to develop their problem-solving skills. A sufficient number of questions of varying degrees of difficulty have been provided to satisfy the needs of every First Year student. Importantly, students are introduced to new topics in a way that is appropriate for mixed-ability classes.

In particular, this new edition of *Text and Tests 1* addresses the challenges of the new syllabus by introducing **Investigations**, **Assignments**, **Problems** and **Reviews**. These elements are based on the content presented in each specific chapter and are intended to be used throughout each unit.

The Investigations and Assignments are designed to allow every student a chance to research and present (communicate) their individual findings. The Problems encourage students to explain and generalise results. The Reviews help students to evaluate their individual progress through the lens of the six elements of the Unifying Strand.

Book 2 (Ordinary Level) and Book 2 (Higher Level) will complete the specification and complement the work started in First Year.

The books encourage the Junior Cycle **Key Skills** of Being Numerate; Working with Others; Communicating; Being Creative; Managing Information and Thinking.

Paul Cooke
O. D. Morris
Deborah Crean

April 2018

Natural Numbers

In this chapter, you will learn to:

- identify **odd**, **even**, **consecutive** and **prime** natural numbers,
- use a **number line**,
- use **powers**, **squares** and **square** roots,
- order **ascending / descending** numbers,
- identify **composite** numbers,
- estimate by **rounding**,
- find **factors**, **multiples**, HCF and LCM,
- check **commutative**, **associative** and **distributive** properties of natural numbers,
- calculate by **estimation**.

Section 1.1 Natural numbers

The counting numbers 1, 2, 3, 4, 5, … are generally called **natural numbers**.

We use the capital letter **N** to represent these numbers.

Thus, N = 1, 2, 3, 4, 5, 6, …

These numbers go on and on …; there is no end number.

> N = 1, 2, 3, 4, 5, 6, …
> Zero is *not* a natural number.

Natural numbers can be divided into two groups, namely **even** numbers and **odd** numbers.

2, 4, 6, 8, 10, … are the **even** natural numbers because they can be divided by 2 with no remainder.

1, 3, 5, 7, 9, … are the **odd** natural numbers.

Tuesday, Wednesday and Thursday are **consecutive** days of the week.

Similarly 6, 7, 8, 9, … are consecutive natural numbers, while 2, 4, 6, 8, … are consecutive even natural numbers.

The Number Line

A very useful and simple way of depicting natural numbers is to place them at equal distances apart on a horizontal line as illustrated below:

The dots on the line represent the numbers 1, 2, 3, 4, …, while the arrow to the right indicates that the line continues on without ending.

Place value

The symbols 2, 3, 5, 8 etc, that we use to represent numbers, are called **numerals**.

In our number system we can write any number, large or small, using the ten numerals 0, 1, 2, 3, 4, 5, 6, 7, 8, 9.

The big advantage of the system is that the same numeral may have different values depending on the place it occupies in the number.

The **place-value diagram** below shows the numbers 368 and 26 427.

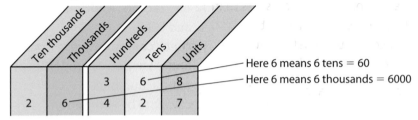

Here 6 means 6 tens = 60
Here 6 means 6 thousands = 6000

The numeral 6 has a different value in each of the numbers as shown above.

Example 1

Find the difference between the largest and smallest numbers that can be made from the digits 3, 7, 4, 9, if each is used once only in the number.

The largest number is 9743.
The smallest number is 3479.

The difference is

$$\begin{array}{r} 9\ 7\ 4\ 3 \\ -\ 3\ 4\ 7\ 9 \\ \hline 6\ 2\ 6\ 4 \end{array}$$

∴ the difference is 6264.

Ascending / Descending order

When numbers are arranged in order of increasing value, we say that they are in **ascending order**, e.g., 34, 423, 1142.

If numbers are placed in order of decreasing value, we say that they are in **descending order**, e.g., 4712, 631, 24, 5.

Example 2

Using all of the digits 3, 7, 2, write down six different 3-digit numbers in descending order.

732, 723, 372, 327, 273, 237.

Exercise 1.1

1. Say whether each of the following is true or false.
   (i) 3 is a natural number
   (ii) $4\frac{1}{2}$ is a natural number
   (iii) -2 is a natural number
   (iv) 101 is a natural number
   (v) The smallest natural number is 2.

2. List the numbers in each of the following:
   (i) the even natural numbers between 7 and 15
   (ii) the odd natural numbers less than 12
   (iii) the first four natural numbers
   (iv) four consecutive natural numbers beginning with 7
   (v) five consecutive odd natural numbers beginning with 5.

3. Describe in words each of the following arrays of numbers:
   (i) 1, 2, 3, 4, 5
   (ii) 1, 3, 5, 7, 9
   (iii) 2, 4, 6
   (iv) 6, 8, 10, 12
   (v) 9, 11, 13, 15, …
   (vi) 101, 102, 103, …

4. Write down the value of the red digit in each of these numbers:
   (i) 384
   (ii) 496
   (iii) 6249
   (iv) 4792
   (v) 1349

5. Write down the three numbers shown in the diagram below.
   Start at the top.

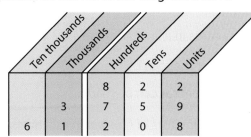

6. Write down
   (i) a four-digit number with a 4 in the thousands column.
   (ii) a two-digit number with a 3 in the tens column.
   (iii) a five-digit number with a 1 in the hundreds column.
   (iv) a three-digit number with a 9 in the units column.
   (v) a four-digit number with a 0 in the tens column.
   (vi) a five-digit number with a 4 in the hundreds column.
   (vii) a four-digit number with a 7 in every column except the tens column.
   (viii) a five-digit number with a 6 in the thousands column and the units column.

7. Using all the digits 4, 3, 1, 7, what is
   (i) the largest   (ii) the smallest   four-digit number that can be formed from them ?

8. What is the difference between the values of the two fours in the number 34746?

9. What is the sum of the values of the threes in the number 34353?

10. What is the difference between the largest and smallest four-digit numbers that can be formed using the digits 2, 9, 3, 5?

11. Write down each of these numbers:
    (i)   seven hundred and nine
    (ii) two thousand, three hundred and nine
    (iii) six thousand and four
    (iv) twenty thousand, four hundred and two
    (v) ninety thousand and ninety
    (vi) three hundred and two thousand and forty five
    (vii) one million and thirty thousand

12. Write these numbers in order, starting with the smallest:
    3297   2988   3079   3190   931   3098

13. Write the next car registration number for each of these:
    (i) 10 D 799   (ii) 11 KE 1019   (iii) 12 KY 7999

14. By placing all these cards in a line, 3 8 2 2 1 6 , write down

    (i) the largest number that can be made

    (ii) the smallest number that can be made.

15. Place each of the following lists of number in ascending order:
    (i) 604, 406, 46, 0, 64.
    (ii) 210, 85, 219, 26, 401, 79, 151.

16. Write down a list, in descending order, of the 5 largest numbers that can be formed using the digits 4, 1, 9, 2.

17. Place each of the following numbers in ascending order;
    1121, 2211, 2112, 1212, 1211, 1122.

Section 1.2 **Factors and primes**

Investigation:

There are 20 sweets in a jar.

(i) Can the sweets be shared equally between three people?

(ii) Write down all the numbers of people between whom the sweets can be shared equally.

How many do they each receive?

In the problem above, you were looking for the numbers that divide evenly into 20.

> A **Factor** divides evenly into a number with no remainder.

These numbers are 1, 2, 4, 5, 10, 20.

Each of these numbers is a **factor** or **divisor** of 20.

By this we mean that each number divides into 20 with no remainder.

When asked for the factors of 24, we can give more than one answer.
For example, $24 = 24 \times 1$ or 12×2 or 8×3 or 6×4.

Each of these is called a **pair of factors** of 24.
Thus, all the numbers 1, 2, 3, 4, 6, 8, 12 and 24 are *factors* or *divisors* of 24.

Similarly, the divisors of 18 are 1, 2, 3, 6, 9, 18.

> Notice that 1 is a factor of every number and every number is a factor of itself.

Highest common factor

The factors of 16 are: 1, 2, 4, **8**, 16.

The factors of 24 are: 1, 2, 3, 4, 6, **8**, 12, 24.

In the above lists, the highest factor common to both is 8.
8 is called the **highest common factor** (or divisor) and is denoted by **HCF**.

Example 1

Find the highest common factor of 36 and 54.

The factors of 36 = {1, 2, 3, 4, 6, 9, 12, **18**, 36}

The factors of 54 = {1, 2, 3, 6, 9, **18**, 27, 54}

The highest common factor = 18.

Prime numbers

The factors of 4 are 1, 2, 4.

The factors of 5 are 1, 5.

The factors of 7 are 1, 7.

Notice that the numbers 5 and 7 have two factors only, i.e., the number itself and 1. Numbers which have 2 factors only are called **prime** numbers.

The first five prime numbers are

    2, 3, 5, 7, 11

> A prime number is a number with 2 factors only.

Note: If a number is not prime it is a **composite** number.

Composite numbers have more than two factors, e.g., 4, 12, 30 etc.

The factors of 30 are 1, 2, 3, 5, 6, 10, 15, 30.

Investigation:

Explain why: (a) 1 is **not** a prime number,

                   (b) 2 is the **only even** prime number.

Expressing a number as a product of prime factors

$$12 = 4 \times 3 \qquad\qquad 18 = 9 \times 2 \qquad\qquad 36 = 9 \times 4$$
$$ = 2 \times 2 \times 3 \qquad\qquad = 3 \times 3 \times 2 \qquad\qquad = 3 \times 3 \times 2 \times 2$$

Each of the numbers above is expressed as a product of prime numbers.

Thus, $12 = 2 \times 2 \times 3$ is expressed as a product of its **prime factors**.

Example 2

Find the prime factors of
(i) 28

(ii) 60

$$28 = 4 \times 7$$
$$ = 2 \times 2 \times 7$$

$$60 = 30 \times 2$$
$$ = 15 \times 2 \times 2$$
$$ = 3 \times 5 \times 2 \times 2$$
$$ = 2 \times 2 \times 3 \times 5$$

Factor trees

A factor tree can also be used to find the prime factors of any number,
e.g., express 16 and 30 as <u>products</u> of their prime factors.

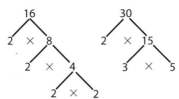

$16 = 2 \times 2 \times 2 \times 2$

$30 = 2 \times 3 \times 5$

Example 3

Write each of the following as a product of their prime factors
(i) 28   (ii) 60

(i) $28 = 4 \times 7$ (ii)
     $\quad\ = 2 \times 2 \times 7$

60
2 × 30
   2   15
   3 × 5

$60 = 2 \times 2 \times 3 \times 5$

The factor tree can be used very effectively to find the highest common factor of numbers.

(i) Find the prime factors of each number.
(ii) Find the common factors and multiply them to find the highest common factor.

Example 4

Find the highest common factor of 36 and 54

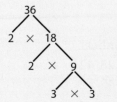 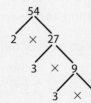

The prime factors of 36 are 2, 2, 3, 3.
The prime factors of 54 are 2, 3, 3, 3.
Common to both numbers are 2, 3, 3.
The highest common factor is
HCF = $2 \times 3 \times 3 = 18$.

Exercise 1.2

1. Say whether each of the following statements is true or false.
   If the statement is true, write the result as a multiplication.
   The first one is done for you.

   (i)   4 is a factor of 20   True, $4 \times 5 = 20$ (ii)   8 is a factor of 12

   (iii)   9 is a factor of 18   (iv)   5 is a factor of 35

   (v)   11 is a factor of 34   (vi)   12 is a factor of 60

   (vii) 16 is a factor of 30   (viii) 16 is a factor of 48

2. 3×4, 6×2 and 12×1 are pairs of factors of 12.
   Write out all the pairs of factors of these numbers.

   (i)   18   (ii)   30   (iii)   36   (iv)   40

3. Which of the numbers 1, 2, 4, 5, 7 is not a factor of 28?

4. List all the factors of each of these numbers:

   (i)   6   (ii)   8   (iii)   15   (iv)   24

   (v)   28   (vi)   35   (vii)   84   (viii)   108

5. Show that the factors of 28 (excluding 28 itself) add up to 28.

6. Is 3 a factor of these numbers?

   (i)   36   (ii)   56   (iii)   141   (iv)   285

   Notice that the sum of the digits in each number that has 3 as a factor is also divisible by 3.
   Investigate if this applies to other numbers that have 3 as a factor.

7. Is 7 a factor of these numbers?

   (i)   49   (ii)   63   (iii)   74   (iv)   252

8. (i)   Write down all the factors of 18.
   (ii)   Write down all the factors of 24.
   (iii)   Write down the factors that are common to 18 and 24.
   (iv)   What is the highest common factor of 18 and 24?

9. Find the highest common factor of each of these pairs of numbers.

   (i)   15, 25   (ii)   14, 49   (iii)   28, 42

   (iv)   42, 70   (v)   36, 63   (vi)   45, 72

10. Find the highest common factor of each of these sets of numbers.

    (i)   18, 27, 36   (ii)   14, 28, 42   (iii)   39, 52, 78

11. In Ms Kirkpatrick's English class there are 12 girls and 18 boys. She wants to select the greatest number of debating teams from her class so that (i) no student is left out (ii) the same number of girls / boys is on each team. How many teams can she make and what is the composition of each team?

12. Write 26 as the sum of two primes in three different ways.

13. Which of these numbers are prime?
    (i) 7   (ii) 19   (iii) 26   (iv) 31   (v) 39

14. Continue the sequence 6, 12, 18, … as far as 48.
    Now write down the numbers which are one smaller and one larger than this sequence, i.e., 5, 7, 11, … 49.
    Which of these numbers are **not** prime?

15. John has 24 chocolate bars and 20 packets of crisps. How many friends could he share them with so that he has none left over and each friend gets the same number of each?

16. Are the following statements true or false? If false, say why.
    (i) All prime numbers are odd numbers.
    (ii) The only even prime number is 2.
    (iii) All odd numbers are prime numbers.
    (iv) There are only three prime numbers between 10 and 20.

17. Write down all the factors of 48.
    How many of these factors are prime?

18. Peter scored 56 points and Sarah 48 points having played the same number of computer games. What was the greatest number of games each could have played? Find also the number of points per game each was awarded. (Note, each game is awarded the same number of points)

19. Write down the prime factors of each of these numbers:
    (i) 12   (ii) 30   (iii) 45   (iv) 84   (v) 108

20. Find a pair of prime numbers that total each of these numbers:
    (i) 12   (ii) 16   (iii) 24   (iv) 32

21. **Twin primes** are prime numbers with a difference of 2. The first pair of twin primes is 3 and 5. What are the next three pairs of twin primes?

22. Think of a number between 1 and 13.
    Multiply it by one less than the number you have chosen and then add 41.
    Do this a few times. Comment on your answers.

23. Barry has 16 white, 40 green and 24 orange beads. How many bracelets can he make using all of the beads if he wants to have the same number of each colour on each bracelet.

How many beads of each colour are on each bracelet?

24. Look at the numbers 3, 4, 5, 9, 10, 12, 15, 18, 30.
  (i) Which numbers are prime?
 (ii) Which numbers are factors of 30?
(iii) Which numbers have 6 as a factor?
(iv) How many of the numbers are divisible by 5?

Section 1.3 Multiples – Lowest common multiple

If we count in groups of 3 we produce multiples of 3.

1 2 **3** 4 5 **6** 7 8 **9** 10 11 **12** 13 14 **15** 16 17 **18** 19 20 **21**

The multiples of 3 are 3, 6, 9, 12, 15, 18, **21**, 24, …

Counting in groups of 7 we produce multiples of 7.

1 2 3 4 5 6 **7** 8 9 10 11 12 13 **14** 15 16 17 18 19 20 **21** …

The multiples of 7 are 7, 14, **21**, 28, 35, …

Notice that **21** is the smallest number common to both sets of multiples.

21 is called the **lowest common multiple (LCM)** of 3 and 7.

Lowest Common Multiple

> The lowest common multiple (LCM) of two or more numbers is the smallest number into which each of the numbers divide.

Example 1

Find the lowest common multiple of 8, 12, 18.

The multiples of 8 are: 8, 16, 24, 32, 40, 48, 56, 64, **72**, …
The multiples of 12 are: 12, 24, 36, 48, 60, **72**, 84, …
The multiples of 18 are: 18, 36, 54, **72**, …
The lowest common multiple (LCM) = 72.

Factor trees can also be used to find **lowest common multiple** as follows:

(i) Find the prime factors of each number.

(ii) List all the factors of the first number and include any factor from each other number that has not been included already.

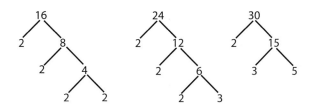

16 as a product of prime factors $= 2 \times 2 \times 2 \times 2$.

24 as a product of prime factors $= 2 \times 2 \times 2 \times$ **3**.

30 as a product of prime factors $= 2 \times 3 \times$ **5**.

The lowest common multiple of 16, 24 and 30 is $2 \times 2 \times 2 \times 2 \times 3 \times 5 = 240$

Exercise 1.3

1. The red dots on the number line show the first six multiples of 3.

   0 1 2 3 4 5 6 7 8 9 10 11 12 13 14 15 16 17 18 19 20 21 22 23 24 25

  (i) What is the difference between any multiple of 3 and the next multiple?

  (ii) What are the next two multiples of 3 after 18?

  (iii) What is the 9th multiple of 3?

  (iv) What is the hundredth multiple of 3?

2. (i) Write out the first six multiples of 7.

  (ii) Is 98 a multiple of 7?

  (iii) 140 is a multiple of 7. Work out the next two multiples of 7.

3. Write out all the multiples of 9 that are less than 80.

4. (i) Write out the first six multiples of 4.

  (ii) Write out the first six multiples of 6.

  (iii) Which of the numbers are common multiples of 4 and 6?

  (iv) What is the lowest common multiple of 4 and 6?

5. Find the lowest common multiple of each of these pairs of numbers.

  (i) 2, 5   (ii) 6, 8   (iii) 4, 7   (iv) 10, 12   (v) 7, 8

6. Find the LCM of each set of numbers.

  (i) 2, 4, 8   (ii) 3, 4, 6   (iii) 3, 5, 10   (iv) 6, 8, 12

7. Use the factor tree method to find the lowest common multiple of:
   (i) 16 and 18
   (ii) 24 and 42.

8. James walks his dog every 3 days. Anna walks her dog every four days. If they both walk their dog on a Monday, on which day of the week will they next walk their dogs together?

9. Jenny is buying food for a barbecue. Burgers are sold in packs of 6 and buns are sold in packs of 8. What is the least number of packs of burgers and buns Jenny should buy so that there is one bun for each burger?

10. The machine below accepts two different inputs. It compares the multiples of each number and outputs the LCM.

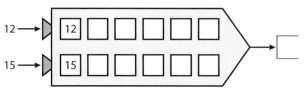

   (i) Copy and complete this machine with inputs of 12 and 15.
   (ii) What are the possible inputs if the output is 12?
   (iii) What are the possible inputs if the output is 42?

11. Describe each of the following statements as *true* or *false*.
    (i) Any multiple of 6 is also a multiple of 3.
    (ii) Any multiple of 5 is also a multiple of 10.
    (iii) The LCM of 6 and 8 is 48.
    (iv) You always get a common multiple of a pair of numbers by multiplying them together.

12. (i) Copy the diagram.
       Write down the first nine multiples of 9 in line 1 and the first nine multiples of 5 in line 2.
    (ii) Line 3 is the difference between each term in lines 1 and 2, and line 4 is the sum. Complete lines 3 and 4 and describe them in words.
    (iii) Line 5 is the difference between line 4 and line 3. Describe line 5.

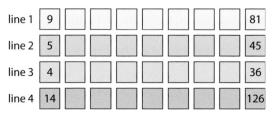

13. One light flashes every 25 seconds. Another light flashes every 30 seconds.
At a certain time they flash together.
How many seconds will it be before they flash together again?

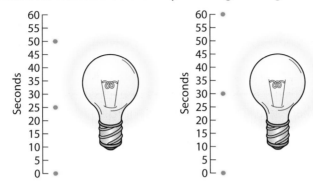

14. A bottle of Orange Juice can fill five 200 ml cups.
Paper cups of the same size are sold in packs of 8.
How many bottles of Orange Juice and packets of paper cups do I need to buy if
I want every cup to be filled with no Orange Juice left over?

15. A newly discovered planet has three moons. On the
day it was discovered, the moons were all aligned.
The closest moon takes 4 days to make one orbit.
The next moon takes 5 days to make one orbit.
The last moon takes 10 days to make the same orbit.
How many days will it take for all three to align again?

Section 1.4 Squares and square roots ——————

A short way of writing 3×3 is 3^2. It is pronounced *three squared*.
The small 2 is called the **index** or **power**.

Similarly   (i) $2 \times 2 \times 2 = 2^3$ ... pronounced *two cubed*.
                (ii) $3 \times 3 \times 3 \times 3 = 3^4$ ... pronounced *three to the power of four*.

The number 3^4 is said to be written in *index form*.

Remember:
$3^4 = 3$ multiplied by ***itself***
4 times.

$4 \times 4 \times 4 \times 4 \times 4 = 4$ *to the power of* 5
 1   **2**   **3**   **4**   **5** $= 4^5$
$7 \times 7 \times 7 \times 7 \times 7 \times 7 = 7^6$ (7 *to the power of* 6)
 1   **2**   **3**   **4**   **5**   **6**

To find the value of 2×5^2, we square the 5 first and then multiply the result by 2.

i.e. $2 \times 5^2 = 2 \times 25 = 50$

Similarly
    (i) $3 \times 4^2 = 3 \times 16 = 48$

    (ii) $3^2 \times 5 = 9 \times 5 = 45$

    (iii) $2^2 + 3^3 = (2 \times 2) + (3 \times 3 \times 3)$

            $= 4 + 27 = 31$

> Always work out the powers first.

Example 1

Find the value of each of the following:

  (i) 4^3 (ii) $4^2 - 3^2$ (iii) 3×4^2 (iv) half of 8^2

(i) $4^3 = 4 \times 4 \times 4$
     $= 64$

(ii) $4^2 - 3^2 = 16 - 9$
             $= 7$

(iii) $3 \times 4^2 = 3 \times 16$
          $= 48$

(iv) half of $8^2 = \frac{1}{2}$ of 64
                $= 32$

Square numbers

$1 = (1^2)$ $4 = (2^2)$ $9 = (3^2)$ $16 = (4^2)$

   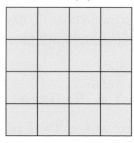

It is easy to see why 1, 4, 9, 16, 25,... are called **square** numbers.

We will meet these numbers again when we find the area of a square.

The square root

$\sqrt{16}$ is read as 'the square root of 16'.

To find $\sqrt{16}$ we look for the number which, when multiplied by itself, gives 16.

This number is 4, i.e., $\sqrt{16} = 4$.

Similarly, $\sqrt{25} = 5$, since $5 \times 5 = 25$.

For harder square roots, you will need your calculator.

Look for the $\boxed{\sqrt{}}$ button to find the square root of a number.

To find $\sqrt{289}$, key in $\boxed{\sqrt{}}$ $\boxed{2}$ $\boxed{8}$ $\boxed{9}$ $\boxed{=}$.

The answer is 17.

Example 2

Find the value of each of these:

(i) $\sqrt{64} + 2^3$ (ii) $3 \times 2^2 + \text{twice } \sqrt{81}$

(i) $\sqrt{64} + 2^3 = 8 + 8$
$= 16$

(ii) $3 \times 2^2 + \text{twice } \sqrt{81}$
$= 3 \times 4 + \text{twice } 9$
$= 12 + 18$
$= 30$

Exercise 1.4

1. Work out each of these:
   (i) 4^2 (ii) 6^2 (iii) 12^2 (iv) 14^2
   (v) $3^2 + 4^2$ (vi) $2^2 + 7^2$ (vii) $9^2 + 5^2$ (viii) $10^2 - 8^2$

2. Find the value of each of these:
   (i) 4×2^2 (ii) 8×3^2 (iii) $10^2 \times 4$ (iv) twice 7^2
   (v) half of 8^2 (vi) $6^2 \div 4$ (vii) $9^2 \div 3$ (viii) $12^2 - 6^2 - 4^2$

3. Work out each of these:
   (i) $2^2 \times 3^2$ (ii) $5^2 + 4^2$ (iii) $8^2 - 7^2$ (iv) half $10^2 - 4^2$

4. The numbers 1, 4, 9, 16, 25, ... are called **square numbers**.
Write down the next four square numbers after 25.

5. Find a square number between each of these pairs of numbers:
   (i) 12, 17   (ii) 30, 40   (iii) 75, 84   (iv) 105 and 130

6. (i) Write two consecutive odd numbers, multiply them together, then add 1.
     Repeat the process several times.
     What do you notice about your final answers?
   (ii) What happens if you use consecutive even numbers instead?

7. Write each of the following as a single number to a power, e.g., 3^4:

    (i) $2 \times 2 \times 2$

    (ii) $3 \times 3 \times 3$

    (iii) $6 \times 6 \times 6 \times 6$

    (iv) 2×2^4

8. Investigate if each of these is true or false:

    (i) $3^2 \times 4^2 = 12^2$

    (ii) $(2 \times 5)^2 = 2^2 \times 5^2$

    (iii) $3^2 + 4^2 = (3 + 4)^2$.

9. Express each of these as a single number to a power:

    (i) 16   (ii) 8   (iii) 27   (iv) 1000   (v) 125   (vi) 121

10. Write down the answer to each of these square roots:

    (i) $\sqrt{9}$ (ii) $\sqrt{25}$ (iii) $\sqrt{64}$ (iv) $\sqrt{144}$ (v) $\sqrt{400}$.

11. Find the missing number in each of the following:

    (i) The square root of 49 is ☐.

    (ii) The square root of ☐ is 9.

    (iii) 12 is the square root of ☐.

    (iv) The square of 9 is ☐.

    (v) ☐ is the square of 8.

    (vi) ☐ is the square root of 1.

12. Write as a single number each of these:

    (i) $\dfrac{10^3}{\sqrt{100}}$

    (ii) $\sqrt{81} + 3^2$

    (iii) $\dfrac{\sqrt{100}}{5}$

    (iv) $\dfrac{3^2 \times \sqrt{81}}{3^3}$.

13. Which is bigger   (i) the sum of the squares of 3 and 5

    or   (ii) the square of the sum of 3 and 5 ?

14. Which is bigger   (i) the square root of the sum of 9 and 16

    or   (ii) the sum of the square roots of 9 and 16 ?

15. $2^2 = 4$. This can be written as the sum of two prime numbers: $2 + 2 = 4$

    $3^2 = 9$. This can be written as the sum of two prime numbers: $2 + 7 = 9$

    Now write   (i) 4^2 (ii) 6^2 (iii) 7^2 (iv) 10^2

    as the sum of two prime numbers.

16. Copy and complete using consecutive whole numbers:

    (i) ☐ $< \sqrt{5} <$ ☐

    (ii) ☐ $< \sqrt{30} <$ ☐

    (iii) ☐ $< \sqrt{46} <$ ☐

17. Use the $\boxed{\sqrt{}}$ button on your calculator to find each of these:

    (i) $\sqrt{169}$ (ii) $\sqrt{225}$ (iii) $\sqrt{441}$ (iv) $\sqrt{676}$ (v) $\sqrt{961}$

18. Find the value of n such that each of the following is true:

(i) $4^n = 16$ (ii) $2^n = 8$ (iii) $8^n = 64$ (iv) $2^n = 16$

19. Copy and complete these.

(i) Describe the pattern in the numbers in the left-hand column.

(ii) What happens to the powers of 10 as the starting numbers increase?

$10 = 10^1$

$100 = 10 \times 10 = 10^2$

$1000 = \square \times \square \times \square = 10^{\square}$

$10\,000 = \square \times \square \times \square \times \square = \square^{\square}$

$100\,000 = \square \times \square \times \square \times \square \times \square = \square^{\square}$

$1\,000\,000 = \square^{\square}$

Section 1.5 Order of operations

When a calculation involves addition and subtraction, you can work from left to right to find the answer.

For example, (i) $3 + 4 + 8 = 7 + 8$ (ii) $14 - 5 - 3 = 9 - 3$

$\qquad\qquad = 15 \qquad\qquad\qquad = 6$

Multiplication and division are equally important operations.

Thus, when calculations involve just $\times$ or $\div$, you work from left to right to find the answers.

(i) $3 \times 4 \times 6 = 12 \times 6$ (ii) $36 \div 6 \div 3 = 6 \div 3$

$\qquad\qquad = 72 \qquad\qquad\qquad = 2$

(iii) $18 \times 4 \div 6 = 72 \div 6$ (iv) $54 \div 9 \times 3 = 6 \times 3$

$\qquad\qquad = 12 \qquad\qquad\qquad = 18$

Multiplication and division are more important operations than addition and subtraction, so you must do these first.

Work out ($\times$ $\div$) before ($+$ $-$)

(i) $4 + 5 \times 6 = 4 + 30$ (ii) $18 - 14 \div 2 = 18 - 7$

$\qquad\qquad = 34 \qquad\qquad\qquad = 11$

(iii) $10 + 6 - 4 \times 2 = 10 + 6 - 8$ (iv) $7 \times 4 + 35 \div 7 = 28 + 5$

$\qquad\qquad\qquad = 16 - 8 \qquad\qquad\qquad = 33$

$\qquad\qquad\qquad = 8$

Powers and roots are more important operations than multiplication and division. They must be done first.

Work out before and then do

(i) $24 - \sqrt{25} + 3^2$

$= 24 - 5 + 9$

$= 19 + 9$

$= 28$

(ii) $63 \div 9 + \sqrt{36}$

$= 63 \div 9 + 6$

$= 7 + 6$

$= 13$

If there are **brackets** in a calculation, do the calculation inside them first.

When a calculation involves brackets as well as other operations, this is the correct order to work out the answers.

First	Second	Third	Fourth
( )	$\square^2$ or $\boxed{\sqrt{}}$	$\times$ or $\div$	$+$ or $-$

B – brackets
I – indices (powers)
R – roots
D – division
M – multiplication
A – addition
S – subtraction

Example 1

Work out   (i) $12 + 8 \div 2 + 4 \times 3$ (ii) $7 \times 8 - 3 - (72 \div 8)$

(i) $12 + 8 \div 2 + 4 \times 3$

$= 12 + 4 + 12$

$= 28$

(ii) $7 \times 8 - 3 - (72 \div 8)$

$= 7 \times 8 - 3 - (9)$

$= 56 - 3 - 9$

$= 53 - 9$

$= 44$

Note: A horizontal line is the same as the $\div$ symbol.

For example,   (i) $\dfrac{15}{3} = 15 \div 3 = 5$ (ii) $\dfrac{20 \div 5}{2} = \dfrac{4}{2} = 2$

Exercise 1.5

Work out numbers (1–15).

1. $5 + 3 \times 4$

2. $6 \times 2 + 5$

3. $9 \times 4 - 8$

4. $22 - 5 \times 4$

5. $18 \div 3 + 7$

6. $16 - 4 + 3 \times 9$

7. $5 + 16 \times 2 - 8$

8. $25 - 16 \div 4$

9. $5 \times 7 - 27 \div 3$

10. $6 \times 3 + 36 \div 4$

11. $5 \times 8 - 6 + 36 \div 3$

12. $15 - 10 \div 2 + 8$

13. $9 - 6 \div 2 + 5 \times 4$

14. $9 \times 6 - 27 \div 3$

15. $34 - 8 + 54 \div 9$

16. Copy and complete these calculations.
Each ☐ stands for an operation ($+$, $-$, $\times$, or $\div$).

(i) $5 \,\square\, 7 \times 2 = 19$

(ii) $21 \,\square\, 3 + 11 = 18$

(iii) $18 + 6 \,\square\, 2 = 21$

(iv) $12 \,\square\, 2 \times 5 = 22$

(v) $15 \,\square\, 2 - 11 = 19$

(vi) $24 \,\square\, 8 \,\square\, 5 = 15$

17. Work out each of these:

(i) $4 \times (5 + 6)$

(ii) $7 \times (12 - 8)$

(iii) $9 \times (7 - 1)$

(iv) $(14 - 3) \times 2$

(v) $(6 - 3) \times 4$

(vi) $48 - 3 \times (9 - 3)$

(vii) $(36 - 12) \div 3 + 9$

(viii) $25 \div (8 - 3) - 2$

(ix) $5 \times 4 + 3 \times (10 - 4)$

18. Find the value of each of these:

(i) $15 - 10 \div 2 + 6 \times 4$

(ii) $5 \times 8 - 3 \times (7 - 4)$

(iii) $15 \div (7 - 4) + 12$

(iv) $(16 + 4) \div 5 + 14 \times 2$

(v) $2 \times (7 - 4) + 28 \div 7$

(vi) $(10 \times 3 - 20) \times 5$

19. Work out each of these:

(i) $\dfrac{22 + 13}{7}$

(ii) $\dfrac{5 + 9 - 2}{6}$

(iii) $\dfrac{100}{2 \times 5}$

(iv) $\dfrac{7 + 9}{10 - 6}$

(v) $26 - \dfrac{15}{3}$

(vi) $\dfrac{6 + 8 \times 3}{5}$

20. Find the value of each of these:

(i) $4 + 5^2$

(ii) $128 - 8^2$

(iii) $4 + 2 \times 3^2$

(iv) $2 \times \sqrt{25} + 4^2$

(v) $6 \times 3^2 - \sqrt{16}$

(vi) $2 \times 5^2 \div 10$

21. Work out each of these:

(i) $(3 + 5) \times 2 - 3^2$

(ii) $\sqrt{16} + 5 \times 2^2$

(iii) $4 \times \sqrt{9} + 6^2$

(iv) $4 \times 3^2 + 8 \div 4$

(v) $5^2 \times 2^2 - 8$

(vi) $2^2 + \sqrt{16} + 5^2$

22. Find the value of each of these:

(i) $\dfrac{8^2}{\sqrt{64}}$

(ii) $\dfrac{\sqrt{81} + 5}{4 \times 4 - 2}$

(iii) $\dfrac{2^2 \times \sqrt{100}}{4 \times (6 - 1)}$

23. Work out each of these:

(i) $3 + 5 \times 2^2 - 6 \times 3$

(ii) $(3 + 4)^2 - 2 \times 3^2$

24. Copy these statements and write in brackets to make them true.

(i) $5 \times 4 + 3 = 35$

(ii) $20 - 3 + 8 = 9$

(iii) $8 + 10 \div 2 = 9$

(iv) $48 \div 16 - 4 = 4$

(v) $11 - 6 \times 2 = 10$

(vi) $5 + 3 \times 4 - 2 = 30$

25. Which of the following has the greatest value? Find this value.

A: $(1 \times 2) \times (3 \times 4)$

B: $(1 \times 2) + (3 \times 4)$

C: $(1 \times 2) \times (3 + 4)$

D: $(1 + 2) \times (3 \times 4)$

E: $(1 + 2) \times (3 + 4)$

26. Which **one** of these calculations is **incorrect**?

A: $4 \times 5 + 67 = 45 + 6 \times 7$

B: $3 \times 7 + 48 = 37 + 4 \times 8$

C: $6 \times 3 + 85 = 63 + 8 \times 5$

D: $2 \times 5 + 69 = 25 + 6 \times 9$

E: $9 \times 6 + 73 = 96 + 7 \times 3$.

27. Which one of these calculations is incorrect?

(i) $(20 - 15)^2 - 10 \div 5 = 3$ (ii) $(20 - 15)^2 - 10 \div 5 = 23$

Section 1.6 Commutative and Associative properties ——

While calculators are now widely used, it is still important to be able to perform the basic operations on numbers without their use.

Here are examples of long multiplication and division.

(i) 134×29

$$
\begin{array}{r}
134 \times 29 \\
29 \\
\hline
1206 \ldots (134 \times 9) \\
2680 \ldots (134 \times 20) \\
\hline
3886
\end{array}
$$

Answer $= 3886$

(ii) $3672 \div 27$

$$
\begin{array}{r}
136 \\
27\overline{)3672} \\
27 \\
\hline
97 \\
81 \\
\hline
162 \\
162 \\
\hline
\end{array}
$$

Answer $= 136$

Properties of natural numbers ————————————————

1. Commutative property

$3 + 5 = 5 + 3$ shows that we can change the order in which two numbers are added without changing the result.

Similarly, $7 \times 8 = 8 \times 7$.

The examples above illustrate a very important property in mathematics, namely, addition and multiplication are **commutative**.

> *Addition of natural numbers is commutative*
> **$3 + 5 = 5 + 3$**
> *Multiplication of natural numbers is commutative*
> **$3 \times 5 = 5 \times 3$**

However, subtraction and division are not commutative as illustrated by the following examples.

> *Subtraction of natural numbers **is not** commutative*
> $$3 - 5 \neq 5 - 3$$
> *Division of natural numbers **is not** commutative*
> $$3 \div 5 \neq 5 \div 3$$

(i) $12 - 8 = 4$ but $8 - 12 = -4$

$\therefore$ $12 - 8 \neq 8 - 12$

(ii) $6 \div 2 = 3$ but $2 \div 6 = \frac{2}{6} = \frac{1}{3}$

$\therefore$ $6 \div 2 \neq 2 \div 6$

2. Brackets

(a) Brackets are used to prioritise part of a calculation. In every calculation the part inside the brackets must be done first.

Consider $5 \times (3 + 4) = 5 \times 7$ ... do what is inside the brackets first.

$$= 35$$

However if $(5 \times 3) + 4 = 15 + 4$ ... do what is inside the brackets first.

$$= 19, \text{ we get a very different answer.}$$

(b) Note that $5 \times (3 + 4) = 5 \times 3 + 5 \times 4$ ... 5 groups of 3 and 5 groups of 4

$$5 \times 7 = 15 + 20$$
$$35 = 35$$

The statement $5(3 + 4) = 5 \times 3 + 5 \times 4$ illustrates that **multiplication is distributive over addition**.

Similarly for subtraction.

$6(8 - 5) = 6 \times 8 - 6 \times 5$

$6(3) = 48 - 30$

$18 = 18$

> *multiplication is distributive over addition.*
> $$5(3 + 4) = 5 \times 3 + 5 \times 4 = 35$$
> *multiplication is distributive over subtraction.*
> $$5(6 - 4) = 5 \times 6 - 5 \times 4 = 10$$

3. The associative property

To perform the operation $6 + 8 + 10$, we could do it in either of these ways:

(i) $6 + 8 + 10 = (6 + 8) + 10 = 14 + 10 = 24$

(ii) $6 + 8 + 10 = 6 + (8 + 10) = 6 + 18 = 24$

Similarly, $3 \times 4 \times 5 = (3 \times 4) \times 5 = 12 \times 5 = 60$

or $3 \times 4 \times 5 = 3 \times (4 \times 5) = 3 \times 20 = 60$

These examples illustrate the **associative property** of addition and multiplication which states that the way in which the numbers are grouped does not change the result.

However $(12 \div 6) \div 2 = 2 \div 2 = 1$ but $12 \div (6 \div 2) = 12 \div 3 = 4$

and $(12 - 6) - 3 = 6 - 3 = 3$ but $12 - (6 - 3) = 12 - 3 = 9$

These examples illustrate that division and subtraction are not associative.

Addition is associative
$(6 + 8) + 10 = 6 + (8 + 10) = 24$
Multiplication is associative
$(6 \times 8) \times 10 = 6 \times (8 \times 10) = 24$

*Subtraction is **not** associative*
$(10 - 5) - 4 \neq 10 - (5 - 4)$
$1 \neq 9$
*Division is **not** associative*
$(16 \div 8) \div 2 \neq 16 \div (8 \div 2)$
$1 \neq 4$

Example 1

State whether each of the following is true or false:

(i) $9 \times 5 = 5 \times 9$ ii) $10 \div 5 = 5 \div 10$ (iii) $(4 \times 5) \times 6 = 4 \times (5 \times 6)$

(i) $9 \times 5 = 45$ and $5 \times 9 = 45$ ... true

(ii) $10 \div 5 = 2$ and $5 \div 10 = \frac{5}{10} = \frac{1}{2}$ ... false

(iii) $(4 \times 5) \times 6 = 20 \times 6 = 120$ and $4 \times (5 \times 6) = 4 \times 30 = 120$ ... true

Multiplying natural numbers

(a)   To multiply 20×26 using the distributive law we proceed as follows;

$26 = (20 + 6)$ ... breaking 26 number into tens and units

therefore $20 \times 26 = 20 \times (20 + 6)$

$$= 20(20) + 20(6)$$
$$= 400 + 120$$
$$= 520$$

(b)   To multiply 32×47 using the distributive law we proceed as follows;

$32 = (30 + 2)$ and $47 = (40 + 7)$ ... breaking each number into tens and units

therefore $32 \times 47 = (30 + 2) \times (40 + 7)$

$$= 30(40 + 7) + 2(40 + 7)$$
$$= (30 \times 40 + 30 \times 7) + (2 \times 40 + 2 \times 7)$$
$$= 1200 + 210 + 80 + 14$$
$$= 1504$$

Using the **array method:**

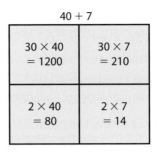

The answer is: $1200 + 210 + 80 + 14 = 1504$

Exercise 1.6

(Do not use a calculator for these exercises.)

1. Work out each of the following:
   (i) $125 + 38 + 9 + 450$
   (ii) $27 + 1037 + 326 + 9$
   (iii) $2017 + 151 + 39 + 6216$
   (iv) $168 + 2167 + 17 + 1076$

2. Copy and complete these subtractions:

   (i)   908
        − 304

   (ii)   673
        − 187

   (iii) 738
        − 354

   (iv)   580
        − 364

   (v)   611
        − 87

3. Complete each of these subtractions:
   (i) $506 − 328$
   (ii) $1296 − 377$
   (iii) $1094 − 29$
   (iv) $7002 − 946$
   (v) $629 − 380$
   (vi) $6200 − 5177$

4. Do these calculations mentally and write down the answers:
   (i) $30 + 10 + 10$
   (ii) $80 − 20 − 10$
   (iii) $80 + 40 − 30$
   (iv) $80 + 30 + 20$
   (v) $60 + 50 − 30$
   (vi) $130 + 70 − 40$

5. Work out each of these mentally:
   (i) 60×2
   (ii) 50×9
   (iii) 300×5
   (iv) 400×6
   (v) 40×10
   (vi) 8×100
   (vii) 40×50
   (viii) 240×10
   (ix) 120×40
   (x) 90×90

6. Write down the answers to these questions:
   (i) $18 \div 3$
   (ii) $180 \div 3$
   (iii) $240 \div 6$
   (iv) $630 \div 9$
   (v) $560 \div 8$

7. Work out each of these multiplications:
   (i) 47×9
   (ii) 426×11
   (iii) 89×29
   (iv) 168×50
   (v) 186×28
   (vi) 765×18
   (vii) 186×47
   (viii) 316×31

8. Five people shared a prize-draw win of €3200 equally.
   How much did each person receive?

9. A bus company owns twelve 48-seater coaches.
   Every Saturday, all the coaches are used for trips.
   (i) How many people can be carried at the same time in the twelve coaches?

   One Saturday, seven of the coaches each carried 39 people.
   The other coaches each had 11 empty seats.
   (ii) How many people went on trips altogether that Saturday?

10. This table shows the numbers of students in each year group at Corbett College.

Year 1	Year 2	Year 3	Year 4	Year 5
112	121	104	98	126

   (i) How many students are at the school altogether?
   (ii) How many fewer students are in Year 4 than in Year 2?
   (iii) Each class in Year 5 has 21 students.
        How many classes are there in Year 5?
   (iv) There are 3 times as many students in St. David's as in Corbett College.
        How many students are in St. David's?

11. The number in the square is found by multiplying the two numbers in the circles on either side of it.
   Copy and complete each of the following:

   (i) 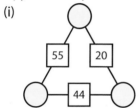   (ii) 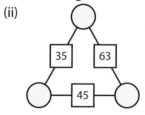   (iii)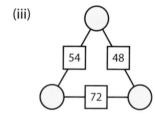

12. The digits of the year 2000 A.D. add up to 2.
   There are nine other years since 1 A.D. that this has happened.
   Name these nine years.

13. Jason bought three boxes of toffees. There were 30 toffees in each box. Jason ate 14 toffees himself and then shared all the rest equally between himself and his three sisters.
   (i) How many toffees did Jason have to start with?
   (ii) When they were shared out, how many toffees did each person get?

14. State whether each of the following is true or false:

 (i) $21 \times 6 = 6 \times 21$ (ii) $10 - 3 = 3 - 10$ (iii) $8 \div 4 = 4 \div 8$

 (iv) $34 \times 5 = 35 \times 4$ (v) $3(4 + 5) = 17$ (vi) $5(6 - 4) = 10$

15. Here are four statements:

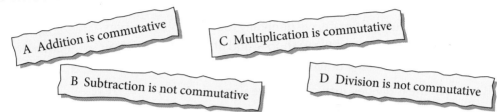

A   Addition is commutative

C   Multiplication is commutative

B   Subtraction is not commutative

D   Division is not commutative

 Which of the statements A, B, C or D does each of the following operations illustrate?

 (i) $12 \times 8 = 8 \times 12$ (ii) $14 - 10 \neq 10 - 14$

 (iii) $14 \div 7 \neq 7 \div 14$ (iv) $16 + 8 = 8 + 16$

16. Using the array method multiply each of the following pairs of numbers:

 (i) 20×37 (ii) 30×52 (iii) 27×80 (iv) 56×40

17. Using the array method multiply each of the following pairs of numbers:

 (i) 21×37 (ii) 33×51 (iii) 27×82 (iv) 56×44

18. State whether each of the following is true or false. Justify your answers.

 (i) $(6 + 8) + 10 = 6 + (8 + 10)$ (ii) $(24 - 8) - 6 = 24 - (8 - 6)$

 (iii) $(7 \times 4) \times 5 = 7 \times (4 \times 5)$ (iv) $(36 \div 6) \div 3 = 36 \div (6 \div 3)$

19. Which of the statements in the boxes below do each of these operations illustrate?

 (i) $(5 + 8) + 10 = 5 + (8 + 10)$ (ii) $15 - (10 - 2) \neq (15 - 10) - 2$

 (iii) $(7 \times 4) \times 3 = 7 \times (4 \times 3)$ (iv) $(20 - 10) - 4 \neq 20 - (10 - 4)$

A   Subtraction is not associative

B   Multiplication is associative

C   Division is not associative

D   Addition is associative

20. Two different whole numbers are each greater than 0 and less than 10.

 These two numbers are (i) multiplied and (ii) added.

 Work out the greatest possible difference between (i) and (ii).

Section 1.7 Rounding off numbers – Estimating

When dealing with numbers, calculators can save a lot of time. However, when using calculators it is very important to have some estimate of the answer you expect. Then you will know if the answer shown on the calculator is reasonable or not.

When making a rough estimate, we generally round whole numbers off to the nearest 10 or 100. If we wish to round off a number to the nearest 10, we examine the units only.

This number line is divided into coloured regions.

You can use it to round numbers to the nearest 10.

Numbers inside a coloured region round to the value at its centre.

44 is in a yellow region. It is nearer to 40 than 50.

44 rounds down to 40, to the nearest 10.

47 is in the green region and rounds up to 50, to the nearest 10.

85 is on the boundary between two regions.

When a number ends in 5, we round up.

So 85 rounds up to 90, to the nearest 10.

When rounding to the nearest 100, your answer will be one of these numbers:
    0, 100, 200, 300, 400, 500, …

When rounding to the nearest 1000, your answer will be one of these numbers:
    0, 1000, 2000, 3000, 4000, …

Significant figures

If the attendance at a football match was 34 176, it would be reasonable to write down 34 200 or 34 000.

    34 200 is written correct to 3 significant figures.

    34 000 is written correct to 2 significant figures.

To round a whole number to a given number of significant figures, you start at the left of the number.

In the number 2834, 2 is the first significant figure and 8 is the second significant figure.

Thus 2834 = 2800, correct to two significant figures.

Notice that all digits that are **not** significant are changed to zeros.

A number with 5 digits when corrected to 2 significant figures must have 3 zeros at the end.

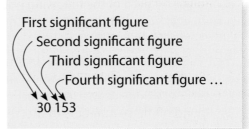

First significant figure
Second significant figure
Third significant figure
Fourth significant figure ...

30 153

> e.g. 30 153 = 30 000

Thus 52 764 = 52 760 correct to 4 significant figures

= 52 800 correct to 3 significant figures

= 53 000 correct to 2 significant figures

= 50 000 correct to 1 significant figure

The number 70 425 = 70 400, correct to 3 significant figures.
Notice here that 7, 0 and 4 are significant but the 2 and the 5 are not and are changed to zeros.

When rounding a number to 1 significant figure,

> Start at the left and find the first two digits.

> If the second digit is 5 or more, add 1 to the first digit.

> If the second digit is 4 or less, leave the first digit as it is.

> Replace all the other digits with zeros.

Here are more examples:

(i)   5210 = 5200 correct to two significant figures

(ii) 75 462 = 80 000 correct to one significant figure

(iii) 80 483 = 80 500 correct to three significant figures.

Exercise 1.7

1. Use the number line below to help you write each of these numbers to the nearest 10.

(i)   634   (ii) 622   (iii) 644   (iv) 598

(v)   604   (vi) 647   (vii) 605   (viii) 645

2. Use the number line above to write the numbers where the yellow and green regions meet.

3. Round off each of the following numbers to the nearest 10:
   (i) 137   (ii) 84   (iii) 677   (iv) 1764   (v) 3785

4. Round off these numbers to the nearest 100:
   (i) 823   (ii) 276   (iii) 2184   (iv) 3099   (v) 3708

5. Round off these numbers to the nearest 1000:
   (i) 2864   (ii) 5726   (iii) 8416   (iv) 9650   (v) 10 890

6. The attendance at an All-Ireland Final in Croke Park was 82 379.
   Write this number   (i) to the nearest 100
                               (ii) to the nearest 1000.

7. Round 28 460   (i) to three significant figures
                       (ii) to two significant figures
                     (iii) to one significant figure.

8. Rounded off to the nearest 100 people, the number of workers at a factory is 800. What is (i) the largest, (ii) the smallest number that could work at the factory?

9. The attendance at a rugby match, correct to the nearest 1000, was 38 000.
   Find (i) the largest and (ii) the smallest number that could have attended.

10. 62 680 people went to a concert.
    (i) The local newspaper reported that about 63 000 people went to the concert. Was this given to the nearest 100, nearest 1000 or nearest 10 000?
    (ii) Another newspaper reported that about 60 000 people went to the concert. Was this given to the nearest 1000 or nearest 10 000?

11. By rounding each number to the nearest 10, find a rough estimate for each of these:
    (i) 38×51 (ii) 48×32 (iii) 69×28 (iv) 288×12

12. By rounding off each number to the nearest 10, calculate a rough estimate of the value of each of the following:
    (i) $\dfrac{124 \times 231}{458}$ (ii) $\dfrac{709 \times 118}{236}$ (iii) $\dfrac{268 \times 147}{176}$

13. The size of a crowd at a concert was given as 23 700, to the nearest hundred.
    (i) What is the smallest number the crowd could be?
    (ii) What is the largest number the crowd could be?

14. The table gives the areas of five European Union states and their populations in 2004.

Country	Area (km²)	Population
Greece	131 944	10 645 343
Italy	301 225	57 436 280
Netherlands	33 812	16 318 199
Germany	356 733	83 251 851
Ireland	70 283	3 883 159

(i)   Round off the areas correct to three significant figures.

(ii) Round off the populations correct to two significant figures.

(iii) When the populations are rounded to one significant figure, which country has three times the population of another country?

Test yourself 1

1. Find the value of each of these:
    (i) $634 + 95 - 237$ (ii) $2 \times (3 + 5) - 3^2$

2. Write down   (i) the highest common factor of 16 and 40
                   (ii) the lowest common multiple of 6 and 9.

3.   (i) List all the prime numbers in this array:
             2, 4, 5, 9, 11, 16, 19, 21
  (ii) List all the factors of 28.
       Now write 28 as a product of its prime factors.

4. Write down the values of the letters A, B, C and D which are marked with arrows in the following diagrams:

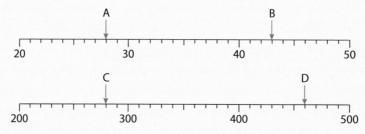

5. Evaluate each of these:
    (i) $2 \times 8 - 5$ (ii) $14 - 3 \times 3$ (iii) $3 \times (7 + 3)$
   (iv) $4 \times 12 \div (8 - 6)$ (v) $44 \div 4 + 3 \times 7$ (vi) $(7 - 3) \times 4 + 16 \div 8$

6. An aeroplane lands at Rome on its way to Cairo.
183 people got off and 42 got on.
If there were then 235 people on the plane, how many people were on the plane before it landed?

7. Fiona has four cards.
Each card has a number written on it.
Fiona puts all four cards on the table to make a number.
  (i) Write the smallest number Fiona can make using all four cards.
  (ii) Write the largest number Fiona can make using all four cards.

Fiona uses the cards to make a true statement.

(iii) Write this calculation.
      Use each of the numbers on Fiona's cards **once**.

8. Choosing numbers from 3, 4, 9, 13, 15, 23, 25, 28, 64, write down
   (i) three prime numbers
   (ii) a multiple of 7
   (iii) three numbers which are factors of 60
   (iv) four numbers whose square roots are whole numbers.

9. Round each number to the nearest 10 and make an estimate of the answer to each of these:

   (i) $\dfrac{63 \times 57}{31}$ 　　　　(ii) $\dfrac{204 \times 96}{53}$ 　　　　(iii) $\dfrac{396 \times 304}{154}$

10. Evaluate each of these:

    (i) $6 \times (5 + 3) - 8 \div 2$ 　　　　(ii) $\dfrac{30 - (3 \times 2)}{4 \times 2 - 2}$

11. There are 576 pupils in a school.
    If there are 48 more boys than girls, how many girls are there in the school?

12. Write these numbers in order, starting with the smallest:

    $9 \qquad \sqrt{49} \qquad 2^3 \qquad 2^2 \times 3 \qquad \sqrt{64} \div 2 \qquad \sqrt{(100 - 64)}$

13. The table on the right gives the areas, in square kilometres, of five member states of the European Union.
    (i) Write each of these areas to the nearest 1000.
    (ii) Which country has the smallest area?
    (iii) One country has about six times the area of another country.
    Name these two countries.
    (iv) One country is about one third the size of another country.
    Name these two countries.

Country	Area
Belgium	30 513
Luxembourg	2576
Spain	504 782
Portugal	92 082
France	547 026

14. Multiply each of the following using the **array** method.
    (i) 30×61 　　(ii) 50×24 　　(iii) 42×61 　　(iv) 73×36

15. Find the value of each of these:
    (i) $15 - 10 \div 2 + 7 \times 4$ 　　　　(ii) $3 \times 4^2 + 36 \div 2^2$

16. State whether each of the following is true or false.
    If a statement is false, give an example to show that it is false.
    (i) All multiples of 8 are also multiples of 4.
    (ii) All factors of 8 are also factors of 4.

(iii) All numbers have an even number of different factors.

(iv) $\sqrt{9} + \sqrt{16} = \sqrt{25}$

(v) There are only three prime numbers which are less than 10.

17. Three cyclists line up together at the start of an indoor cycling track.
The fastest cyclist can complete a lap in 30 seconds, the second can complete a lap in 45 seconds and the third can complete a lap in 1 minute.
How many laps will each cyclist have completed before they are all side by side again?

Learning Experience   *Unit 1*

Assignment 1

Looking back through history, many different number systems were used in different cultures. Our present-day system has its origin in Arabia.
The chart below compares our system with the Roman and Mayan (from Central America) cultures.

1	2	3	4	5	6	7	8	9	10	Arabic
I	II	III	IV	V	VI	VII	VIII	IX	X	Roman
.	..	...	....	—	·	..	...	....	═	Mayan

> Investigate this chart and extend it to count up to 20
> Research one other number system
> Write 36 in Roman and Mayan number systems
> State some reasons why the *Arabic* system is used today.

Assignment 2

Julia used all the digits 2, 3, 4, 5, 6 to do the subtraction.

$$462 - 35$$

Describe how she could do a similar subtraction using all of the digits 2, 3, 4, 5, 6 so as to produce the smallest positive answer.

Problem 1

Two students were given an empty 5 litre and an empty 3 litre bucket.

Their task was to fill the 5 litre bucket with exactly 4 litres of water.

Describe how they completed the task.

Problem 2

Using the following 4 clues identify the number.

State the order in which you used the clues.

1. the sum of the digits is 8

2. the number reads the same forwards as backwards

3. the number is less than 2000

4. the number has four digits

Chapter 1 review 1

Using the terms from the chapter, copy and complete the following sentences:

1. Whole positive numbers are called _____ numbers.

2. A number that divides evenly into a second number with no remainder is called a _____ of the second number.

3. A _____ number has 2 factors only.

4. LCM stands for _____ _____ _____.

5. HCF stands for _____ _____ _____.

6. A number multiplied by itself to give a second number is called the _____ of the second number.

7. 1, 4, 9, 16, 25, … are called _____ numbers.

8. BIRDMAS stands for _____, _____, _____,

_____, _____, _____, _____.

9. If $(a * b) = (b * a)$ then the operation $*$ is said to be _____.

10. If $a * (b * c) = (a * b) * c$ then the operation $*$ is said to be

_____.

11. Brackets are used to _____ an operation.

12. When making a rough estimate of a calculation we generally _____ whole numbers off to the nearest 10 or 100.

13. If we estimate 32 657 as 33 000 we are using the first two _____

_____.

Chapter 1 review 2

You should now be able to;

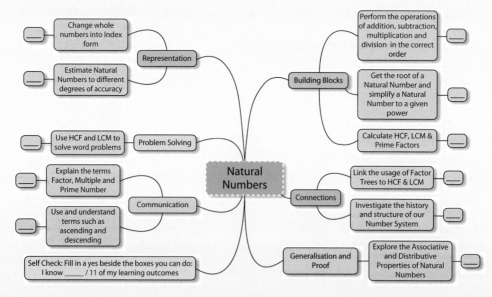

Integers

In this chapter, you will learn to:

- identify **integers**,
- add, subtract, multiply and divide positive and negative numbers,
- use a **number line to compare integer numbers**,
- use **temperature** to explain negative numbers,

- check **commutative**, **associative** and **distributive** properties of integers,
- put integers in **order**.

Section 2.1 Negative numbers

This thermometer is showing a temperature of $-10°C$ or $10°C$ below zero.

Numbers greater than zero are called **positive numbers.**
        1, 2, 3, 4, … are positive.

Numbers less than zero are called **negative numbers**.
        $-1, -2, -3,$ … are negative.

The set of positive and negative whole numbers, together with zero, is called the set of **integers**. We use the letter **Z** to represent the set of integers.
These integers can be represented on a number line as shown below.

$$Z = …-4, -3, -2, -1, 0, 1, 2, 3, 4, …$$

Decreasing   Increasing

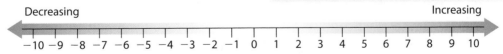

$$-10 \; -9 \; -8 \; -7 \; -6 \; -5 \; -4 \; -3 \; -2 \; -1 \quad 0 \quad 1 \quad 2 \quad 3 \quad 4 \quad 5 \quad 6 \quad 7 \quad 8 \quad 9 \quad 10$$

Negative numbers are always written with the negative sign, $-$, before them, e.g., $-3, -5, -8$.
However it is not necessary to write the plus sign, $+$, before positive numbers.

Using the number line to compare numbers

On the number line, the smaller number will appear to the left of the bigger one.

From the number line above,

    (i) $-3 < -1$ as -3 is to the left of -1

    (ii) $-2 > -4$ as -2 is to the right of -4.

> $<$ means 'is less than'
>
> $>$ means 'is greater than'

Exercise 2.1

1. Use the number line to help you find the missing terms in these sequences.

    (i) 6, 4, 2, ☐, ☐, ☐   (ii) 5, 3, 1, ☐, ☐, ☐

    (iii) 8, 4, 0, ☐, ☐, ☐   (iv) $-3, -1, 1,$ ☐, ☐, ☐

    (v) $-4, -2, 0,$ ☐, ☐, ☐   (vi) 8, 5, ☐, ☐, $-4,$ ☐

2. Which is the higher temperature in each of the following?

    (i) 8°C or 10°C   (ii) -2°C or 5°C

    (iii) 0°C or -5°C   (iv) -8°C or -5°C

    (v) -12°C or -6°C   (vi) -8°C or -14°C

3. What temperature is

    (i) 3°C warmer than 7°C   (ii) 5°C colder than 8°C

    (iii) 6°C colder than 3°C   (iv) 3°C colder than -4°C

    (v) 4°C warmer than -10°C   (vi) 8°C warmer than -8°C ?

4. Write these numbers in order, starting with the smallest:

    (i) $3, 6, -3, 0, -4, 1$ (ii) $6, -5, -8, -2, 0, 4$

    (iii) $-5, 3, 1, -2, -8, 9$ (iv) $-3, 5, -7, 0, -1, 3, -4$

5. How many degrees difference is there between

    (i) -1°C and 10°C   (ii) 13°C and -5°C   (iii) -3°C and -14°C ?

6. The temperature in a freezer is -15°C and the temperature in the room is 17°C. How many degrees difference is this?

7. List the next four integers:

    (i) greater than 2   (ii) less than -1 (iii) greater than -7.

8. Say if each of the following is true or false:
   (i) $9 > 0$ (ii) $-1 < 4$ (iii) $2 < -3$ (iv) $-4 > -1$
   (v) $0 > -4$ (vi) $-12 > 6$ (vii) $-1 < -7$ (viii) $6 > -7$.

9. The temperature of the fridge compartment of
   a fridge-freezer is set at 5°C.
   The freezer compartment is set at -18°C.
   What is the difference between these temperature
   settings?

10. The table gives the highest and lowest temperatures recorded in several cities
    during one year.

	New York	Paris	Rome	Moscow	Sydney
Highest temperature	27°C	32°C	34°C	28°C	34°C
Lowest temperature	-9°C	-6°C	8°C	-21°C	7°C

    (i) Which city recorded the lowest temperature?
    (ii) Which city recorded the biggest difference between its highest and lowest
         temperatures?
    (iii) Which city recorded the smallest difference between its highest and lowest
          temperatures?

11. Copy and complete the following by putting the symbols $>$ or $<$ in the box.
    (i) $2 \,\square\, 5$ (ii) $2 \,\square\, -3$ (iii) $0 \,\square\, 4$ (iv) $0 \,\square\, -2$
    (v) $-3 \,\square\, 4$ (vi) $-3 \,\square\, -4$ (vii) $-5 \,\square\, -1$ (viii) $-3 \,\square\, 0$

Section 2.2 Adding and subtracting integers

If the temperature is 2°C and drops 6°C, it is then -4°C.
That is, $2 - 6 = -4$.

When combining negative and positive numbers such as $2 - 6$, it can be very helpful to
use the number line.

To find $2 - 6$ on the number line, start at 0, move 2 places to the right and then move
6 places to the left.

You finish at -4.

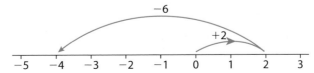

To find the value of $-1 - 4$, start at 0, move 1 place to the left and then move 4 places to the left.

The result is -5, as shown below.

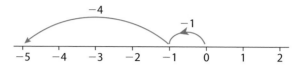

Rules for adding integers

When there are too many numbers, it may be no longer convenient to use a number line to add integers.

Take these numbers: $4 - 6 + 8 - 3$

Write the positive numbers first: $4 + 8 - 6 - 3$

Now combine the positive numbers and negative numbers separately.
$$4 + 8 - 6 - 3 = 12 - 9$$
$$= 3$$

Rules for adding integers

1. When the signs are the same, add the numbers and retain the sign.

2. When the signs are different, subtract the numbers (start with the numerically bigger number) and keep the sign of the numerically bigger number.

$$4 + 8 = 12$$
$$4 - 8 = -4$$
$$-4 + 8 = 4$$
$$-4 - 8 = -12$$

Example 1

Express each of these as a single integer:

(i) $-4 - 8$ (ii) $-7 + 2$ (iii) $-2 + 5 - 13 + 6$

(i) $-4 - 8 = -12$ ... retain the sign and add the numbers

(ii) $-7 + 2 = -5$ ... retain sign of bigger number and take 2 from 7

(iii) $-2 + 5 - 13 + 6$

We rewrite this as $-2 - 13 + 5 + 6$
$$= -15 + 11$$
$$= -4$$

Remember; as with the scale on a thermometer, a number line can be drawn vertically as well as horizontally as the following investigation will show.

Investigation:

A lift in an hotel travels between a top floor $+4$ and an underground carpark at -3.

1. If the lift starts at ground level goes up two floors, down three floors, up one floor and down two floors, what level does it finish at? Represent the movement as an integer sum.

2. The lift starts at ground level as 4 people get in, goes up three floors where 3 people leave and 4 people get in, goes down five levels where 4 people leave as 5 people get in and then goes up three levels. Using integers investigate: (i)   which level the lift is at now and
(ii)   how many people are still in the lift?

Exercise 2.2

1. Work out the following calculations using the number line.

   (i) $3 - 5$ (ii) $2 - 6$ (iii) $0 - 3$ (iv) $1 - 4$

   (v) $-1 + 4$ (vi) $-2 + 7$ (vii) $-1 - 3$ (viii) $-2 - 4$

2. Write down the calculation represented by each diagram:

   (i)

   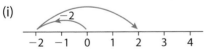

   (ii)

   (iii)

   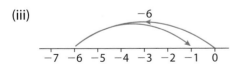

   (iv)

3. Express each of the following as a single number.

   (i) $3 + 7$ (ii) $6 - 4$ (iii) $12 - 5$ (iv) $-8 + 6$

   (v) $-10 + 3$ (vi) $2 - 8$ (vii) $-12 + 7$ (viii) $-16 + 12$

4. Simplify each of these:

   (i) $-1 - 2$ (ii) $-9 + 3$ (iii) $-4 - 2$ (iv) $1 - 8$

   (v) $-7 - 4$ (vi) $-2 + 12$ (vii) $-12 - 3$ (viii) $-20 - 30$

Express numbers **5.** to **16.** as a single number.

    5. $6 + 7 - 5$ **6.** $12 + 4 - 8$ **7.** $14 - 3 - 2$

    8. $16 - 5 - 3$ **9.** $20 - 5 - 8$ **10.** $3 - 7 + 9$

  11. $6 - 2 - 9$ **12.** $-3 + 7 - 1$ **13.** $6 - 9 + 12$

  14. $12 - 9 + 4 - 3$ **15.** $12 - 8 + 9 - 4$ **16.** $-7 - 3 + 4 + 8$

  17. Copy and complete these calculations:

    (i) $\square + 6 = 9$ (ii) $-7 + \square = 4$ (iii) $\square + 3 = -6$

    (iv) $-9 + \square = -6$ (v) $-6 - \square = 14$ (vi) $\square + 5 = -4$

  18. Copy and complete these addition squares:

    (i) 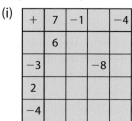   (ii)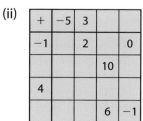

  19. Copy and complete these addition pyramids.

    (i) 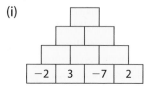   (ii)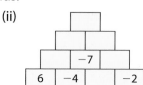

  20. In a magic square each row, each column and each diagonal adds up to the same number.

    Now copy and complete each of these magic squares.

    (i) 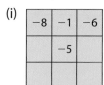   (ii)    (iii)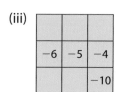

21. At 7 p.m. the temperature in Berlin was 2°C. By midnight it had dropped by 5°C. By 4 a.m. it had dropped a further 5°C. What was the temperature at 4 a.m.?

22. John had €180 in his bank account. He lodged a further €135 to his account and then withdrew €115. How much was then in his account?

23. The lift in a hotel starts in the carpark at level −2 goes up 5 floors before going down 2 floors. At what floor is the lift now?

24. In a shopping centre a customer enters a lift at level −2 goes up 5 floors and then up two more before finally coming down 6 floors to his car. At what level did he leave the lift?

Section 2.3: **Multiplying and dividing integers**

Four groups of -2 is $-2-2-2-2 = -8$

This can be written as $4 \times (-2) = -8$

Also $(-2) \times 4 = -8$ …multiplication of integers is commutative

$$4 \times 2 = 8$$
$$4 \times (-2) = -8$$
$$(-4) \times 2 = -8$$
$$(-4) \times (-2) = 8$$

The example above illustrates that a positive number multiplied by a negative number results in a negative number.

Now look at the multiplication grid opposite.

From the grid, we can see that two minus numbers multiplied together give a positive number.

×	−3	−2	−1	1	2	3
3	−9	−6	−3	3	6	9
2	−6	−4	−2	2	4	6
1	−3	−2	−1	1	2	3
−1	1	2	1	−9	−6	−3
−2	6	4	2	−6	−4	−2
−3	9	6	3	−3	−2	−1

The same rules apply to division as apply to multiplication.

Remember

When multiplying or dividing integers
> like signs give plus
> unlike signs give minus

Example 1

Write as a single integer
  (i) -3×5
  (ii) -3×-7
  (iii) $-2 \times 3 \times -4$

  (i) $-3 \times 5 = -15$ ... unlike signs give minus
  (ii) $-3 \times -7 = 21$ ... like signs give plus
  (iii) $-2 \times 3 \times -4 = -6 \times -4$ ... take two at a time
                    $= 24$

Example 2

Find the value of
  (i) $-14 \div 2$
  (ii) $-26 \div (-2)$
  (iii) $\dfrac{-5 \times (-8)}{4}$

  (i) $-14 \div 2 = -7$
  (ii) $-26 \div (-2) = 13$
  (iii) $\dfrac{-5 \times (-8)}{4} = \dfrac{40}{4} = 40 \div 4 = 10$

Removing brackets

$-4(-2)$ is the same as $-4 \times (-2) = 8$.

Now consider $-(-4)$.

  $-(-4)$ is the same as $-1(-4) = -1 \times -4$
                    $= 4$

$-(-4) = 4$

Example 3

Find the value of
  (i) $6 - (-5)$
  (ii) $-7 - (-3 + 2)$
  (iii) $-7 \times 4 - (-5)$

  (i) $6 - (-5) = 6 + 5 = 11$
  (ii) $-7 - (-3 + 2) = -7 - (-1) = -7 + 1$
                    $= -6$
  (iii) $-7 \times 4 - (-5) = -28 - (-5)$
                    $= -28 + 5$
                    $= -23$

Investigation:

Considering integers as directed numbers, investigate the principle involved in each of the following lines, particularly line (iii)

(i) +4 ...

(ii) −4 ...

(iii) −(−4) ...

Try to find a practical example to illustrate (iii)

Exercise 2.3

1. Write down the answer to each of the following:

  (i) 6×4 (ii) -5×4 (iii) $7 \times (-8)$

  (iv) $5 \times (-9)$ (v) -6×9 (vi) $(-9) \times (-4)$

  (vii) $(-8) \times (-6)$ (viii) $10 \times (-7)$ (ix) -9×8

  (x) $(-6) \times (-11)$ (xi) $4 \times (-20)$ (xii) $(-18) \times 3$

2. Work out each of these:

  (i) $-12 \div 2$ (ii) $36 \div (-4)$ (iii) $-20 \div 5$

  (iv) $-15 \div (-5)$ (v) $-30 \div (-10)$ (vi) $-24 \div 8$

3. Write down the answer to each of these:

  (i) $\dfrac{16}{2}$ (ii) $\dfrac{-8}{4}$ (iii) $\dfrac{-27}{3}$ (iv) $\dfrac{15}{-3}$ (v) $\dfrac{-42}{-7}$

  (vi) $\dfrac{-35}{7}$ (vii) $\dfrac{54}{-6}$ (viii) $\dfrac{-54}{-9}$ (ix) $\dfrac{-63}{7}$ (x) $\dfrac{55}{-11}$

4. Find the missing number in each of the following:

  (i) $6 \times \boxed{} = -48$ (ii) $-4 \times \boxed{} = 24$ (iii) $-5 \times \boxed{} = -40$

  (iv) $-20 \div \boxed{} = -4$ (v) $36 \div \boxed{} = -9$ (vi) $\boxed{} \div (-7) = -3$

5. This is a 'multiplication wall'.
The number on each brick is found by multiplying the two numbers on the bricks below.
What will be the number on the top brick of this wall?

6. Copy and complete these multiplication walls.

(i)

(ii)

(iii)

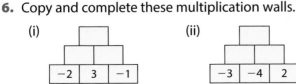

7. Express as a single integer:

    (i) $6 \times 2 \times (-3)$ (ii) $4 \times (-3) \times (-2)$ (iii) $(-6) \times 5 \times (-3)$
    (iv) $(-4) \times (-3) \times 5$ (v) $(-2) \times 6 \times (-8)$ (vi) $(-3) \times (-2) \times (-7)$

8. Express each of the following as a single integer:

    (i) $\dfrac{3 \times (-6)}{9}$ (ii) $\dfrac{(-5) \times (-10)}{-10}$ (iii) $\dfrac{(-12) \times 4}{8}$

    (iv) $\dfrac{(-8) \times (-9)}{-12}$ (v) $\dfrac{9 \times (-6)}{-2}$ (vi) $\dfrac{(-8) \times 3 \times (-6)}{-12}$

9. Choose pairs of numbers from the loop to make these calculations correct.

    (i) $\square \div \square = -3$ (ii) $\square \times \square = 14$
    (iii) $\square \times \square = -6$ (iv) $\square \div \square = -5$
    (v) $\square \div \square = 5$ (vi) $\square \times \square = -63$

    $-7 \quad -3 \quad 7 \quad -2 \quad 3 \quad 10 \quad 21 \quad -10$

10. Given that $(-4)^2 = (-4) \times (-4) = 16$, work out each of these:

    (i) $(-3)^2$ (ii) $(-6)^2$ (iii) $(-7)^2$ (iv) $(-2)^3$

11. Noting that you multiply and divide before you add and subtract, simplify each of the following:

    (i) $3 - 8 + 8 \times (-2)$ (ii) $15 + 6 \div 2 + 12 \times (-2)$
    (iii) $(16 - 4) \div 2 + 5 \times (-4)$ (iv) $(15 - 10) \times -3 + 5 \times (-6)$
    (v) $14 + 4 \times (-2) - (7 - 15)$ (vi) $100 \div (13 - 3) + (-4) \times (-7)$.

12. Since $3 \times 4 = 12$, we call 12 the product of the two numbers 3 and 4.
    Now copy and complete the table shown below.

	Sum	Product	Two numbers
(i)	-7	10	
(ii)	-13	30	
(iii)	-5	6	
(iv)	5	-6	
(v)	-8	12	
(vi)	-2	-15	

13. In a quiz, there are ten questions.
Each correct answer gains five points.
Each wrong answer loses two points.

   (i) Jane gave ten correct answers.
      How many points did she get altogether?

  (ii) Shane gave seven correct answers and three wrong answers.
      How many points did he get altogether?

 (iii) Elena answered all ten questions.
      Explain how Elena could get 43 points altogether.

Test yourself 2

1. Express each of the following as a single integer:

(i) $6 - 4$ (ii) $-6 + 4$ (iii) $-3 - 7$ (iv) $2 - 4 - 5$

(v) -3×5 (vi) $-6 \times (-3)$ (vii) $-18 \div 6$ (viii) $-24 \div (-12)$

2. List these numbers in order of size, starting with the smallest:

(i) $4, -3, 9, 0, -12, -1, 6$ (ii) $-3, 2, 14, -9, -4, 7$

3.

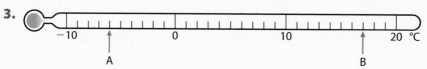

(i)   What is the temperature reading marked A?

(ii) What temperature is 4°C warmer than the temperature at A?

(iii) What temperature is 12°C colder than the temperature at B?

(iv) What is the difference between the temperatures at A and B?

4. Copy each of the following and insert the symbols $>$ (greater than) or $<$ (less than) between each pair of numbers:

(i) $3 \,\square\, -2$ (ii) $-5 \,\square\, -4$ (iii) $0 \,\square\, -7$ (iv) $-1 \,\square\, -8$

5. Choose pairs of numbers from the loop to make these calculations correct.

(i) $\square + \square = -6$ (ii) $\square \times \square = -15$

(iii) $\square \times \square = 40$ (iv) $\square + \square = -13$

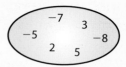

6. Copy and complete this multiplication pyramid.

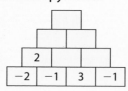

7. Simplify each of these:

(i) $6 - 8 + 5 - 10$ (ii) $6 - (-4) + 3$ (iii) $4 \times (-3) \times (-5)$

8. Copy and complete these multiplication grids.

(i)    (ii)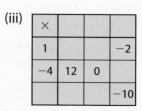

9. On a cold day, wind chill can make it *feel* even colder.
   If the wind chill is −10°C, then a temperature of 4°C would feel like −6°C.
   What does each of these temperatures feel like with a wind chill of −10°C?

   (i) 1°C   (ii) 3°C   (iii) −2°C   (iv) −15°C

10. In this grid, each letter corresponds to a number.
    For example, K corresponds to 20
    because 5 × 4 = 20.

    (i)   What number corresponds to the letter J?
    (ii) What letter corresponds to the number −10?
    (iii) For each set of numbers, work out the
          corresponding letters to spell a word.

    (a) 9, 10, 15, 12   (b) 30, −30, −4, 15   (c) −10, 10, −30, 20

11. Copy and complete the addition grid shown on the right.

+	−7	3	0	
	−11			
−2				−6
0				
		−2		

12. The top of Mount Kenya, in Africa, is about 5000 metres above sea level.
    When you climb a mountain, the temperature drops by 6 degrees Celsius for every
    1000 metres climbed.
    When the temperature at sea level is 26°C, what will the temperature be on the top
    of Mount Kenya?

13. Work out the answers and write them in order, lowest first.
    The letters will spell the name of a city.

K	A	L	C	U	N	D	A
−2 × 3	3 × (−4)	−7 + 2	1 − 9	−8 − 2	5 − 5	−3 + 7	−1 − 3

14. In a certain test, there are 10 questions. Candidates score
    3 for every question answered correctly,
    −2 for every question answered incorrectly and
    −1 for every question they do not answer.
    Declan answered 5 questions correctly, answered 3 questions incorrectly and did
    not answer 2 questions.
    Calculate his total score.

Learning Experience   *Unit 2*

Problem 1

A: Investigate how numbers are arranged on a die.

B: A die has the numbers 1, ….. 6 on its faces except that the odd numbers are negative.

If two such dice are thrown, discuss how to find which of the following **totals** cannot be achieved.

A 3   B 4   C 5   D 7   E 8   F 1

Draw a chart to explain your answer.

Assignment 1

In banking, the terms "in the black" and "in the red" are often used.

Investigate the historical significance of these terms and explain how they are connected to integer numbers.

In bank accounts today find out what the term "overdrawn" refers to?

How is a negative number recorded in a bank statement?

Problem 2

The sum of ten consecutive **integers** is 5.

Explain what is meant by the word consecutive.

Describe how to find the largest of these integers.

Assignment 2

In the early years mathematicians had difficulty dealing with the number of apples in an empty box. The Romans did not have a symbol for "nothing".

Question; how does zero behave?

Answer; generally, very well except for one problem. Find the problem.

Study zero with the operations of addition, subtraction, multiplication and division.

Draw a poster with your conclusions e.g.

$0 + \text{any integer} = ?$

$\text{any integer} + 0 = ?$

$0 - \text{any integer} = ?$

$\text{any integer} - 0 = ?$

$0 \times \text{any integer} = ?$

$\text{any integer} \times 0 = ?$

$0 \div \text{any integer} = ?$

$\text{any integer} \div 0 = ?$

Chapter 2 review 1

Using the terms from the chapter, copy and complete the following sentences:

1. The set of positive and negative whole numbers including _____ is called the set of integers.

2. When multiplying or dividing integers with like signs the answer is always _____.

3. When multiplying or dividing integers with different signs the answer is always _____.

4. Using an integer number line, numbers to the left are _____ than numbers on the right.

5. If the temperature is −5°C it is often described as 5°C _____ _____.

6. If *a* and *b* are numbers and *a* > *b* then *a* is _____ _____ *b*.

7. If *c* and *d* are numbers and *c* > *d* then *c* is _____ _____ *d*.

8. If *e*, *f* and *g* are integer numbers and *e* > *f* and *f* > *g* then *g* is _____ _____ *e*.

Chapter 2 review 2

You should now be able to:

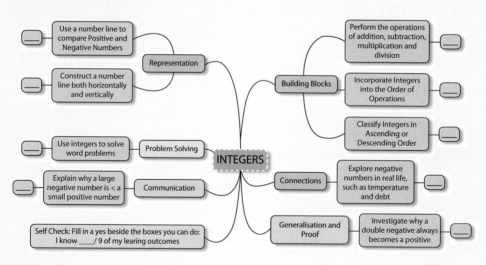

Related lines

Fractions

In this chapter, you will learn to fractions

- recognise **rational numbers** (fractions),
- recognise **numerators** and **denominators**,
- use **equivalent fractions** to simplify fractions,
- identify **proper** and **improper** fractions,
- find a fraction of an amount,
- add and subtract fractions,
- multiply and divide fractions,
- find the **reciprocal** of a fraction,
- use fractions in problem solving.

Section 3.1 Recognising fractions – Equivalent fractions

The circle on the right is divided into 4 equal parts.

The shaded part is $\frac{1}{4}$.

The unshaded part is $\frac{3}{4}$.

$\frac{1}{4}$ and $\frac{3}{4}$ are examples of **fractions**.

$\dfrac{3}{4}$ The top number is called the **numerator**.
The bottom number is called the **denominator**.

In the previous chapter we studied integer numbers, positive and negative whole numbers. Now we study numbers that are not whole numbers called **rational numbers** or **fractions**.

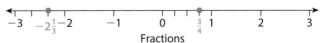

Fractions

$\frac{3}{4}$; the gap between 0 and 1 is divided into 4 equal parts.

$-2\frac{1}{3}$; the gap between −2 and −3 is divided into 3 equal parts.

When any unit is broken into smaller parts we get fractions.

Any number of the form $\frac{a}{b}$ is called a rational number (fraction).

The letter **Q** is used to represent the set of rational numbers. (See definition page 56)

Equivalent Fractions

The diagrams below show that the fractions $\frac{1}{2}$, $\frac{2}{4}$, $\frac{3}{6}$ and $\frac{4}{8}$ are all equal.

Each fraction represents half of the circle.

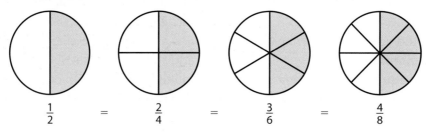

$$\frac{1}{2} \quad = \quad \frac{2}{4} \quad = \quad \frac{3}{6} \quad = \quad \frac{4}{8}$$

These fractions are said to be **equivalent** as they all have the same value.

Simplifying fractions

Fractions can be **simplified** if the top and bottom can be divided by a common factor.

Take $\frac{4}{8}$ for example.

The top and bottom can both be divided by 4.

$$\frac{4}{8} \quad \boxed{\begin{array}{l}\text{4 divided by 4 is 1}\\ \text{8 divided by 4 is 2}\end{array}} \quad \frac{1}{2}$$

$\frac{4}{8}$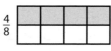

So $\frac{4}{8}$ can be simplified to $\frac{1}{2}$ $\frac{1}{2}$

Similarly, $\qquad \dfrac{12}{15} = \dfrac{12 \div 3}{15 \div 3} = \dfrac{4}{5}$

Since $\frac{4}{5}$ cannot be reduced any more, it is said to be expressed in its **simplest form**.

Example 1

Express the following fractions in their simplest form:

  (i) $\frac{18}{27}$ (ii) $\frac{21}{35}$ (iii) $\frac{22}{77}$ (iv) $\frac{48}{72}$

(i) $\dfrac{18}{27} = \dfrac{18 \div 9}{27 \div 9} = \dfrac{2}{3}$ (ii) $\dfrac{21}{35} = \dfrac{21 \div 7}{35 \div 7} = \dfrac{3}{5}$

(iii) $\dfrac{22}{77} = \dfrac{22 \div 11}{77 \div 11} = \dfrac{2}{7}$ (iv) $\dfrac{48}{72} = \dfrac{48 \div 8}{72 \div 8} = \dfrac{6}{9}$

                                          Now $\dfrac{6}{9} = \dfrac{6 \div 3}{9 \div 3} = \dfrac{2}{3}$

Exercise 3.1

1. What fraction of each of these diagrams is shaded?

(i)   (ii) 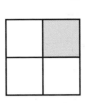   (iii) 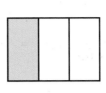   (iv)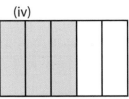

(v)   (vi)   (vii) 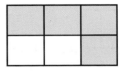   (viii)

2. What fraction of each of the diagrams above is unshaded?

3. Write down the shaded part of this figure as a fraction in two different ways.
What are these two fractions known as?

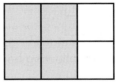

4. (i) What fraction of a week is 1 day?
(ii) What fraction of a year is 3 months?
(iii) What fraction of a year is 9 months?
(iv) What fraction of an hour is 20 minutes?

5. A cake is cut into eighths.
(i) How many people can have 1 piece each?
(ii) How many people can have 2 pieces each?

6. Fill in the missing number in each of the following:

(i) $\dfrac{4}{8} = \dfrac{\Box}{2}$ (ii) $\dfrac{6}{8} = \dfrac{\Box}{4}$ (iii) $\dfrac{4}{6} = \dfrac{\Box}{3}$ (iv) $\dfrac{10}{15} = \dfrac{\Box}{3}$

(v) $\dfrac{9}{12} = \dfrac{3}{\Box}$ (vi) $\dfrac{9}{15} = \dfrac{3}{\Box}$ (vii) $\dfrac{18}{27} = \dfrac{2}{\Box}$ (viii) $\dfrac{\Box}{21} = \dfrac{2}{3}$

7. Write each of the following fractions in its lowest terms:

(i) $\dfrac{2}{4}$ (ii) $\dfrac{3}{9}$ (iii) $\dfrac{4}{12}$ (iv) $\dfrac{8}{24}$ (v) $\dfrac{5}{30}$

(vi) $\dfrac{6}{18}$ (vii) $\dfrac{16}{24}$ (viii) $\dfrac{15}{25}$ (ix) $\dfrac{9}{27}$ (x) $\dfrac{7}{35}$

8. What fraction of this rectangle is shaded? Write it in its simplest form.

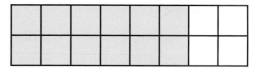

9. Write, in its simplest form, the fraction of each rectangle that is shaded.

(i)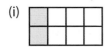

(ii)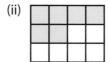

(iii)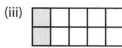

(iv)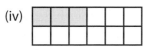

(v)

(vi)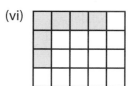

(vii)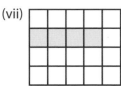

(viii)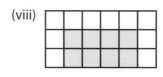

10. Write each of the following fractions as an equivalent fraction with denominator 24:

(i) $\frac{1}{2}$ (ii) $\frac{3}{4}$ (iii) $\frac{2}{3}$ (iv) $\frac{5}{8}$ (v) $\frac{11}{12}$

Use your answers to find which is the bigger fraction in each of the following:

(a) $\frac{2}{3}$ or $\frac{5}{8}$?   (b) $\frac{3}{4}$ or $\frac{2}{3}$?   (c) $\frac{5}{8}$ or $\frac{11}{12}$?

11. To what fraction is each of the following arrows pointing?

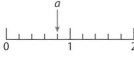 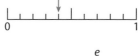 

 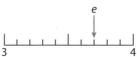 

12. You can use a fraction wall to compare fractions.

Using this fraction wall to help you, copy and complete each statement using $<$ or $>$.

(i) $\frac{2}{7}\ \square\ \frac{1}{3}$ (ii) $\frac{3}{5}\ \square\ \frac{4}{7}$

(iii) $\frac{2}{3}\ \square\ \frac{7}{8}$ (iv) $\frac{3}{8}\ \square\ \frac{2}{5}$

(v) $\frac{4}{5}\ \square\ \frac{6}{7}$ (vi) $\frac{5}{6}\ \square\ \frac{2}{3}$

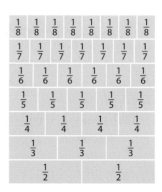

Section 3.2 Types of fractions – Fraction of a number

Fractions such as $\frac{2}{3}$ and $\frac{3}{4}$ are less than 1 since the numerator is less than the denominator.

Fractions which are less than 1 are called **proper fractions**.

Take the fraction $2\frac{1}{2}$.

$2\frac{1}{2}$ is five halves or $\frac{5}{2}$.

Fractions such as $\frac{5}{2}$ or $\frac{8}{3}$ are all greater than 1.

These are called **improper fractions**.

The number $4\frac{2}{3}$ consists of a whole number and a fraction.

It is called a **mixed number**.

> Fractions less than 1 are **proper fractions** e.g. $\frac{4}{5}$
>
> Fractions greater than 1 are **improper fractions** e.g. $\frac{6}{5}$

Example 1

Change (i) $4\frac{2}{3}$ to an improper fraction

(ii) $\frac{15}{4}$ to a mixed number.

(i) $4\frac{2}{3} = 4 + \frac{2}{3}$

$\quad = \frac{12}{3} + \frac{2}{3} = \frac{14}{3}$

> You will get the same result if you multiply 3 by 4 and then add 2, i.e., $(3 \times 4) + 2 = \frac{14}{3}$.

(ii) To change an improper fraction to a mixed number, divide the numerator (top) by the denominator (bottom) as follows:

$\frac{15}{4} = 3 + \frac{3}{4} = 3\frac{3}{4}$

Investigation:

Rational numbers take the form $\frac{a}{b}$.

Investigate the set of numbers to which a and b belong.

Are there any restrictions on the value of b?

Comparing fractions

It is much easier to compare fractions if they are written with the same denominator.
Take the fractions $\frac{4}{5}$ and $\frac{3}{4}$.

The smallest number into which both 5 and 4 divide evenly is 20.

Thus, $\dfrac{4}{5} = \dfrac{4 \times 4}{5 \times 4} = \dfrac{16}{20}$

$\dfrac{3}{4} = \dfrac{3 \times 5}{4 \times 5} = \dfrac{15}{20}$ ...20 is the LCM of 5 and 4

It is now clear that $\dfrac{16}{20} > \dfrac{15}{20}$, i.e., $\dfrac{4}{5} > \dfrac{3}{4}$.

Investigation:

Explain the connection between *fractures* and *fractions*.

Finding a fraction of a number

$\dfrac{1}{4}$ of $60 = \left[\dfrac{1}{4} \times \dfrac{60}{1} = \dfrac{60}{4}\right] = 60 \div 4 = 15$

$\dfrac{3}{4}$ of $60 = \left[\dfrac{3}{4} \times \dfrac{60}{1} = \dfrac{3 \times 60}{4}\right] = 3 \times 15 = 45$

"of" = "×"

Example 2

Find $\dfrac{7}{8}$ of 120.

$\dfrac{1}{8}$ of $120 = 120 \div 8 = 8\overline{)120} \div 8$ i.e. 15
$\phantom{\dfrac{1}{8} \text{ of } 120 = 120 \div 8 = 8)120 \div 8 } 15$

$\dfrac{7}{8}$ of $120 = 15 \times 7 = 105$

A **rational number**, Q, is a number of the form $\dfrac{a}{b}$, where a and b are **integers** and $b \neq 0$.

Exercise 3.2

1. State whether each of the following is a proper or improper fraction:

   (i) $\dfrac{3}{5}$ (ii) $\dfrac{7}{4}$ (iii) $\dfrac{1}{8}$ (iv) $\dfrac{9}{5}$ (v) $\dfrac{15}{12}$

2. Write these improper fractions as mixed numbers:

   (i) $\dfrac{6}{5}$ (ii) $\dfrac{8}{3}$ (iii) $\dfrac{11}{2}$ (iv) $\dfrac{11}{4}$ (v) $\dfrac{16}{3}$

   (vi) $\dfrac{25}{6}$ (vii) $\dfrac{29}{3}$ (viii) $\dfrac{47}{11}$ (ix) $\dfrac{63}{10}$ (x) $\dfrac{43}{8}$

3. Express each of these mixed numbers as an improper fraction:

   (i) $1\frac{2}{3}$ (ii) $2\frac{2}{5}$ (iii) $2\frac{3}{8}$ (iv) $3\frac{3}{4}$ (v) $3\frac{4}{5}$

   (vi) $4\frac{2}{3}$ (vii) $6\frac{2}{3}$ (viii) $5\frac{2}{9}$ (ix) $3\frac{7}{10}$ (x) $5\frac{4}{9}$

4. By writing each pair of fractions with the same denominator, find which is the bigger fraction in each case:

   (i) $\frac{3}{5}$ or $\frac{2}{3}$ (ii) $\frac{2}{3}$ or $\frac{3}{4}$ (iii) $\frac{2}{5}$ or $\frac{3}{7}$ (iv) $\frac{3}{4}$ or $\frac{4}{7}$

   (v) $\frac{4}{7}$ or $\frac{3}{5}$ (vi) $\frac{5}{8}$ or $\frac{4}{5}$ (vii) $\frac{2}{9}$ or $\frac{1}{5}$ (viii) $\frac{7}{10}$ or $\frac{3}{4}$

5. Work out each of these:

   (i) $\frac{1}{4}$ of 24   (ii) $\frac{3}{4}$ of 36   (iii) $\frac{2}{5}$ of 65

   (iv) $\frac{3}{10}$ of 80   (v) $\frac{4}{9}$ of 63   (vi) $\frac{4}{7}$ of 490

6. Find these amounts:

   (i) $\frac{5}{6}$ of 36 km   (ii) $\frac{3}{8}$ of €192   (iii) $\frac{7}{8}$ of 72 litres

   (iv) $\frac{5}{9}$ of 207 cm   (v) $\frac{5}{11}$ of €165   (vi) $\frac{6}{7}$ of 161 metres

7. Find the missing number in each of these:

   (i) $\frac{1}{3}$ of $\square$ = 8   (ii) $\frac{1}{\square}$ of 40 = 5   (iii) $\frac{1}{\square}$ of 12 = 3

   (iv) $\frac{2}{\square}$ of 18 = 12   (v) $\frac{\square}{5}$ of 30 = 18   (vi) $\frac{\square}{10}$ of 80 = 24

8. Put the digits in the boxes to make the calculation correct:

   (i) $\frac{\square}{\square}$ of $\square$ = $\square$ (ii) $\frac{\square}{\square}$ of $\square$ = $\square$ (iii) $\frac{\square}{\square}$ of $\square$ = $\square$

      3 4 6 8   9 2 6 3   15 25 3 5

9. A store employs 115 people and $\frac{2}{5}$ of these are men.
   How many women does the store employ?

10. Darina sold 560 sandwiches today.
   $\frac{1}{4}$ were ham sandwiches, $\frac{2}{5}$ were salad, $\frac{1}{8}$ were tuna and the rest were cheese.
   How many of each type did Darina sell?

11. What words do these make?

   (i) The first $\frac{1}{3}$ of CAMERA and the second $\frac{1}{2}$ of LIVE.

   (ii) The last $\frac{2}{5}$ of HIPPO, the first $\frac{1}{2}$ of LITTER and the last $\frac{3}{11}$ of MATHEMATICS.

12. A diagram of Jim's garden is shown.

    (i)   Copy the diagram and shade $\frac{3}{4}$ of it.

    (ii) How many sixteenths are there in $\frac{3}{4}$?

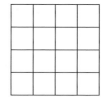

Section 3.3 Adding and subtracting fractions

It is easy to add (or subtract) fractions which have the same denominator.

For example $\frac{4}{7} + \frac{5}{7} = \frac{9}{7} = 1\frac{2}{7}$

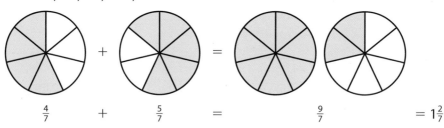

$$\frac{4}{7} \qquad + \qquad \frac{5}{7} \qquad = \qquad \frac{9}{7} \qquad = 1\frac{2}{7}$$

The diagrams above show that when adding fractions with the same denominator, you add the numerators and keep the **same** denominator.

Thus $\frac{2}{9} + \frac{3}{9} = \frac{5}{9}$ and $\frac{6}{11} - \frac{2}{11} = \frac{4}{11}$

Fractions with different denominators

How do we add $\frac{2}{3} + \frac{4}{5}$?

We must first write each fraction so that they have the same denominator.

The smallest number into which both 3 and 5 divide is 15.

$$\frac{2}{3} = \frac{2 \times 5}{3 \times 5} = \frac{10}{15} \quad \text{and} \quad \frac{4}{5} = \frac{4 \times 3}{5 \times 3} = \frac{12}{15}$$

Now $\frac{10}{15} + \frac{12}{15} = \frac{22}{15} = 1\frac{7}{15}$

Similarly, $\frac{8}{9} - \frac{5}{6} = \frac{16}{18} - \frac{15}{18}$ ... 18 is the LCM of 9 and 6

$$= \frac{1}{18}$$

Shorter method

We added fractions above using this method:

$$\frac{3}{4} + \frac{4}{5} = \frac{15}{20} + \frac{16}{20} = \frac{31}{20} = 1\frac{11}{20}$$

Your work could also be laid out in the following way:

$$\frac{3}{4} + \frac{4}{5} = \frac{3(5) + 4(4)}{20}$$

$$= \frac{15 + 16}{20} = \frac{31}{20} = 1\frac{11}{20}$$

Adding and subtracting mixed numbers

To find $4\frac{3}{4} + 2\frac{1}{6}$, first add the whole numbers 4 and 2, then add the two fractions $\frac{3}{4}$ and $\frac{1}{6}$.

Thus $\quad 4\frac{3}{4} + 2\frac{1}{6} = 4 + 2 + \frac{3}{4} + \frac{1}{6}$

$$= 6 + \frac{9}{12} + \frac{2}{12}$$

$$= 6\frac{11}{12}$$

Another way

$$4\frac{3}{4} + 2\frac{1}{6} = \frac{19}{4} + \frac{13}{6}$$

$$= \frac{19(6) + 13(4)}{24}$$

$$= \frac{114 + 52}{24}$$

$$= \frac{166}{24} = \frac{83}{12}$$

$$= 6\frac{11}{12}$$

When subtracting mixed numbers such as $3\frac{1}{4} - 2\frac{3}{8}$, first change each number to an improper fraction and then subtract as follows:

$$3\frac{1}{4} - 2\frac{3}{8} = \frac{13}{4} - \frac{19}{8}$$

$$= \frac{26}{8} - \frac{19}{8} = \frac{7}{8}$$

Example 1

Simplify $1\frac{3}{4} + 4\frac{5}{6} - 3\frac{2}{3}$.

First add $1\frac{3}{4}$ and $4\frac{5}{6}$

$$1\frac{3}{4} + 4\frac{5}{6} = 1 + 4 + \frac{3}{4} + \frac{5}{6}$$

$$= 1 + 4 + \frac{9}{12} + \frac{10}{12}$$

$$= 5 + \frac{19}{12} = 5 + 1\frac{7}{12} = 6\frac{7}{12}$$

Now $6\frac{7}{12} - 3\frac{2}{3} = \frac{79}{12} - \frac{11}{3}$

$$= \frac{79}{12} - \frac{44}{12} = \frac{35}{12} = 2\frac{11}{12}$$

Now try it this way! $\quad 1\frac{3}{4} + 4\frac{5}{6} - 3\frac{2}{3}$

$$= \frac{7}{4} + \frac{29}{6} - \frac{11}{3}$$

Exercise 3.3

1. Copy and complete the fraction additions shown by these two diagrams:
   (no need to copy diagrams)

   (i)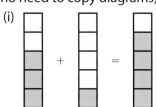

   $$\frac{\square}{5} + \frac{\square}{5} = \frac{\square}{5}$$

   (ii)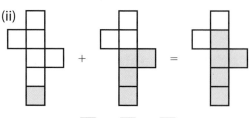

   $$\frac{\square}{7} + \frac{\square}{\square} = \frac{\square}{\square}$$

   (iii)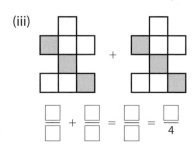

   $$\frac{\square}{\square} + \frac{\square}{\square} = \frac{\square}{\square} = \frac{\square}{4}$$

   (iv)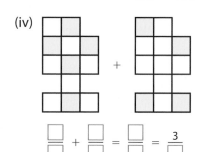

   $$\frac{\square}{\square} + \frac{\square}{\square} = \frac{\square}{\square} = \frac{3}{\square}$$

2. Work out each of these and simplify your answer where possible.
   (i) $\frac{2}{5} + \frac{1}{5}$
   (ii) $\frac{3}{7} + \frac{2}{7}$
   (iii) $\frac{1}{9} + \frac{2}{9} + \frac{4}{9}$
   (iv) $\frac{4}{11} + \frac{2}{11} + \frac{1}{11}$
   (v) $\frac{8}{9} - \frac{2}{9}$
   (vi) $\frac{9}{10} - \frac{4}{10}$
   (vii) $\frac{5}{7} + \frac{4}{7} - \frac{6}{7}$
   (viii) $\frac{9}{13} - \frac{3}{13} + \frac{5}{13}$
   (ix) $\frac{7}{8} + \frac{5}{8} - \frac{3}{8}$

3. Simplify these calculations as far as possible:
   (i) $\frac{1}{4} + \frac{3}{8}$
   (ii) $\frac{3}{10} + \frac{2}{5}$
   (iii) $\frac{5}{6} + \frac{2}{3}$
   (iv) $\frac{3}{7} + \frac{1}{14}$
   (v) $\frac{5}{12} + \frac{3}{4}$
   (vi) $\frac{2}{5} - \frac{1}{15}$
   (vii) $\frac{2}{3} - \frac{1}{4}$
   (viii) $\frac{9}{14} - \frac{1}{7}$
   (ix) $\frac{11}{20} - \frac{1}{5}$

4. Work out each of the following and simplify your answers:
   (i) $\frac{1}{3} + \frac{2}{5} + \frac{1}{15}$
   (ii) $\frac{3}{8} + \frac{1}{6} + \frac{2}{3}$
   (iii) $\frac{5}{12} + \frac{3}{4} + \frac{1}{3}$
   (iv) $\frac{2}{9} + \frac{1}{3} + \frac{1}{6}$
   (v) $\frac{3}{4} + \frac{1}{2} - \frac{1}{3}$
   (vi) $\frac{7}{12} + \frac{1}{8} - \frac{1}{6}$

5. Work these out and simplify your answers:
   (i) $2\frac{1}{3} + 1\frac{1}{6}$
   (ii) $2\frac{1}{4} + 1\frac{1}{3}$
   (iii) $3\frac{1}{2} + 2\frac{3}{5}$
   (iv) $3\frac{3}{10} + 1\frac{4}{5}$
   (v) $1\frac{3}{4} + 2\frac{5}{12}$
   (vi) $4\frac{1}{5} + 1\frac{1}{3}$
   (vii) $2\frac{7}{10} + 1\frac{3}{5}$
   (viii) $3\frac{1}{5} + 2\frac{2}{3}$
   (ix) $3\frac{2}{3} - 2\frac{1}{2}$

6. Match each calculation with its result.

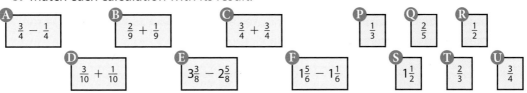

A $\frac{3}{4} - \frac{1}{4}$ B $\frac{2}{9} + \frac{1}{9}$ C $\frac{3}{4} + \frac{3}{4}$ P $\frac{1}{3}$ Q $\frac{2}{5}$ R $\frac{1}{2}$

D $\frac{3}{10} + \frac{1}{10}$ E $3\frac{3}{8} - 2\frac{5}{8}$ F $1\frac{5}{6} - 1\frac{1}{6}$ S $1\frac{1}{2}$ T $\frac{2}{3}$ U $\frac{3}{4}$

7. Work out each of these and verify your answers by using your calculator.

(i) $\frac{7}{8} + \frac{3}{4}$ (ii) $\frac{5}{6} + \frac{7}{12}$ (iii) $\frac{11}{15} - \frac{2}{5}$

(iv) $4\frac{3}{4} - 2\frac{1}{2}$ (v) $2\frac{7}{8} - 1\frac{3}{4}$ (vi) $5\frac{2}{3} - 3\frac{1}{4}$

8. Work out each of these and verify your answers by using a calculator.

(i) $5\frac{3}{4} - 2\frac{1}{3}$ (ii) $4\frac{3}{10} - 2\frac{2}{5}$ (iii) $5\frac{2}{9} + 3\frac{1}{3}$

(iv) $4\frac{3}{8} + 2\frac{1}{2} + 1\frac{3}{4}$ (v) $2\frac{7}{10} + 2\frac{3}{5} - 3\frac{1}{2}$ (vi) $3\frac{5}{8} + 2\frac{3}{4} - 4\frac{1}{6}$

9. In a magic square, each row, each column and each diagonal add up to the same number. Copy and complete this magic square.

$5\frac{1}{3}$		
$\frac{2}{3}$	$3\frac{1}{3}$	6

Section 3.4 Multiplying fractions

If you study the diagram on the right, you will see that $\frac{1}{2}$ of $\frac{2}{3}$ is $\frac{1}{3}$.

Also $\frac{1}{2} \times \frac{2}{3} = \frac{1 \times 2}{2 \times 3} = \frac{2}{6} = \frac{1}{3}$.

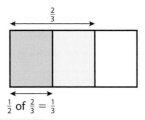

$$\frac{1}{2} \text{ of } \frac{2}{3} = \frac{1}{3}$$

This illustrates that 'of' is the same as 'multiply by'.

Now $\frac{1}{2}$ of $\frac{4}{5} = \frac{2}{5}$ and $\frac{1}{2} \times \frac{4}{5} = \frac{4}{10} = \frac{2}{5}$

> When multiplying two fractions, multiply the numerators together and the denominators together.

When multiplying mixed numbers such as $2\frac{1}{4} \times 1\frac{2}{3}$, change the mixed numbers to improper fractions as follows:

$$2\frac{1}{4} \times 1\frac{2}{3} = \frac{9}{4} \times \frac{5}{3} = \frac{45}{12} = 3\frac{9}{12} = 3\frac{3}{4}$$

Example 1

Simplify   (i) $\frac{4}{5} \times \frac{2}{3}$ (ii) $2\frac{1}{3} \times 3\frac{1}{2}$

$$\frac{4}{5} \times \frac{2}{3} = \frac{8}{15}$$

$$2\frac{1}{3} \times 3\frac{1}{2}$$
$$= \frac{7}{3} \times \frac{7}{2} = \frac{49}{6} = 8\frac{1}{6}$$

Simplifying fractions

Sometimes when multiplying two fractions, we can simplify our work by dividing the numerator and denominator by a common factor.

Now $\quad \dfrac{3}{8} \times \dfrac{4}{9} = \dfrac{12}{72} = \dfrac{1}{6}$ $\quad$ or $\quad \dfrac{{}^{1}\cancel{3}}{\cancel{8}_{2}} \times \dfrac{{}^{1}\cancel{4}}{\cancel{9}_{3}} = \dfrac{1 \times 1}{2 \times 3} = \dfrac{1}{6}$

Example 2

Work out $\quad$ (i) $\;1\frac{3}{4} \times 2\frac{2}{3}$ $\qquad\qquad$ (ii) $\;1\frac{3}{7} \times \frac{21}{35}$

$$1\frac{3}{4} \times 2\frac{2}{3} = \frac{7}{{}_{1}\cancel{4}} \times \frac{\cancel{8}^{2}}{3}$$

$$= \frac{14}{3} = 4\frac{2}{3}$$

$$1\frac{3}{7} \times \frac{21}{35} = \frac{{}^{2}\cancel{10}}{{}_{1}\cancel{7}} \times \frac{{}^{3}\cancel{21}}{\cancel{35}_{7}}$$

$$= \frac{2 \times 3}{1 \times 7} = \frac{6}{7}$$

Calculators

Calculators allow us to perform calculations quickly. The calculator has two special keys.

(i) $\boxed{\frac{\blacksquare}{\square}}$ for proper and improper fractions.

and (ii) $\boxed{\blacksquare\frac{\blacksquare}{\square}}$ for mixed numbers.

When using a calculator to find the answer to a calculation involving fractions it is important to check the screen of the calculator regularly to make sure that you are inputting all of the digits correctly.

 When using your calculator to work out $\frac{3}{4} \times \frac{2}{5}$, key in

$\boxed{\frac{\blacksquare}{\square}}\;\boxed{3}\;\boxed{\downarrow}\;\boxed{4}\;\boxed{\rightarrow}\;\boxed{\times}\;\boxed{\frac{\blacksquare}{\square}}\;\boxed{2}\;\boxed{\downarrow}\;\boxed{5}\;\boxed{\rightarrow}\;\boxed{=}$

The result is $\frac{3}{10}$.

To find the value of $2\frac{1}{3} \times 3\frac{1}{2}$, key in

$\boxed{\text{SHIFT}}\;\boxed{\frac{\blacksquare}{\square}}\;\boxed{2}\;\boxed{\rightarrow}\;\boxed{1}\;\boxed{\downarrow}\;\boxed{3}\;\boxed{\rightarrow}\;\boxed{\times}\;\boxed{\frac{\blacksquare}{\square}}\;\boxed{3}\;\boxed{\rightarrow}\;\boxed{1}\;\boxed{\downarrow}\;\boxed{2}\;\boxed{\rightarrow}\;\boxed{=}$

The answer is $8\frac{1}{6}$.

Note 1 If you convert $2\frac{1}{3} \times 3\frac{1}{2}$ to $\frac{7}{3} \times \frac{7}{2}$, it can be done much more quickly on a calculator.

To find $\frac{7}{3} \times \frac{7}{2}$, key in $\boxed{\frac{\blacksquare}{\square}}\;\boxed{7}\;\boxed{\downarrow}\;\boxed{3}\;\boxed{\rightarrow}\;\boxed{\times}\;\boxed{\frac{\blacksquare}{\square}}\;\boxed{7}\;\boxed{\downarrow}\;\boxed{2}\;\boxed{\rightarrow}\;\boxed{=}$

The result is $8\frac{1}{6}$.

Note 2 When multiplying a fraction by a whole number, e.g. $3\frac{1}{2} \times 8$, write 8 as $\frac{8}{1}$ and proceed as follows:

$$3\frac{1}{2} \times 8 = \frac{7}{2} \times \frac{8}{1} = \frac{56}{2} = 28$$

Exercise 3.4

Work out each of the following and give your answer in its simplest form.

1. $\frac{1}{2} \times \frac{3}{4}$
2. $\frac{3}{4} \times \frac{1}{5}$
3. $\frac{3}{4} \times \frac{3}{5}$

4. $\frac{4}{5} \times \frac{2}{3}$
5. $\frac{4}{7} \times \frac{2}{3}$
6. $\frac{3}{4} \times \frac{8}{9}$

7. $\frac{3}{4} \times \frac{4}{5}$
8. $\frac{8}{9} \times \frac{3}{10}$
9. $\frac{3}{4} \times \frac{2}{21}$

10. $\frac{5}{6} \times \frac{2}{15}$
11. $\frac{7}{12} \times \frac{18}{35}$
12. $\frac{3}{16} \times \frac{8}{9}$

13. $\frac{2}{3} \times \frac{6}{7} \times \frac{3}{4}$
14. $\frac{3}{7} \times \frac{5}{9} \times \frac{21}{5}$
15. $\frac{1}{2} \times \frac{7}{12} \times \frac{6}{7}$

16. $2\frac{2}{3} \times 1\frac{1}{4}$
17. $4\frac{1}{5} \times \frac{5}{7}$
18. $1\frac{4}{5} \times 2\frac{1}{3}$

19. $3\frac{3}{4} \times 1\frac{2}{5}$
20. $1\frac{2}{5} \times 2\frac{1}{7}$
21. $3\frac{3}{4} \times 1\frac{1}{5}$

22. $4\frac{3}{5} \times 5$
23. $1\frac{7}{8} \times 8$
24. $\frac{7}{10} \times 20$

25. $3\frac{5}{7} \times 14$
26. $28 \times 2\frac{3}{7}$
27. $\frac{5}{21} \times 14$

28. Work out each answer and use the code to change it to a letter. (You may need to simplify your answer.)

S	O	B	H	K	L	T	E	A	C	N	D
$\frac{2}{3}$	$\frac{3}{4}$	$1\frac{1}{2}$	$1\frac{2}{5}$	$1\frac{3}{5}$	$1\frac{4}{5}$	$2\frac{1}{3}$	$2\frac{1}{2}$	$2\frac{2}{3}$	$2\frac{3}{4}$	$3\frac{3}{4}$	$4\frac{3}{4}$

Then rearrange each set of letters to spell a piece of furniture.

(i) $\frac{1}{4}$ of 19 $\frac{1}{5}$ of 8 $\frac{1}{3}$ of 2 $\frac{1}{4}$ of 10

(ii) $\frac{1}{4}$ of 3 $\frac{1}{3}$ of 7 $\frac{1}{5}$ of 9 $\frac{1}{8}$ of 6 $\frac{1}{6}$ of 4

(iii) $\frac{1}{2}$ of 3 $\frac{1}{4}$ of 11 $\frac{1}{5}$ of 7 $\frac{1}{4}$ of 15 $\frac{1}{2}$ of 5

29. Work these out. Cancel first and then simplify your answer where possible:

(i) $\frac{3}{4} \times \frac{5}{7} \times \frac{2}{3}$ (ii) $\frac{9}{20} \times \frac{5}{6} \times \frac{4}{5}$ (iii) $3\frac{1}{3} \times 1\frac{4}{5} \times 2$

(iv) $2\frac{3}{4} \times 1\frac{1}{11} \times \frac{1}{4}$ (v) $7\frac{1}{2} \times \frac{9}{10} \times 1\frac{1}{3}$ (vi) $3\frac{1}{5} \times 2\frac{1}{2} \times 1\frac{3}{4}$

Section 3.5 Dividing fractions

To find how many sixes in 24 we divide 24 by 6, i.e. $24 \div 6 = 4$.
In the same way, to find the number of *halves* in 3, we find $3 \div \frac{1}{2}$.

(i) The diagram shows that there are 6 halves in 3, i.e. $3 \div \frac{1}{2} = 6$

(ii) Also to find out how many $\frac{1}{2}$ units are in $\frac{3}{4}$ of a unit we divide $\frac{3}{4}$ by $\frac{1}{2}$.

i.e. $\frac{3}{4} \div \frac{1}{2} = 1\frac{1}{2}$

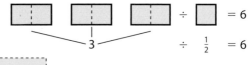

$\frac{3}{4}$ unit $\div$ $\frac{1}{2}$ unit $= 1\frac{1}{2}$

In (i) we notice that $3 \div \frac{1}{2} = 3 \times \frac{2}{1} = 6$

Also in (ii) we have $\frac{3}{4} \div \frac{1}{2} = \frac{3}{4} \times \frac{2}{1} = \frac{6}{4} = 1\frac{1}{2}$

> To divide a number by a fraction, multiply the number by the **fraction turned upside down.**

Reciprocal

If the fraction $\frac{1}{4}$ is turned upside down the fraction $\frac{4}{1}$ is made.

$\frac{4}{1}$ is called the **reciprocal** of $\frac{1}{4}$.

Also $\frac{4}{5}$ is the reciprocal of $\frac{5}{4}$.

Note; the reciprocal of $7 \left(= \frac{7}{1} \right)$ is $\frac{1}{7}$.

Since $\frac{3}{1} \div \frac{1}{2} = \frac{3}{1} \times \frac{2}{1}$, dividing by a fraction is the same as multiplying by the reciprocal of the fraction.

> $\frac{b}{a}$ is the **reciprocal** of $\frac{a}{b}$

> To divide a number by a fraction, multiply the number by the **reciprocal** of the fraction.

Example 1

Find the reciprocal of the following numbers:
  (i) $\frac{2}{5}$ (ii) $1\frac{4}{9}$ (iii) 5

  (i) $\frac{5}{2}$ is the reciprocal of $\frac{2}{5}$

  (ii) $1\frac{4}{9} = \frac{13}{9}$ $\therefore \frac{9}{13}$ is the reciprocal of $1\frac{4}{9}$

  (iii) $5 = \frac{5}{1}$ $\therefore \frac{1}{5}$ is the reciprocal of 5.

Example 2

Work out   (i) $15 \div \frac{5}{8}$ (ii) $4\frac{1}{6} \div 1\frac{2}{3}$

  (i) $15 \div \frac{5}{8} = \frac{3\cancel{15}}{1} \times \frac{8}{\cancel{5}_1} = \frac{24}{1} = 24$

  (ii) $4\frac{1}{6} \div 1\frac{2}{3} = \frac{25}{6} \div \frac{5}{3} = \frac{5\cancel{25}}{2\cancel{6}} \times \frac{\cancel{3}^1}{\cancel{5}_1} = \frac{5}{2} = 2\frac{1}{2}$

Exercise 3.5

1. Shane has $\frac{4}{5}$ of a bar of chocolate. He shares it equally between two people. What fraction of the bar do they each get?

2. Find the reciprocal of each of the following fractions:
   (i) $\frac{7}{3}$ (ii) $\frac{4}{9}$ (iii) 6   (iv) $\frac{1}{5}$ (v) $\frac{3}{11}$

3. Find the reciprocal of each of the following fractions:
   (i) $2\frac{1}{3}$ (ii) $1\frac{2}{9}$ (iii) 10   (iv) $3\frac{4}{5}$ (v) $1\frac{1}{4}$

4. Rewrite each of these as a multiplication and then work out the answer.
   (i) $\frac{3}{4} \div \frac{1}{2}$ (ii) $\frac{5}{6} \div \frac{2}{3}$ (iii) $\frac{2}{5} \div \frac{9}{10}$ (iv) $\frac{7}{12} \div \frac{1}{6}$
   (v) $6 \div \frac{3}{4}$ (vi) $12 \div \frac{4}{9}$ (vii) $16 \div \frac{8}{9}$ (viii) $27 \div \frac{3}{4}$

5. Work out each of the following:
   (i) $3\frac{3}{4} \div \frac{3}{8}$ (ii) $2\frac{5}{8} \div \frac{3}{4}$ (iii) $2\frac{1}{10} \div \frac{3}{5}$ (iv) $2\frac{5}{8} \div \frac{7}{16}$
   (v) $1\frac{1}{8} \div 2\frac{1}{4}$ (vi) $8\frac{1}{4} \div 1\frac{3}{8}$ (vii) $5\frac{5}{8} \div 6\frac{1}{4}$ (viii) $3\frac{1}{8} \div 3\frac{3}{4}$

6. Which diagram below matches $\frac{1}{4} \div 2$?

    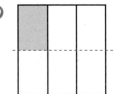

7. Work out each of these:
   (i) $5\frac{3}{7} \div 1\frac{3}{7}$ (ii) $10\frac{5}{6} \div 3\frac{1}{4}$ (iii) $6\frac{2}{3} \div 2\frac{4}{9}$ (iv) $1\frac{4}{5} \div \frac{27}{10}$

8. Match each calculation to a diagram.

      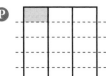 

9. Simplify each of the following by first working out what is inside the brackets:

   (i) $\left(\frac{3}{4} \times \frac{2}{9}\right) \div \frac{1}{12}$

   (ii) $1\frac{1}{3} \times \left(\frac{3}{10} \div \frac{1}{2}\right)$

   (iii) $\left(\frac{3}{4} \div \frac{7}{12}\right) \times 4\frac{2}{3}$

10. Denise has $\frac{1}{3}$ of a cake.
    She shares it equally between herself, her brother and her sister.
    What fraction of the cake do they each get?

11. Put these calculations into pairs which give the same answer.
    Write down the answer to each pair.

    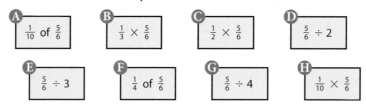

A	B	C	D
$\frac{1}{10}$ of $\frac{5}{6}$	$\frac{1}{3} \times \frac{5}{6}$	$\frac{1}{2} \times \frac{5}{6}$	$\frac{5}{6} \div 2$

E	F	G	H
$\frac{5}{6} \div 3$	$\frac{1}{4}$ of $\frac{5}{6}$	$\frac{5}{6} \div 4$	$\frac{1}{10} \times \frac{5}{6}$

12. Simplify each of the following by first working out what is inside the brackets:

    (i) $\left(\frac{3}{5} + \frac{1}{3}\right) \div \frac{2}{3}$

    (ii) $\left(\frac{4}{9} + \frac{1}{3}\right) \times \frac{6}{7}$

    (iii) $\frac{5}{8} \div \left(3\frac{1}{2} - 1\frac{1}{4}\right)$

13.

S	G	R	I	O	A	D	P	W	L	E	M
$\frac{1}{12}$	$\frac{1}{10}$	$\frac{1}{9}$	$\frac{1}{8}$	$\frac{1}{6}$	$\frac{3}{16}$	$\frac{1}{5}$	$\frac{1}{4}$	$\frac{3}{8}$	$\frac{1}{2}$	$\frac{2}{5}$	$\frac{3}{4}$

Work out each answer and use the code to change it to a letter.
Then rearrange each set of letters to spell a city.

(i) $\frac{4}{5} \div 2$ $\frac{1}{2}$ of $\frac{2}{9}$ $\frac{1}{2}$ of $1\frac{1}{2}$ $\frac{5}{6} \div 5$

(ii) $\frac{1}{10} \times \frac{5}{6}$ $\frac{1}{3}$ of $\frac{3}{4}$ $\frac{1}{16}$ of 3 $\frac{3}{8} \div 3$ $2 \times \frac{1}{18}$

(iii) $\frac{3}{5} \div 3$ $\frac{1}{2} \times \frac{2}{5}$ $\frac{1}{4}$ of 3 $\frac{1}{3} \times \frac{1}{3}$ $\frac{3}{8} \div 2$ $\frac{1}{4} \times \frac{1}{2}$

14. How many shelves could Carl make with $2\frac{1}{3}$ m of wood if each shelf measures $\frac{1}{6}$ m.

15. Show that if you divide $\frac{2}{3}$ m by $\frac{3}{4}$ m you get $\frac{8}{9}$. Interpret this result.

Section 3.6 Problems involving fractions ───────

When solving problems involving fractions, you must decide whether to add, subtract, multiply or divide.

(i) to find $\frac{3}{4}$ of 16, multiply $\frac{3}{4} \times \frac{16}{1} = \frac{48}{4} = 12$

(ii) to find 150 g as a fraction of 1 kg, convert both to the same units and divide

$1 \text{ kg} = 1000 \text{ g}$ $\quad \therefore \frac{150}{1000} = \frac{3}{20}$ (150 g is $\frac{3}{20}$ of 1 kg)

(iii) if you spend $\frac{4}{5}$ of your money, you have $\frac{1}{5}$ left.

Example 1

Express 18 minutes as a fraction of an hour.
Give your answer in its simplest form.

To express one quantity as a fraction of another quantity, both quantities must be in the same units.

$\therefore \dfrac{18 \text{ minutes}}{1 \text{ hour}} = \dfrac{18}{60}$ ..... both in minutes

$\qquad\qquad = \dfrac{3}{10}$ ..... divide above and below by 6

Example 2

Ciara spent $\frac{3}{7}$ of her money and had €12 left.
How much had she at first?

If she spent $\frac{3}{7}$, she had $\frac{4}{7}$ left.

$\frac{4}{7} = €12$

$\therefore \frac{1}{7} = €3$ ..... divide by 4

$\therefore \frac{7}{7} = €21$

$\therefore$ she had €21 at first.

Exercise 3.6

1. Express the first quantity as a fraction of the second quantity, and give each fraction in its lowest terms:

   (i) 16, 24 (ii) 3 days, 1 week (iii) 40 c, €2

   (iv) 24 mins, 2 hours (v) €1.20, €3 (vi) 8 hours, 3 days

2. Hannah spends $\frac{1}{5}$ of her pocket money on sweets and $\frac{2}{3}$ on clothes.
   She saves the rest.
   What fraction of her pocket money does Hannah save?

3. The first $\frac{1}{2}$ of TANK is TA. The last $\frac{1}{3}$ of IRRITABLE is BLE.
Put them together and you get TABLE.
What words do these make?

   (i)   The first $\frac{1}{3}$ of TRIANGLES and the second $\frac{1}{2}$ of STICKS

  (ii)   The first $\frac{2}{5}$ of PRECIPICES and the last $\frac{2}{5}$ of VICTORIOUS

 (iii)   The first $\frac{1}{3}$ of DISCUSSED, the first $\frac{1}{4}$ of APPLICATIONS and the last $\frac{3}{4}$ of FEAR

4. A journey to school consists of a $\frac{2}{5}$ km walk, then a $3\frac{1}{4}$ km bus journey, and finally a $\frac{1}{2}$ km walk from the bus stop to the school.
Find the total length of the journey to school.

5. Find $\frac{3}{8}$ of €576.

6. In a bag of 56 coloured counters, $\frac{1}{4}$ are red, $\frac{2}{7}$ are blue and the rest are yellow.
How many of the counters are yellow?

7. Emer bought a 3-hour blank video tape. She recorded programmes lasting $1\frac{1}{2}$ hours, $\frac{3}{4}$ hour and $\frac{2}{3}$ hour on this tape.
How many minutes recording time were left on the tape?

8. Three quarters of a certain number is 27.

    Find   (i) $\frac{1}{4}$ of the number.
           (ii) the whole number.

9. Alan spent $\frac{4}{9}$ of his money. If he had €65 left, how much had he at first?

10. How many $1\frac{1}{4}$ litre cartons of orange juice can be filled from a container holding 40 litres?

11. $\frac{3}{7}$ of the students in first-year are girls.
If there are 64 boys in first-year, find the number of girls in the year.

12. $\frac{2}{5}$ of the spectators at a football match were in the terraces and the remaining 17 580 were in the stands. Find the total number of spectators at the match.

13. How many $\frac{1}{4}$ litre glasses can be filled from a container which contains $4\frac{1}{2}$ litres?

14. A ferry completes one crossing in $1\frac{1}{2}$ hours.
What is the greatest number of crossings it can make in a 24 hour period?

15. Which of the letters on the line below corresponds to $\frac{5}{8}$?

16. A class of 30 students went to a fast-food bar.
$\frac{3}{10}$ of them bought a hamburger, $\frac{2}{5}$ of them bought a pizza
and the remainder bought chips.

  (i) What fraction of the students bought chips?

  (ii) How many students bought a pizza?

Test yourself 3

1. Express each of the following fractions in its simplest form:

   (i) $\frac{5}{15}$ (ii) $\frac{12}{16}$ (iii) $\frac{16}{24}$ (iv) $\frac{18}{30}$ (v) $\frac{21}{28}$

2. Express each of the following as an improper fraction (e.g. $1\frac{1}{4} = \frac{5}{4}$)

   (i) $1\frac{1}{2}$ (ii) $2\frac{1}{4}$ (iii) $3\frac{2}{3}$ (iv) $4\frac{3}{4}$ (v) $2\frac{4}{5}$

3. Copy and complete the following:

   (i) $\frac{1}{6} = \frac{?}{12}$ (ii) $\frac{2}{5} = \frac{6}{?}$ (iii) $\frac{4}{7} = \frac{12}{?}$

4. Perform the following operations and simplify your answers where possible:

   (i) $\frac{1}{2} + \frac{1}{3}$ (ii) $\frac{5}{8} + \frac{3}{4}$ (iii) $\frac{5}{6} + \frac{2}{3}$ (iv) $\frac{5}{7} + \frac{3}{14}$

   (v) $\frac{1}{2} - \frac{1}{3}$ (vi) $\frac{1}{3} - \frac{1}{4}$ (vii) $\frac{3}{4} - \frac{2}{3}$ (viii) $\frac{3}{4} - \frac{5}{12}$

5. To what fraction is each of the following arrows pointing?

    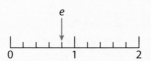 

6. Express each pair of fractions with the same denominator and then state the bigger fraction:

   (i) $\frac{3}{4}$ or $\frac{2}{3}$ (ii) $\frac{1}{3}$ or $\frac{2}{5}$ (iii) $\frac{2}{3}$ or $\frac{7}{12}$ (iv) $\frac{7}{11}$ or $\frac{20}{33}$

7. Express each of the following as a single fraction, mixed number or whole number.

   (i) $\frac{3}{4} \times \frac{2}{5}$ (ii) $\frac{1}{4} \times 8$ (iii) $3\frac{1}{4} \times \frac{1}{2}$ (iv) $4\frac{1}{2} \times \frac{2}{3}$

   (v) $\frac{3}{4} \div \frac{1}{2}$ (vi) $\frac{5}{8} \div \frac{3}{4}$ (vii) $\frac{4}{9} \div \frac{2}{3}$ (viii) $2\frac{2}{3} \div \frac{2}{3}$

8. Work out each answer and use the code to change it to a letter. Then rearrange each set of letters to spell an item of food.

R	A	D	S	C	B	E	H	I	F	T	P
$\frac{6}{7}$	$1\frac{1}{5}$	$1\frac{1}{3}$	$1\frac{1}{2}$	$1\frac{2}{3}$	$2\frac{1}{4}$	$2\frac{2}{5}$	$2\frac{4}{5}$	$3\frac{1}{5}$	$3\frac{1}{3}$	$3\frac{3}{4}$	$6\frac{3}{4}$

   (i) $\frac{2}{5} \times 8$ $\frac{2}{3} \times 5$ $\frac{2}{5} \times 7$ $\frac{3}{4} \times 2$

   (ii) $\frac{2}{5}$ of 6 $\frac{3}{7}$ of 2 $\frac{2}{5}$ of 3 $\frac{2}{3}$ of 2 $\frac{3}{4}$ of 3

   (iii) $\frac{3}{10}$ of 4 $\frac{3}{5}$ of 2 $\frac{3}{8}$ of 4 $\frac{3}{4}$ of 9 $\frac{5}{8}$ of 6

9. Simplify each of these:

   (i) $\frac{8}{9} + \frac{2}{3}$ (ii) $2\frac{9}{10} - 1\frac{3}{5}$ (iii) $2\frac{2}{3} \times 2\frac{1}{4}$ (iv) $2\frac{4}{5} \div \frac{7}{10}$

10. A mother walks from home to the shop and then on to the school. If she then walks $1\frac{1}{2}$ km back to her home as show on the right, find how many km she walked in total.

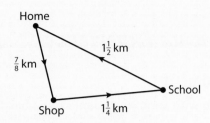

11. Niamh spent $\frac{1}{4}$ of her pocket money and had €10.50 left. How much pocket money did she have at first?

12. 24 boys and 36 girls applied to go on a mountaineering course. $\frac{3}{4}$ of the boys and $\frac{2}{3}$ of the girls were selected. Find the total number that went on the course.

13. (i) What fraction of this figure is shaded?
    (ii) How many more squares would have to be shaded for $\frac{3}{4}$ of the figure to be shaded?

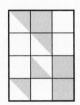

14. A farmer had 240 animals on his farm. $\frac{5}{8}$ of them were sheep, $\frac{1}{10}$ were pigs, six of them were horses and the rest were cows. How many cows did he have?

15. Simplify each of the following by first working out what is inside the brackets.
    (i) $\left(\frac{2}{3} \times \frac{1}{2}\right) \div \frac{3}{4}$
    (ii) $\left(3\frac{1}{7} - 1\frac{1}{2}\right) \times 14$
    (iii) $\left(1\frac{3}{5} + 2\frac{2}{3}\right) \times \frac{5}{8}$

16.

	Men	Women	Children
Fraction of people	$\frac{3}{10}$	$\frac{1}{10}$	A
Number of people	B	50	C

The table above shows information about the number of people watching a fireworks display.
    (i) Find the fraction marked A.
    (ii) Work out the numbers marked B and C.

Learning Experience   Unit 3

Assignment 1

Working with another student drop a ball from a height
of 2 m.
Measure the height of the rebound.
Calculate the height of the rebound as a fraction of the
original height.
Drop the ball from the rebound height.
Measure the new rebound height and check if the fraction is the same.
Repeat with different balls and different surfaces.

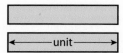

Problem 1

A ball is dropped onto a hard surface and each time it bounces it rebounds to
exactly one third of the previous height. If after the second bounce the ball rises
to a height of 9 cm, describe how to find the height from which it was dropped
originally.

Assignment 2

Design two cardboard strips, each of length 1 unit,
to show that $\frac{1}{2}$ divided by $\frac{1}{6}$ is 3.

Problem 2

Each morning Alan walks at a steady rate to school. When he has gone a quarter
of the way he passes the clock tower; at one third of the way he passes the
railway station. The clock on the tower shows 8.30 am and the clock at the
railway station shows 8.35 am.

Describe how to find the time Alan leaves his house and the time he arrives at
school.

Chapter 3 review 1

Using the terms from the chapter copy and complete the following sentences:

1. When any unit is broken into parts, _____ of the unit are created.

2. The bottom number of a fraction is called a _____.

3. $\frac{1}{2}, \frac{2}{4}, \frac{3}{6}$ are examples of _____ fractions.

4. Fractions less than 1 are called _____ fractions.

5. Improper fractions are fractions that are _____ than 1.

6. To compare two fractions it is best to convert them to fractions with the same _____.

7. The top number of a fraction is called a _____.

8. If you are asked to find a fraction of a fraction you _____ the fractions.

9. Fractions are also called _____
_____.

10. To divide fractions, the second fraction must be _____
_____ _____ and multiplied by the first fraction.

Chapter 3 review 2

You should now be able to:

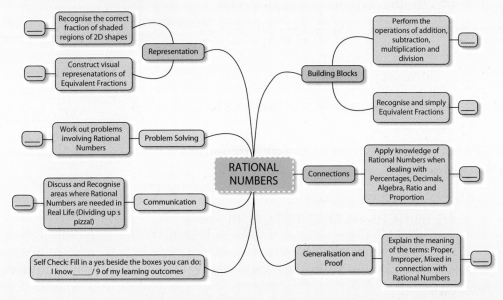

Probability

4

In this chapter, you will learn to:

- list the **outcomes** of an experiment,
- use the **fundamental principle of counting**,
- use **two-way** tables,
- link **events and outcomes**,
- link **chance** with probability,
- check for **equally likely** outcomes,
- use **fractions** to measure probability,
- identify **favourable** outcomes,
- make a **probability scale**,
- understand **fair / biased** experiments,
- apply probability to, the tossing of coins, the rolling of dice, spinning of spinners, picking of cards form a deck of cards etc.

Section 4.1 Listing outcomes

When a die is thrown, you will get

1, 2, 3, 4, 5 or 6.

These are called results or **outcomes**.

If you toss a coin, the outcomes are **head** and **tail**.

When this spinner is spun, the number outcomes are

1, 2, 3, 4, 5, 6.

The colour outcomes are blue and green.

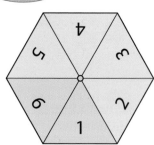

In the three examples above, we have **listed** all the possible outcomes.

We will now list the outcomes when a die is thrown and a coin is tossed.

Here is the list of possible outcomes:

H1, H2, H3, H4, H5, H6, T1, T2, T3, T4, T5, T6

Notice that there are 12 outcomes.

Notice also that there were **2** outcomes when a coin is tossed and **6** outcomes when a die is thrown.

The **12** outcomes listed above could be found much more easily by multiplying **6** by **2** to get **12**.

The preceding example illustrates the **Fundamental Principle of Counting** which is given on the right.

> If one event has **m** possible outcomes and a second event has **n** possible outcomes, the two events have **m** × **n** possible outcomes.

Example 1

This is the choice for a two-course meal at *The Red Robin Cafe*.

If a diner has a starter and main course, how many choices does she have?

List the choices.

The Red Robin Cafe

Starters
Avocado   (A)
Soup   (S)

Main Courses
Beef   (B)
Chicken   (C)
Plaice   (P)

There are 2 starters and 3 main courses.

Number of choices = 2 × 3
            = 6

These choices are as follows:

AB, AC, AP, SB, SC, SP.

The **Fundamental Principle of Counting** can be extended to any number of events.

If a menu consists of 2 starters, 4 main courses, and 3 desserts, then a three-course meal can be selected in

2 × 4 × 3, i.e., 24 ways.

If an operation consists of choosing *x* first **and** *y* second, we **multiply** the numbers.

Two-way tables

In experiments that involve two parts, the outcomes can be arranged in an organised way by using a **two-way** table.

e.g. tossing a coin and rolling a die:

Tossing a coin gives a **H**ead or a **T**ail outcome.

Rolling a die gives a **1, 2, 3, 4, 5, 6** outcome.

There are 12 possible outcomes.

(T, 2) means a Tail on the coin and a 2 on the die.

Coin outcomes	Die outcomes					
	1	2	3	4	5	6
H	H,1	H,2	H,3	H,4	H,5	H,6
T	T,1	T,2	T,3	T,4	T,5	T,6

e.g. tossing two coins:

First coin gives a **H**ead or a **T**ail outcome.

Second coin gives a **H**ead or a **T**ail outcome.

A total of 4 possible outcomes (2 × 2)

Note; since the coins are different, (**T, H**) is different from (**H, T**)

	Second coin	
First coin	H	T
H	H, H	H, T
T	T, H	T, T

Example 2

Two spinners are spun and the outcomes from the two spinners are added.

Find the number of outcomes possible. Using a two-way table find how many outcomes result in:

(i) a total of 5   (ii) an even number total.

Number of outcomes = 4 × 3 = 12

(i) a total of 5, 2 outcomes (3, 2), (1, 4)

(ii) an even number total, 4 outcomes (4, 6, 8, 10)

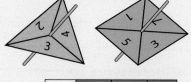

	2	3	4
1	3	4	5
3	5	6	7
5	7	8	9
7	9	10	11

Exercise 4.1

1. A coin is tossed and this spinner is spun.
   (i) How many different outcomes are possible?
   (ii) List all these outcomes.

2. An 'early-bird' menu consists of 2 starters and 4 main courses. How many different 2-course meals can you have?

3. Two coins are tossed. List all the possible outcomes, using H for head and T for tail.

4. A coin is tossed and this spinner is spun.
   (i) How many possible outcomes are there?
   (ii) List these outcomes.

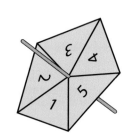

5. A certain car is available in saloon or estate.
   Each of these is available in three different engine sizes and five different colours.
   How many different versions of the car are available?

6. There are four roads from *A* to *B* and five roads from *B* to *C*.
   In how many different ways can a person travel from *A* to *C*?

7. These two spinners are spun.
   (i) How many different outcomes
      are possible?
   (ii) List all these outcomes.

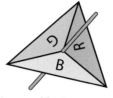 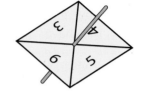

8. Paint comes in the colours green, blue, lilac and beige.
   Jamie wants to paint the walls of his cafe.
   He wants to paint the top half one colour and the bottom half a different colour.
   In how many different ways can he do this?

9. A code for a lock consists of one letter and one digit.
   The letters can be A, B, C, D or E.
   The digits can be 1, 3, 5, 7, 9.
   How many different codes are possible?

10. Darren is dressing up for his first interview.
    He has 5 shirts, 3 ties and 3 jackets to choose from.
    If he is to wear a shirt, a tie and a jacket, how many different choices can he make?

11. A factory makes shirts as follows:

Material	silk	cotton	denim	
Size	small	medium	large	extra large
Sleeve	long	short		

   Calculate how many different types of shirt the factory makes.

12. Three coins are tossed.
    Make a list of all possible outcomes.
    Start with HHH, HHT, …
    How many different outcomes are there?

13. A lunch consists of a soup, a main course and a dessert.

    The Restaurant offers   2 types of soup
                              3 main courses
                              4 desserts.

    How many different lunch selections are possible?

14. A couple want to buy a house.
They can choose between a terraced, a
semi-detached or a detached house.
Each of these types comes with two
bedrooms, three bedrooms or four
bedrooms.
How many different choices of house do
they have?

15. Draw a two-way table showing the possible
outcomes from rolling a die and spinning
the spinner shown.

What is the total number of possible
outcomes from this experiment.

16. Design a two-way table to show the possible
outcomes from spinning both spinners
and multiplying the results.

What is the total number of possible
outcomes from this experiment.

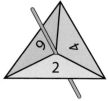
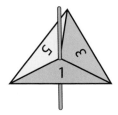

17. The following two-way table shows the possible
outcomes from spinning two spinners.
  (i) What operation was carried out on the separate
       numbers?
  (ii) How many different outcomes were there?

	1	2	3
1	2	3	4
3	4	5	6
5	6	7	8

18. There are 4 roads from town A to town B and 3 roads from town B to town C.
Draw a two-way table to show the number of ways a person can travel from A to C.

19. (i) The digits 0,1, 2 are written on discs and placed in a bag.
            The digits 2, 3, 4 are written on discs and placed in a second bag.
            If a digit is taken from the first bag and then the second bag in that order
            without looking and placed on the table, using the fundamental principle of
            counting find how many different numbers can be formed from the two digits.
            List the numbers.

   (ii) The digits 1, 2, 3 are written on discs and placed in a bag.
         The digits 3, 4 are written on discs and placed in a second bag.
         The digits 5, 8 are written on discs and placed in a third bag.

If a digit is taken from each bag in order, without looking and placed side by side on a table, using the fundamental principle of counting find how many different numbers can be formed from the three digits.

List the numbers.

Investigation:

To send a text message using an old mobile-phone a key had to be pressed a number of times to get the letter required. 2 pressed twice gave the letter B, 6 pressed three times produced the letter O.

If the numbers 4, 6, 6, 3 were pressed investigate the 4-letter variations (not all English words) possible.

	4	6	6	3	P
letters					
Number of letters					
Word 1	H	O	O	D	
Word 2					
Word 3					

Phone keypad:

1 ᴏₒ	2 ABC	3 DEF
4 GHI	5 JKL	6 MNO
7 PQRS	8 TUV	9 WXYZ
*+	0 ‿	# ↑↟

MY PHONE
HOOD

Describe how you would calculate the total number of arrangements(outcomes) possible from these 4 keys.

One variation(outcome) is the word HOOD.

Copy and complete the chart, writing down at least 2 other words.

In the column marked P write down the number of presses needed to write each word. Find the word that requires 11 presses of the keys.

Find also a combination of keys that would give 48 three-letter variations.

Section 4.2 Chance and Probability

In the previous section, we learned
how to list the **outcomes** when a
die was thrown, a coin was
tossed or a spinner was spun.

We saw that tossing a coin has two possible outcomes.

These are **head** (H) or **tail** (T).

On any occasion, no one knows what the outcome will be.

It is down to **chance**.

The coin is as **likely** to show a head as a tail.

There is an **even chance** that either will occur.

We could also say that there is a **fifty-fifty chance** of getting a head or a tail.

When a die is thrown, the possible outcomes are 1, 2, 3, 4, 5 or 6.

It is equally likely that any of these numbers will show in a single
throw of the die.

We are equally likely to get green or blue when this spinner
is spun.

Events / Outcomes

An **event** is a commonly used word.

It might be a single occurrence e.g. (i) going to a concert.

It could also be a series of happenings e.g. (ii) picking an even number between 0 and 9.

An **event** is a collection of outcomes.

In (i) the outcome is you go to the concert.

In (ii) the outcome could be any of the numbers 2, 4, 6, 8.

> An event is a collection of
> outcomes.

Investigation:

Make a list of some events and possible outcomes that have been
experienced by the class in the last week.
e.g. In the event of being late for class…?
    In the event of a 400 m race…?

The probability scale

We know that some events are more likely to happen than others.

For example, it is more likely to rain in Ireland tomorrow than it is to get three months of sunshine.

If we want to measure how likely something is to happen, we will begin the study of a new branch of Mathematics called **probability**.

We first use a **probability scale** to show how likely any event is to happen.

A probability scale ranges from **certain** to **impossible**. This is shown in the diagram below.

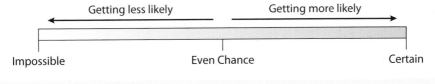

Investigation:

Describe an event that could occur during an average day in school, for each of the following probabilities:

a. Impossible

b. Highly Unlikely

c. Unlikely

d. Evens

e. Likely

f. Highly Likely

g. Certain

As stated above, some events are **more likely** to happen than others.

Example   These squares are put in a bag.

The green square is more likely to be chosen as there are more green squares than yellow squares.

Some events have an **equal chance** of happening.

Example   These circles are put in a bag.

If one is taken without looking, there is an equal chance of it being yellow or green.

How do we measure the chances of something happening?

Probability, as we stated above, is a way of measuring the chance that a particular event will happen. We will now put some numbers on the **probability scale** mentioned earlier. **Impossible** is at one end and **certain** is at the other. This scale goes from 0 to 1.

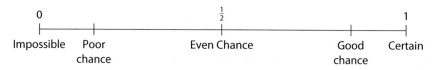

The probability of an event that is **impossible** to happen is **zero**.

The probability of an event that is **certain** to happen is **1**.

The probability of all other events is between 0 and 1.

The more likely an event is to happen, the closer the probability is to 1.

Exercise 4.2

1. The diagram below shows a scale ranging from impossible to certain.

The letters a, b, c and d are marked on the scale to match these labels:

| Likely | Very Likely | Unlikely | Very Unlikely |

Match the letters to the labels.

2. The probability scale below shows how likely the five events A, B, C, D and E are to happen.

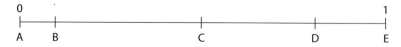

(i) Which event is certain to occur?

(ii) Which event is very unlikely but possibly may occur?

(iii) Which event has an even chance of occurring?

(iv) Which event is impossible?

(v) Which event is likely but not certain to occur?

3. Which of these labels best describes the likelihood of each of the events below occurring?

| Certain | Impossible | Even chance | Likely | Unlikely |

   (i)   Tomorrow a baby will be born in Ireland.
  (ii)   The next winner of the Lotto will be a woman.
 (iii) You score 8 when you roll an ordinary die.
 (iv) It will rain in Galway sometime in the next week.
   (v) Someone in your class will be absent one day next week.
 (vi) The next baby born will be a boy.
(vii) Ireland will win the next soccer World Cup.
(viii) The sun will set this evening.
 (ix) You will get an even number when you throw a die.
  (x) You will do three hours homework tonight.
 (xi) You will live to be 200 years old.

4. The probability scale below shows the probability of the events A, B, C, D and E occurring.

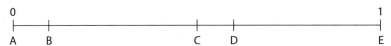

   (i) Which event has a 100% chance of happening?
  (ii) Which event has a 50% chance of occurring?
 (iii) Which event is impossible?
 (iv) Which event is very unlikely to occur?
  (v) Which event has a little more than an even chance of occurring?

5. Draw a scale like this one.

Write the letter, which is beside each statement below, on the line above to show how likely it is to happen.
A: A monkey will be driving the next car you see.
B: You will win the next raffle at your local club.
C: Clouds will appear in the sky tomorrow.
D: The traffic lights will be red when you reach a junction.
E: There will be twelve months in the next year.

6. All of these spinners are spun at the same time.

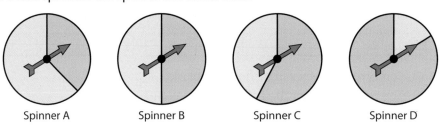

Spinner A   Spinner B   Spinner C   Spinner D

   (i)   Which spinner has the greatest chance of stopping on green?

  (ii)   Which spinner has the greatest chance of stopping on blue?

 (iii)   Which spinner has an even chance of stopping on blue?

 (iv)   Which spinner has the least chance of stopping on blue?

7. The probability scale below shows seven events – A, B, C, D, E, F and G.

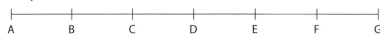

Match each letter to the phrases or fractions or decimals given below:

| Impossible | 0.5 | $\frac{5}{6}$ | Likely | $\frac{1}{3}$ | Certain | Very Unlikely |

8. Make a copy of this probability scale.

Show where each of these events might be on the scale.
(The first one is done for you.)

   (i)   Your neighbour will live for 150 years.

  (ii)   This spinner will stop on Red. ⟶

 (iii)   You will get a head when you toss a coin.

 (iv)   You will get 1 if you throw a fair die.

  (v)   A blue bead, without looking, will be drawn from the bag. ⟶

 (vi)   A red bead, without looking, will be drawn from the same bag.

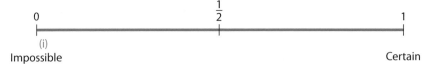

9. Choose the probability $0, \frac{1}{4}, \frac{1}{2}, \frac{3}{4}$ or 1 for the following events:

   (i)   Your next holiday will be to the moon.

  (ii)   Picking a left shoe from a matching pair.

(iii) Scoring an even number with a throw of a die.

(iv) Getting a diamond when a card is drawn from a deck
of 52 playing cards.

(v) Picking a red bead from this bag.

(vi) Next year Christmas will fall in the month of December.

10.

The numbers 1 to 10 are written on cards.

The cards are shuffled and then put face down in a line.

(i) The first card is turned over. It is a 6. Is the next card to be turned over likely to
be higher or lower than this? Why?

(ii) The next card turned over is a 4. Is the next card likely to be higher or lower
than 4? Why?

(iii) The next two cards turned over are 7 and 5.

Is the next card to be turned over
(a) more likely   (b) less likely   (c) equally likely   to be more than 5?
Explain your answer.

Section 4.3 Equally likely outcomes

We have already listed the outcomes in the event a die is thrown.

Each of the numbers 1, 2, 3, 4, 5, 6 has the same chance of appearing.

These are called **equally likely outcomes**.

We are equally likely to get green, blue or yellow when this
spinner is spun.

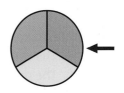

Example 1

A card is selected at random from these coloured digit-cards.

1 2 3 4 5 6

When a card is selected at random, each card has the same chance of being selected.

Write down the number of outcomes for these events:
 (i) the card is blue
 (ii) the number on the card is greater than 4
 (iii) the number on the card is at least 3
 (iv) the number on the card is even
 (v) the card is not red
 (vi) the card is blue and the number is even.

 (i) 3 (ii) 2 (iii) 4 (iv) 3 (v) 4 (vi) 2

Exercise 4.3

1. When this spinner is spun, list all the possible outcomes.

List the possible outcomes if
 (i) a red number shows
 (ii) an even number shows
 (iii) a green number shows
 (iv) the number is 4 or more
 (v) the number is odd and red
 (vi) the number is green and even.

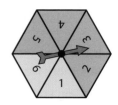

2. A card is selected at random from these coloured digit-cards:

Write down the number of outcomes for these events:
 (i) The card is blue.
 (ii) The number on the card is 6 or more.
 (iii) The number on the card is odd.
 (iv) The card is green and the number is odd.
 (v) The card is not red and the number is even.

3. The cards below show numbers enclosed in a circle or a triangle.

Niamh selects a card at random.

Write down the number of outcomes for these events:

(i) The card contains a circle.

(ii) The card has an odd number on it.

(iii) The card has a circle and an even number on it.

(iv) The card has a triangle and an odd number.

(v) The card has a multiple of 3 on it.

(vi) The card has a circle and a number that is 5 or more.

4. The cards in Question 3 are mixed and turned face down.

Niamh turns over one card.

It has on it. She turns over another card. Is it more likely that she gets a number greater than 6 than a number less than 6?

Explain your answer.

5. State whether or not each of the following are equally likely events:

(i) Getting a head or getting a tail when a fair coin is tossed.

(ii) Getting a yellow or getting a blue when this spinner is spun.

(iii) Getting a black card or getting a red card when a card is drawn from a deck of 52 playing cards.

(iv) Getting an even number or getting an odd number when a card is drawn from the five cards shown.

6. Here are three spinners

  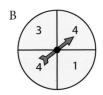 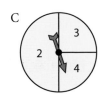

When all these spinners are spun,

(i) which spinner has the greatest chance of landing on 4?

(ii) which spinner has an even chance of landing on 2?

(iii) which spinner has no chance of landing on 2?

All the spinners have the same chance of landing on a certain number.

(iv) Which number is this?

7. Here are four spinners with different colours:

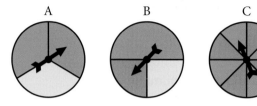
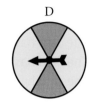

If the spinners are spun,
(i) Which spinner has an even chance of showing blue?
(ii) Which spinner has an even chance of showing red?
(iii) Which spinner has the least chance of showing yellow?
(iv) Which spinner has one chance in three of showing yellow?
(v) Which spinner has one chance in four of showing red?
(vi) Which spinner has the greatest chance of showing red?

8. The spinner shown has 12 equal sectors.

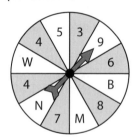

When the spinner is spun, write down the number of outcomes for these events:
(i) the spinner stops on pink
(ii) the spinner stops on a letter
(iii) the spinner stops on a number in a white sector
(iv) the spinner stops on a letter in a white sector
(v) the spinner stops on an even number.

Section 4.4 Calculating probability

When a coin is tossed, there are two **equally likely** outcomes.

They are **head** or **tail**.

The probability of getting a head is one chance in two.

We write this as $P(\text{head}) = \frac{1}{2}$.

A favourable outcome is an outcome that you want.

For **equally likely outcomes**,

$$\text{Probability of an event} = \frac{\text{Number of favourable outcomes}}{\text{Number of possible outcomes}}$$

Example 1

Here are 12 cards of various colours with numbers on them.

3 10 4 12 7 2 8 6 1 9 11 5

Jane picks a card at random. Find the probability, as a fraction in its lowest terms, that she picks

(i) a blue card
(ii) a card showing 9
(iii) a red card
(iv) a 2-digit number
(v) a blue card with an odd number on it
(vi) a card that is not red.

(i) There are 4 blue cards.

$\therefore$ $P(\text{blue}) = \dfrac{\text{Number of blue cards}}{\text{Total number of cards}} = \dfrac{4}{12} = \dfrac{1}{3}$

(ii) There is one card showing 9.

$\therefore$ $P(9) = \dfrac{1}{12}$

(iii) There are 5 red cards.

$\therefore$ $P(\text{red}) = \dfrac{5}{12}$

(iv) There are three 2-digit numbers.

$\therefore$ $P(\text{2-digits}) = \dfrac{3}{12} = \dfrac{1}{4}$

(v) The blue cards with odd numbers are 7 and 11, i.e. 2 cards.

$\therefore$ $P(\text{odd blue}) = \dfrac{2}{12} = \dfrac{1}{6}$

(vi) The number of cards that are not red is 7.

$\therefore$ $P(\text{not red}) = \dfrac{7}{12}$

Example 2

(i) Find the probability of getting an odd number, when a die is rolled.
(ii) Find the probability of getting the same face, when two coins are tossed.

(i) Rolling a die.
Number of **possible outcomes** = 6   .....P(odd number) $= \frac{3}{6} = \frac{1}{2}$
Number of **favourable outcomes** = 3

(ii) Tossing two coins.
Number of **possible outcomes** = 4
Number of **favourable outcomes** = 2
.....P(same face on both coins) $= \frac{2}{4} = \frac{1}{2}$

	H	T
H	H, H	H, T
T	T, H	T, T

Note: Fair / Biased

If we rolled a die 12 times we would not be surprised if we got the result,
2, 4, 6, 3, 2, 1, 2, 4, 3, 6, 1, 2.

We would not assume that the die is **biased** because a 5 was not rolled.

A die is **fair** if after a large number of trials the probability of rolling
each number is the same.

A die is **biased** if the probability of rolling each number is not the same.

After a large number of tosses, we say that the coin is a fair coin,
i.e. there is no bias, if the probability of tossing each face $= \frac{1}{2}$

Exercise 4.4 ————————————————————————————

1. These counters are put into a bag and one is selected at random.

(i)   What is the probability that the selected counter is red?
(ii) What is the probability that the selected counter is green?
(iii) What is the probability that the selected counter is yellow or green?
(iv) What is the probability that the selected counter is not green?

2. Find the probability, as a fraction in its lowest terms, that
this spinner lands on

  (i) blue   (ii) red
  (iii) green   (iv) red or yellow
  (v) not blue   (vi) green or blue.

3. If I throw a fair die, what is the probability
that I get

  (i) 4   (ii) an odd number   (iii) 5 or 6?

4. This spinner is equally likely to end on 1, 2, 3, 4 or 5.

  (i) What is the probability of getting 4?
  (ii) What is the probability of getting 4 or more?
  (iii) What is the probability of getting an even number?

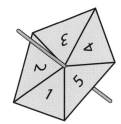

5. What is the probability of getting orange on each of these spinners?

  (i)   (ii)   (iii)

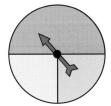 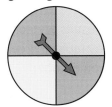 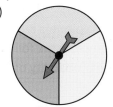

6. Sean puts these beads into a bag.
He picks one bead from the bag without looking.

  (i) Which colour is Sean least likely to pick?
  (ii) What is the probability that he picks a yellow bead?
  (iii) What is the probability that the bead is not black?
  (iv) Sean wants all colours to have an equal chance of being picked.
        What beads does Sean need to add to the bag?
  (v) If the probability of getting a yellow bead is to be twice the probability of
       getting a blue bead, what bead does Sean need to add to the bag?

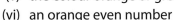

7. When this spinner is spun, find the probability that it will stop on

  (i) 5   (ii) 8 or higher
  (iii) an even number   (iv) the colour orange
  (v) the colour orange or green
  (vi) an orange even number
  (vii) a colour that is not yellow
  (viii) green and an even number.

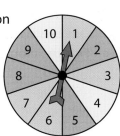

8. Sharon has 12 cards, as shown below.

| 9 | 5 | 6 | 2 | 5 | 5 | 7 | 6 | 8 | 4 | 3 | 2 |

She picks a card at random. Find the probability, as a fraction in its lowest terms,
that the card selected

(i)   is yellow

(ii)   is blue

(iii)   is orange or yellow

(iv)   shows an even number

(v)   shows an even orange number

(vi)   shows a 5

(vii)   shows a number that is 6 or more

(viii)   is blue and shows an even number.

9. In a casino game, a pointer is spun and you win the
amount shown in the sector where the pointer comes to
rest. Assuming that the pointer is equally likely to come to
rest in any sector, what is the probability that you win

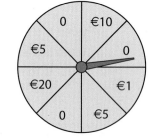

(i)   €5

(ii)   no money

(iii)   €10 or €20

(iv)   some money ?

10. Two spinners are spun and the results added.
Complete the following two-way table and calculate
the probability of getting an even number.

	2	4	6
1			
3			
5			

11. A card is drawn from a pack of 52 playing cards.
What is the probability that the card is

(i)   a red card   (ii)   a spade   (iii)   a king   (iv)   a red king ?

> There are four suits in a pack of cards: hearts and diamonds
> which are red; clubs and spades which are black.
> Each suit contains 2, 3, 4, 5, 6, 7, 8, 9, 10, jack, queen, king and ace.
> The picture cards are jack, queen and king.

12. A bag contains 5 red, 3 blue and 2 yellow beads, as shown.
One bead is taken out at random.
Find the probability that it is

(i)   red

(ii)   blue

(iii)   not red

(iv)   red or yellow.

13. A die has its faces numbered 2, 4, 5, 5, 5, 7.
Find the probability of rolling

(i) 7   (ii) 5   (iii) an even number   (iv) 5 or 7.

14. One card is selected at random from the nine
cards shown. Find the probability of selecting

(i) an ace of diamonds
(ii) an ace
(iii) a king
(iv) a red card.

15. One letter is chosen at random from the letters of the word *DEALING*.

(i) Find the probability that the letter chosen is *G*.
(ii) Find the probability that the letter chosen is a vowel.
(iii) Find the probability that the letter chosen is a vowel or *G*.

16. This box contains 9 counters.
The counters are either blue or green.
The probability of picking a blue counter is $\frac{4}{9}$.

(i) How many blue counters are in the box?
(ii) How many green counters are in the box?
(iii) If a black counter is added to the box, what now
is the probability of picking a blue counter?

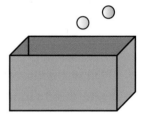

17. A die is rolled and a coin is tossed. Draw a two-way table of the possible outcomes.
Find the probability a getting a Head and an odd number.

18. There are 15 cars in a car-park. 7 are red, 6 are blue and 2 are silver.
Calculate the probability that the next car to leave the car-park is

(i) red   (ii) silver   (iii) not blue   (iv) red or silver.

19. At a fund-raiser for a school, class 5A makes a spinning wheel game, as shown.

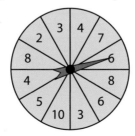

What is the probability that the pointer lands on

(i) 8   (ii) 6 or 8   (iii) an odd number
(iv) a multiple of 5   (v) a number that is even and greater than 5 ?

20. If two coins are tossed find using a two-way table the probability of getting
  (i) 2 Heads
  (ii) 2 Heads or 2 Tails

21. A student rolled a die a number of times and obtained the following results.
  2, 5, 2, 6, 1, 2, 3, 4, 6, 6, 1, 3, 2, 4, 3, 5, 3, 2, 6, 1, 5, 5, 3, 2, 4, 1, 4, 2, 5, 6,
  1, 4, 2, 5, 5, 6, 1, 2, 4, 1, 3, 2, 5, 2, 4, 3, 6, 6, 1, 4, 5, 2, 4, 5, 2, 4, 1, 5, 2, 1,
  3, 1, 6, 1, 3, 2, 4, 5, 6, 1, 6, 3, 3, 4, 4, 3, 4, 6, 3, 4, 1, 5, 5, 6, 1, 2, 5, 6, 6, 1.
  Decide if the die is a fair die.

22. Seven of the eight discs shown have numbers on them.
  The remaining disc is blank. Anne intends to write a
  number on the disc before she puts them all into the bag.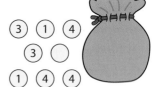
  (i) What number should she write on the disc so that
     the probability of drawing a 3 is $\frac{3}{8}$?
  (ii) What number should she not write on the disc so
     that the probability of drawing a 1 is $\frac{1}{4}$?
  (iii) What number should she write on the disc so that the probability of getting a
     5 is $\frac{1}{8}$?
  (iv) If she wrote 4 on the disc, what is the probability of getting a 4?
  She wrote a number on the blank disc and put all the discs in the bag. If the
  probability of then getting a 3 was $\frac{1}{4}$, say whether each of the following is *true*,
  could be true or *false*.
  (a) She wrote a 3 on the disc.
  (b) She wrote a 4 on the disc.
  (c) She could have written any number except 3 on the disc.

23. A fair six-sided spinner is numbered from 1 to 6, as shown.
  The spinner is spun once. Copy the probability scale below
  and on it mark A, B, C and D to correspond to the
  following probabilities.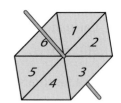
  A: The spinner lands on an even number.
  B: The spinner lands on 4 or 5.
  C: The spinner lands on 8.
  D: The spinner lands on a number which is less than 8.

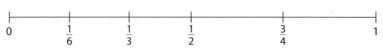

24. The fair spinner shown is spun.
Work out the probability of the arrow pointing to:
  (i) yellow (Y),
  (ii) green (G),
  (iii) red (R),
  (iv) blue (B),
  (v) red or blue (R or B).

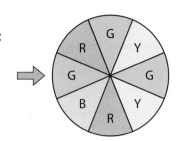

25. Elena has 3 different spinners.

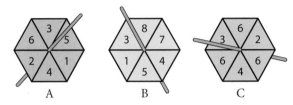

She spins each spinner 100 times.

  (i) Draw a number line as shown and draw arrows labelled A, B and C to show your estimate of how many times each spinner will land on a six.

  (ii) Explain how you worked out your estimate for spinner C.

Test yourself 4

1. Write **impossible**, **unlikely**, **evens**, **likely** or **certain** for each of these:

    (i) A rabbit will be driving the next bus you see.

    (ii) Someone in your class will be absent tomorrow.

    (iii) You will get a head when you toss a coin.

    (iv) You will have only one birthday next year.

    (v) It will not rain in your area in the next week.

2.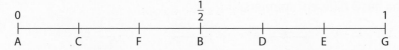

   From the probability scale above, which letter best describes the following:

    (i) impossible   (ii) even chance   (iii) very likely   (iv) certain

    (v) very unlikely   (vi) likely   (vii) unlikely ?

3. Barry spun this spinner.

   Copy and finish this list of possible outcomes:

       10, 15, __, __, __, __

   Do each of these outcomes have the same chance of happening? Explain.

4. Write down the probability that this spinner will land on these colours:

    (i) yellow

    (ii) blue

    (iii) green

    (iv) either blue or green

    (v) not blue.

5. A card game uses these ten digits.

   A card is chosen at random.

    (i) How many possible outcomes are there?

    (ii) What is the probability that the card chosen has an odd number?

    (iii) What is the probability that the card chosen has a 6 or greater on it?

    (iv) What is the probability that the card chosen is yellow?

    (v) What is the probability that the card chosen is yellow and has an even number on it?

    (vi) What is the probability that the card is yellow or green?

6. This table shows the colours of 100 tickets sold in a raffle.

All the tickets were put into a hat.

One ticket was pulled out without looking.

Find the probability that the colour of the ticket is
  (i) yellow   (ii) pink
  (iii) yellow or blue   (iv) not green.

green	20
pink	60
blue	5
yellow	15
Total	100

7. A special die and spinner are shown.

Opposite sides of the die have the same colour.

Draw a two-way table to show the possible outcomes.

Calculate the probability that the same colour shows on both die and spinner.

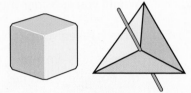

8. For each of the bags shown below,
  (i) find the probability of choosing a red bead
  (ii) find the probability of choosing a blue bead.

  A   B   C

9. In a game, a person is given a choice of two bags to take a bead from.
The person wins if they choose a red bead.

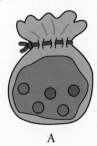

  A   B

Is it better to take a bead from bag A or bag B, or doesn't it matter?

Give your reasons.

10. A letter is chosen at random from the word MATHEMATICS.

    (i) What is the probability that the letter is M?

    (ii) What is the probability that the letter is either A, E or I?

    (iii) What is the probability that the letter is not T?

11. Sean tossed a coin a number of times and listed his results as follows:

    H, H, T, T, H, T, T, H, H, H, T, H, H, H, H, T, T, H, T, H, H, T, T, T, T, H, T, T, H, H,
    T, H, T, T, T, T, H, T, H, T, T, H, H, H, T, H, H, T, H, H, H, T, T, H, H, T, T, T, H, H.
    Would you consider the coin biased. Explain your answer.

12. A die is rolled with a spinner with numbers 1, 2 and 3.

    If the results are added complete the table to show the possible outcomes.

    Using the fundamental principle of counting how many outcomes are possible?

    Find the probability of getting an odd number total.

	1	2	3	4	5	6
1						
2			5			
3						9

Learning Experience   Unit 4

Assignment 1

Luke has 3 sisters (S_1, S_2, S_3) and 4 brothers (B_1, B_2, B_3, B_4).

Luke and his brothers and sisters all buy each other one Easter egg.

Draw a large diagram(poster) to show clearly that 56 eggs were bought in total.

Assignment 2

Use a tally chart to determine if a die is **fair or biased** by rolling a die 100 times.

[Note: ||||| = 5]

Based on the results calculate the probability of each face occurring.

Compare the experimental probability with the expected probability of a fair die.

Can you say that the die is a fair die?

Face	1	2	3	4	5	6
Total						
Probability						
Expected probability						

Assignment 3

A student in your class says that "**the odds** of winning a game are 2 to 1".

Explain to the class the meaning of "odds".

Explain how this expression would be changed if you used probability.

Change the expression into a probability statement(ratio).

Tell the class what "**the odds** of rolling a 6" using a fair die, would be.

Problem 1

A list of 10 numbers contains two of each of the numbers 0, 1, 2, 3, 4.

The two 0s are next to each other, the two 1s are separated by one number, the two 2s by two numbers, the two 3s by three numbers and the two 4s by four numbers.

The list starts 3, 4, _, _, _, _, _, _, _, _.

Describe how you would find the last number?

Problem 2

You are told that 30 pupils have 25 different birthdays between them.

Explain why the largest number of these pupils who could share the same birthday is 6.

Chapter 4 review 1

Using the terms from the chapter copy and complete the following sentences:

1. The results of a trial or experiment are called _____.

2. If one event has **m** possible outcomes and a second event has **n** possible outcomes, the two events have _____ possible outcomes.

3. The result in the previous question is referred to as "The Fundamental Principle of _____.

4. To show how likely/unlikely any event is to happen we use a _____ scale.

5. The probability of an event that is certain is _____.

6. If an event has a probability of 0 then the event is _____.

7. If outcomes have the same chance (probability) of occurring, the outcomes are called _____-_____ outcomes.

8. For equally likely outcomes, the probability of an event is equal to the number of _____ outcomes divided by the number of _____ outcomes.

9. A _____-_____ table shows the possible outcomes from two independent trials.

10. If an event has a fifty-fifty chance of occurring then the chance of it happening equals the chance of it _____ _____.

Chapter 4 review 2

You should now be able to:

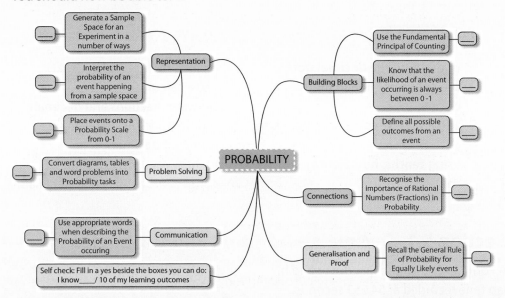

Generate a Sample Space for an Experiment in a number of ways

Interpret the probability of an event happening from a sample space

Place events onto a Probability Scale from 0-1

Representation

Convert diagrams, tables and word problems into Probability tasks

Problem Solving

Use appropriate words when describing the Probability of an Event occuring

Communication

Self check: Fill in a yes beside the boxes you can do:
I know_____/ 10 of my learning outcomes

PROBABILITY

Use the Fundamental Principal of Counting

Know that the likelihood of an event occurring is always between 0 -1

Define all possible outcomes from an event

Building Blocks

Recognise the importance of Rational Numbers (Fractions) in Probability

Connections

Recall the General Rule of Probability for Equally Likely events

Generalisation and Proof

Chapter 5 Decimals

In this chapter, you will learn to:

- understand the **decimal point**,
- use a **number line** to represent decimals,
- add and subtract decimal numbers,
- change decimals to fractions using **tenths, hundredths** and **thousandths**,
- change fractions to decimals,
- use a **calculator** to convert between fractions and decimals,
- multiply and divide decimals,
- round off decimals,
- identify **recurring** decimals,
- connect probability and decimals.

Section 5.1 Decimals – Addition and subtraction

A Formula One Grand Prix driver had his lap time recorded at 54.653 seconds.

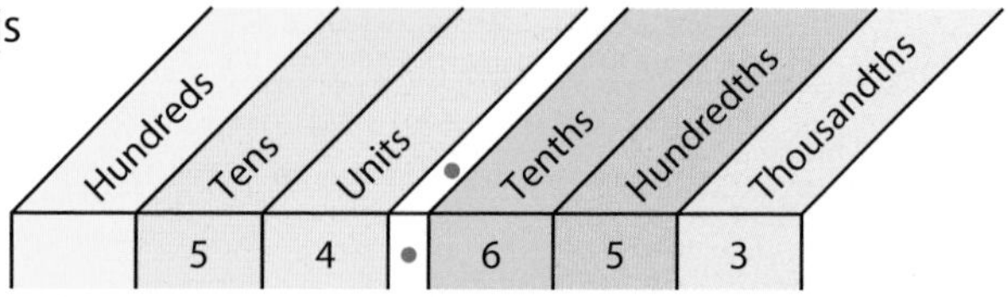

This is a decimal number.

The decimal point separates the whole number from fractions.

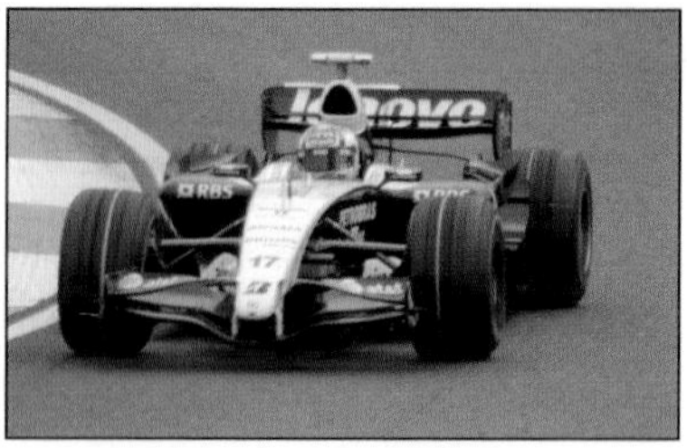

In the number 54.653,

the digit 6 $= \frac{6}{10}$; the digit 5 $= \frac{5}{100}$; the digit 3 $= \frac{3}{1000}$

$$\begin{aligned}\text{Thus, } 54.653 &= 54 + \tfrac{6}{10} + \tfrac{5}{100} + \tfrac{3}{1000} \\ &= 54 + \tfrac{600}{1000} + \tfrac{50}{1000} + \tfrac{3}{1000} \\ &= 54\tfrac{653}{1000}\end{aligned}$$

$3.614 = 3\frac{614}{1000}$

If you examine the numbers below, you will see how a decimal can be changed to a fraction and then simplified.

(i) $0.7 = \frac{7}{10}$

(ii) $0.25 = \frac{25}{100} = \frac{5}{20} = \frac{1}{4}$

(iii) $0.125 = \frac{125}{1000} = \frac{25}{200} = \frac{5}{40} = \frac{1}{8}$

The first digit after the decimal point has 10 as denominator; the first two digits have 100 as denominator; the first three digits have 1000 as denominator.

Example 1

Find the value of the underlined digit in each of these:
  (i) 12.4$\underline{8}$ (ii) 28.4$\underline{6}$3   (iii) 6.75$\underline{4}$ (iv) 3$\underline{5}$.079

  (i) In the decimal 12.48, the 4 represents $\frac{4}{10}$.
  (ii) In the decimal 28.463, the 6 represents $\frac{6}{100}$.
  (iii) In the decimal 6.754, the 4 represents $\frac{4}{1000}$.
  (iv) In the decimal 35.079, the 5 represents 5 units.

A **number line** may be used to represent decimals.

The number line below shows 10 divisions between each whole number.

Each division has a value of 0.1.

$A = 0.3 = \frac{3}{10}$, $C = 1.6 = 1\frac{6}{10}$,

$B = 0.8 = \frac{8}{10}$, $D = -0.4 = -\frac{4}{10}$

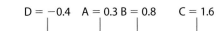

Example 2

Write each of these fractions as a decimal:
  (i) $\frac{9}{10}$ (ii) $\frac{17}{100}$ (iii) $\frac{113}{1000}$ (iv) $\frac{6}{100}$ (v) $\frac{27}{1000}$

  (i) $\frac{9}{10} = 0.9$ (ii) $\frac{17}{100} = 0.17$ (iii) $\frac{113}{1000} = 0.113$

  (iv) $\frac{6}{100} = 0.06$ (v) $\frac{27}{1000} = 0.027$

Adding and subtracting decimals

Decimals are added and subtracted in the same way as whole numbers provided that the decimal points are lined up directly beneath one another.

Example 3

Find   (i) 146.076 + 12.34 + 1.6   (ii) 39.45 − 12.876

  (i) 146.076
        12.34
          1.6
      ─────────
      160.016

  (ii) 39.450
        12.876
      ─────────
        26.574

Exercise 5.1

1. Write the value of the **highlighted** digit in each of the following:
   - (i) 2.7**4**
   - (ii) 12.3**6**
   - (iii) 1.**2**74
   - (iv) 13.21**7**
   - (v) 16.0**7**3
   - (vi) 28.10**9**
   - (vii) 1**3**6.8
   - (viii) 0.00**7**

2. Write the value of each **highlighted** digit in words:
   - (i) **2**6.32
   - (ii) 14.**5**7
   - (iii) 1.2**6**5
   - (iv) 0.70**4**

3. Write these numbers as decimals:
   - (i) four and three tenths
   - (ii) sixteen and seven hundredths
   - (iii) seventeen hundredths
   - (iv) six and three hundredths
   - (v) twelve and twenty eight thousandths

4. Write the following decimals as fractions in their lowest terms:
   - (i) 0.1
   - (ii) 0.3
   - (iii) 0.5
   - (iv) 0.8
   - (v) 0.6

5. Write each of these as a fraction and simplify your answer:
   - (i) 0.25
   - (ii) 0.75
   - (iii) 0.28
   - (iv) 0.05
   - (v) 0.08

6. Write each of the following fractions as a decimal:
   - (i) $\frac{9}{10}$
   - (ii) $\frac{1}{10}$
   - (iii) $\frac{5}{10}$
   - (iv) $\frac{8}{10}$
   - (v) $\frac{7}{10}$
   - (vi) $\frac{16}{100}$
   - (vii) $\frac{28}{100}$
   - (viii) $\frac{25}{100}$
   - (ix) $\frac{75}{100}$
   - (x) $\frac{9}{100}$

7. Write as a decimal the number shown by each arrow:

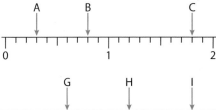
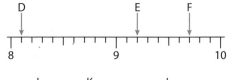
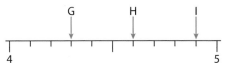

8. Simplify each of these without using a calculator:
   - (i) 12.24 + 6.72 + 14.4
   - (ii) 3.04 + 6.128 + 13.2
   - (iii) 8.056 + 14.2 + 6.17
   - (iv) 0.462 + 1.8 + 3.07

9. Subtract each of the following:
   - (i) 18.4 − 3.8
   - (ii) 14.05 − 1.62
   - (iii) 12.98 − 3.7
   - (iv) 27.062 − 1.95
   - (v) 7.1 − 3.94
   - (vi) 3.016 − 0.99

10. Simplify each of these without using a calculator:
    - (i) 26.84 + 5.06 − 12.97
    - (ii) 131.6 − 8.97 + 13.52
    - (iii) 14.08 + 126.3 − 94.071
    - (iv) 39.01 − 16.94 + 27.494

11. Insert a decimal point in each of the following numbers:
- (i)   257 so that the 5 represents *five tenths*
- (ii)   147 so that the 4 represents *four units*
- (iii)   854 so that the 8 represents *eighty*
- (iv)   6253 so that the 3 represents *three hundredths*
- (v)   2146 so that the 6 represents *six thousandths*
- (vi)   14 so that the 4 represents *four thousandths*

12. What decimal of each of the following figures is shaded?
- (i)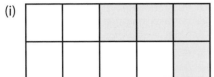
- (ii)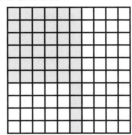

13. Find the decimal that is half-way between the numbers in each of these pairs:
- (i)   0.5 and 0.6   (ii)   3.4 and 3.5   (iii)   4.6 and 4.7
- (iv)   7.6 and 8   (v)   2.46 and 2.47   (vi)   0 and 0.1

14. Rearrange each of these decimals in order of size, starting with the smallest.
- (i)   0.4, 0.3, 0.45, 0.36, 0.08, 0.5   (ii)   2.4, 2.52, 1.96, 2.73, 2.09, 2.17

15. In the number 138.274, which digit represents
- (i)   tens   (ii)   units   (iii)   hundreds   (iv)   tenths   (v)   hundredths ?

16. (i)   Make the largest number you can with these cards. There must be at least one digit after the decimal point. The last digit must not be zero.

- (ii)   Make the smallest number you can with the cards above. There must be at least one digit before the decimal point. The first digit must not be zero.

17. Using a diameter growth rate of 4.3 mm per year, find the number of years it will take for a tree with a diameter of 20 mm to reach a diameter of 50 mm.

18. Find the number halfway between:
- (i) 6.8 and 6.9   (ii) 4.3 and 4.4   (iii) 1.6 and 1.9

Section 5.2 Multiplying and dividing decimals

1. Multiplying and dividing by 10, 100, 1000, ...

To **multiply** a decimal by 10, move the decimal point **one place** to the **right**, e.g.,

$1.46 \times 10 = 14.6$

When multiplying a number by **100**,
move the decimal point **2 places** to the right.

When multiplying a number by **1000**,
move the decimal point **3 places** to the right.

	× 10	× 100	× 1000
4.29	42.9	429	4290
16.1	161	1610	16100
0.27	2.7	27	270

Examples: (i) $12.367 \times 100 = 1236.7$
  (ii) $1.489 \times 1000 = 1489$

	÷ 10	÷ 100	÷ 1000
4.29	0.429	0.0429	0.00429
16.1	1.61	0.161	0.0161
0.27	0.027	0.0027	0.00027

Similarly, when **dividing** by 10, 100 or 1000,
move the decimal point 1, 2 or 3 places to the **left**.

Examples: (i) $28 \div 10 = 2.8$ (ii) $128.3 \div 100 = 1.283$ (iii) $14.9 \div 1000 = 0.0149$

2. Multiplying decimals

If you multiply 8.4 by 1.2 on your calculator, you will get the answer 10.08.

Notice that there is **one** digit after the decimal point in each of the numbers that we multiplied.

Notice also that there are **two** digits after the decimal point in the answer.

$8.\underline{4} \times 1.\underline{2} = 10.\underline{08}$

one + one = two

Similarly, (i) $1.46 \times 1.1 = 1.606$ (ii) $1.273 \times 9 = 11.457$
            (2 places) × (1 place) = (3 places)   (3 places) × (no place) = (3 places)

Rule When multiplying two decimals, the number of digits after the decimal
point in the answer will be equal to the sum of the numbers of digits after
the decimal point in the two decimals to be multiplied.

Example 1

Find   (i) 14.72×1.8 (ii) 0.4×0.02

(i) 14.72×1.8 $= 26.496$
    (2 places) × (1 place) = (3 places)
    (To perform 14.72×1.8, first multiply the whole numbers 1472 and 18
    and then insert the decimal point in your answer.)

(ii) 0.4×0.02 $= 0.008$
    (1 place) × (2 places) = (3 places)

3. Dividing decimals

When dividing decimals by a whole number, keep the decimal points in line as shown below.

(i) $16.45 \div 5$ is $\quad 5\overline{)16.45}$
$\qquad\qquad\qquad\qquad 3.29$

(ii) $77.16 \div 12$ is $\quad 12\overline{)77.16}$
$\qquad\qquad\qquad\qquad\qquad 6.43$

When dividing a number by a decimal, e.g. $\dfrac{9}{0.3}$, change the denominator into a whole number as follows:

$$\frac{9}{0.3} = \frac{9 \times 10}{0.3 \times 10} = \frac{90}{3} = 30$$

Similarly, $\qquad \dfrac{1.284}{0.12} = \dfrac{1.284 \times 100}{0.12 \times 100}$

$$= \frac{128.4}{12} = 10.7$$

> Remember: When making equivalent fractions you must multiply numerator and denominator by the same number.

Exercise 5.2

(Do not use a calculator in these exercises.)

1. Write down the answer to each of these:
   (i) 72×10
   (ii) 12×100
   (iii) 4×1000
   (iv) 1.6×10
   (v) 1.34×100
   (vi) 14.8×100
   (vii) 2.136×1000
   (viii) 4.85×1000
   (ix) 0.74×1000

2. Find the value of each of the following:
   (i) $174 \div 10$
   (ii) $18.4 \div 10$
   (iii) $1.74 \div 10$
   (iv) $387 \div 100$
   (v) $12.8 \div 100$
   (vi) $1.8 \div 100$
   (vii) $387 \div 1000$
   (viii) $14.6 \div 1000$
   (ix) $8.9 \div 1000$

3. Work these out:
   (i) 2.3×100
   (ii) 6.74×100
   (iii) $86 \div 100$
   (iv) 100×0.34
   (v) $3.28 \div 100$
   (vi) $4 \div 100$
   (vii) 0.047×100
   (viii) $158 \div 100$

4. Write down the answer to each of these:
   (i) 1.2×4
   (ii) 3.1×5
   (iii) 8×0.12
   (iv) 1.2×0.4
   (v) 3.3×0.2
   (vi) 2.3×0.3
   (vii) 0.8×0.2
   (viii) 0.7×0.12

5. Work out the value of each of these:
   (i) 4.6×8
   (ii) 12.34×4
   (iii) 2.53×8
   (iv) 1.2×0.6
   (v) 14.8×0.8
   (vi) 127×0.6
   (vii) 42.5×0.06
   (viii) 0.48×0.7

6. What goes in each box?
   (i) $\boxed{} \times 3 = 0.9$
   (ii) $\boxed{} \times 0.2 = 1$
   (iii) $\boxed{} \times 3 = 1.2$
   (iv) $7 \times \boxed{} = 2.8$
   (v) $0.2 \times \boxed{} = 0.08$
   (vi) $1.1 \times \boxed{} = 0.55$

7. Work out each of these:
    (i) 12.8 ÷ 2   (ii) 128.4 ÷ 4   (iii) 4.08 ÷ 3   (iv) 78.61 ÷ 7

8. Work out each of these:
    (i) $\dfrac{0.8}{0.2}$ (ii) $\dfrac{4.2}{0.6}$ (iii) $\dfrac{13.85}{0.5}$ (iv) $\dfrac{6.14}{0.4}$

    (v) $\dfrac{4.8}{0.08}$ (vi) $\dfrac{20.4}{0.04}$ (vii) $\dfrac{0.92}{0.4}$ (viii) $\dfrac{1.08}{0.03}$

9. Choose one number from each box to multiply together to give these:

0.8	1.2	0.5	3
4	0.2	60	0.9

    (i) 4.8   (ii) 30   (iii) 2.7   (iv) 0.24
    (v) 0.6   (vi) 0.16   (vii) 0.1   (viii) 1.08

10. Use the fact that $48 \times 11 = 528$ to write down the answer to
    (i) 4.8×11 (ii) 48×1.1 (iii) 4.8×1.1
    (iv) 4.8×0.11 (v) 0.48×0.11

11. In each of the following choose the **larger** of the two numbers, explaining your choice:
    (i) 0.98 or 0.89   (ii) 2.750 or 2.057   (iii) 104.040 or 104.104

12. (i) Write down two numbers whose *product* is 1482.
    (ii) Using your answer to (i), explain how to find two numbers whose product is
        (a) 148.2   (b) 1.482   (c) 0.01482

13. Work out each of these:
    (i) $\dfrac{1.2 \times 0.4}{0.3}$ (ii) $\dfrac{12}{0.6 \times 0.5}$ (iii) $\dfrac{2.7 \times 0.3}{0.9}$ (iv) $\dfrac{0.12 \times 0.4}{0.8}$

14. A car on a motorway travels 26.4 m every second.
    How far does it travel in each of these times?
    (i) 10 seconds   (ii) 50 seconds   (iii) 2 minutes

15. You are told that $364 \div 14 = 26$.
    Using this information, write down the answers to these:
    (i) $\dfrac{36.4}{1.4}$ (ii) $\dfrac{3.64}{0.14}$ (iii) $\dfrac{36400}{14}$ (iv) $\dfrac{364}{1.4}$ (v) $\dfrac{3640}{0.14}$

16. Five friends go apple-picking. These are the amounts they pick.
        7.8 kg   9.43 kg   6.72 kg   11.27 kg   10.43 kg.
    They agree to put all the apples together and share out the weight equally.
    How much do they each get?

17. If 9 square metres of carpet costs €622.80, find the cost of one square metre.

18. How many pieces of timber, each 0.8 metres long, can be cut from a piece of length 25.6 metres?

19. Sheets of metal, 0.15 cm thick, are piled one on top of the other until they reach a height of 13.2 cm. How many sheets are there in the pile?

20. How many cups, each containing 0.3 litres, can be filled from a container holding 16.2 litres?

21. Four matching pairs of divisions give the same answer.
Which is the odd one out?

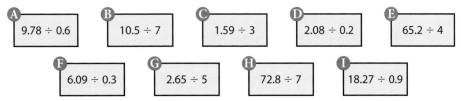

A $9.78 \div 0.6$ B $10.5 \div 7$ C $1.59 \div 3$ D $2.08 \div 0.2$ E $65.2 \div 4$

F $6.09 \div 0.3$ G $2.65 \div 5$ H $72.8 \div 7$ I $18.27 \div 0.9$

22. Which **one** of the following is less than 0.8?

(i) 0.8×2 (ii) $\dfrac{0.8}{0.2}$ (iii) 0.8×1.2 (iv) $(0.8)^2$

23. At Alfredo's Pizza take away you order 2 medium pizzas, one with cheese and ham, one with pepperoni and mushrooms and a large pizza with ham, pepperoni and pineapple. Each medium pizza costs €11.50 and a large pizza costs €14.90 and each topping costs €1.25. You also buy 4 drinks at €2.50 each.
(i) Estimate the total cost of the bill for you and three friends.
(ii) Calculate the exact cost and how much each should pay if the bill is to be divided equally.

Section 5.3 Rounding off decimals

The length of the line shown below is somewhere between 3.3 and 3.4 cm. We see an enlarged view of the ruler between 3 and 4 cm to illustrate the point A where the line ends.

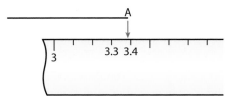

Notice that the arrow at the point A is nearer to 3.4 than to 3.3.

Thus we say that the length of the line is 3.4 cm, *correct to one decimal place*.

If the point A is 3.37, we can see that 3.37 is nearer to 3.4 than it is to 3.3.

When we omit some of the ending digits in a decimal, we are **rounding off** the given decimal to a certain number of decimal places.

Thus   (i) 3.86 = 3.9, correct to 1 decimal place as 86 is nearer to 90 than 80.
     (ii) 7.43 = 7.4, correct to 1 decimal place as 43 is nearer to 40 than 50.

The following rules are important when rounding off decimals to a given number of decimal places.

> **1.** If the last digit is 5 or more, we increase the previous digit by 1.
> e.g. 163.<u>68</u> = 163.<u>7</u>   … a number rounded to 1 place of decimals
>
> **2.** If the last digit is 4 or less, we leave the previous digit as it is.
> e.g. 163.<u>683</u> = 163.<u>68</u>   … a number rounded to 2 places of decimals

Here are some examples:
  (i) 24.6 = 25, correct to the nearest whole number
 (ii) 1.238 = 1.2, correct to one decimal place
(iii) 16.425 = 16.43, correct to two decimal places

Expressing a fraction as a decimal

To change a fraction to a decimal, divide the top line by the bottom line.

$$\frac{3}{4} = 4\overline{)3.00} \qquad \frac{5}{8} = 8\overline{)5.000}$$
$$0.75 0.625$$

$$\frac{3}{4} = 0.75 \qquad \frac{5}{8} = 0.625$$

We will now express $\frac{2}{3}$ as a decimal: $3\overline{)2.0000}$
                          $0.6666\ldots$

Here we see that the sixes continue on and on …

This decimal is written as $0.66666\ldots = 0.\dot{6}$, where the dot over the 6 indicates that this digit repeats and is an example of a **recurring decimal**.

Also $8.24242424\ldots = 8.\dot{2}\dot{4}$, where two dots are needed to show the recurring decimals.

When decimals continue on like that shown above, we generally give our answer correct to a given number of decimal places.

Using a calculator

As with fractions, decimals can be added, subtracted, multiplied and divided very quickly using a calculator. Always check the screen on the calculator to make sure that you have entered the decimals correctly. Remember to use the $\boxed{\text{S} \leftrightarrow \text{D}}$ key to change the fraction to a decimal.

Example 1

Evaluate the following (i) $\dfrac{2.9 - 1.01}{3.6}$ (ii) $\dfrac{13.7 - 2.1}{4.5 - 2.25}$

(i) $\dfrac{2.9 - 1.01}{3.6} = 0.525$

(ii) $\dfrac{13.7 - 2.1}{4.5 - 2.25} = 5.155555... = 5.1\dot{5}$ ... a recurring decimal.

Rough estimates

With the widespread use of electronic calculators, it is important to have a rough estimate of the answer so that you will know whether the answer you actually get is reasonable or not. The most common way to make a rough estimate is to round off whole numbers to the nearest 10, 100 or 1000 ... and to round off decimals to one or two decimal places.

Example 2

By correcting each decimal to the nearest whole number, find the value of
$$\frac{3.16 \times 9.673}{5.38}$$

$$\frac{3.16 \times 9.673}{5.38} \approx \frac{3 \times 10}{5} = \frac{30}{5} = 6$$

(We use the symbol $\approx$ to denote *is approximately equal to*.)

The correct answer, using a calculator, is 5.68. (Correct to two decimal places.)

Exercise 5.3

1. Which whole number is the nearest to each of these?
   (i) 38.6   (ii) 12.4   (iii) 4.27   (iv) 15.96   (v) 23.5

2. Write these numbers correct to one decimal place:
   (i) 1.94   (ii) 13.73   (iii) 0.381   (iv) 3.152   (v) 6.049

3. Write these numbers correct to two decimal places:
   (i) 8.538   (ii) 0.348   (iii) 0.1792   (iv) 3.008   (v) 9.1592

4. Round these to the nearest kilometre:
   (i) 135.4 km   (ii) 87.47 km   (iii) 135.51 km   (iv) 327.89 km

5. Round these numbers to one decimal place:
   (i) 1.07   (ii) 0.762   (iii) 12.73   (iv) 0.05   (v) 1.75

6.

A	E	C	K	R	H	S	B	D
4.0	4.1	4.2	4.3	4.4	4.5	4.6	4.7	4.8

Round each number below to one decimal place and find a letter for each one. Rearrange each set of letters to spell an item of food.
   (i) 4.0937, 4.03, 4.1875, 4.3453
   (ii) 4.477, 4.134, 4.059, 4.567, 4.235, 4.088
   (iii) 4.392, 4.778, 4.7341, 4.079, 4.032

7. The numbers in the rectangles are written to three decimal places in the loops. Find three matching pairs.

8. Express the following fractions as decimals:
   (i) $\frac{1}{2}$ (ii) $\frac{1}{4}$ (iii) $\frac{3}{4}$ (iv) $\frac{1}{8}$ (v) $\frac{3}{8}$
   (vi) $\frac{5}{8}$ (vii) $\frac{9}{20}$ (viii) $\frac{3}{25}$ (ix) $\frac{7}{16}$ (x) $\frac{15}{32}$

9. Write each of the following fractions as decimals, correct to two decimal places.
   (i) $\frac{5}{6}$ (ii) $\frac{3}{7}$ (iii) $\frac{4}{11}$ (iv) $\frac{4}{9}$ (v) $\frac{5}{14}$

10. By expressing each fraction as a decimal correct to two decimal places, find which is the greater in each of the following:

    (i) $\frac{3}{5}$ or $\frac{4}{7}$ (ii) $\frac{5}{8}$ or $\frac{7}{11}$ (iii) $\frac{5}{9}$ or $\frac{7}{12}$ (iv) $\frac{5}{13}$ or $\frac{6}{15}$

11. Without using a calculator, write each number correct to the nearest whole number and then work out your answer:

    (i) 11.8×7.4 (ii) 3.84×2.75 (iii) $43.8 \div 10.6$

    (iv) $\dfrac{15.2 \times 6.8}{13.7}$ (v) $\dfrac{16.3 \times 8.54}{17.67}$ (vi) $\dfrac{12.37 \times 6.08}{3.49}$

12. Which *one* of the following is less than 0.6?

    (i) 0.6×2 (ii) $\dfrac{0.6}{0.2}$ (iii) 0.6×1.2 (iv) $(0.6)^2$

13. Rewrite each number correct to one decimal place and then simplify without using a calculator:

    (i) $\dfrac{1.48 \times 6.34}{0.27}$ (ii) $\dfrac{1.78 \times 0.33}{0.94}$ (iii) $\dfrac{1.84 \times 0.18}{3.62}$

    Now use your calculator to find the exact value of each of the above, correct to one decimal place.

14. A group of 38 people are going to a concert. Tickets are €29.75 each.

    (i) Estimate roughly the total cost of the tickets.
    (ii) Is your rough estimate bigger or smaller than the exact amount?
        How can you tell without working out the exact amount?

15. Put these letters in order of size, starting with the smallest:

    A: $\dfrac{0.1 + 0.2}{0.2 + 0.3}$ B: $\dfrac{0.2 + 0.4}{0.2 + 0.3}$ C: $\dfrac{0.1 + 0.2}{0.4 + 0.6}$ D: $\dfrac{0.1 + 0.4}{0.1 + 0.3}$ E: $\dfrac{0.3 + 0.4}{0.2 + 0.4}$

16. What is two and thirty four hundredths when written as a decimal?

    A: 0.234   B: 2.034   C: 2.34   D: 234.00   E: 23400

Section 5.4 **Probability and decimals**

In the previous chapter the number line from 0 to 1 was used to work out the probability of an event happening.

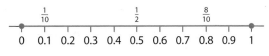

It is easier to compare probabilities when decimals numbers are used instead of fractions.

Example 1

If $P(A) = \frac{8}{25}$ and $P(B) = \frac{1}{4}$, find out which event, A or B, is more likely to happen?

$P(A) = \frac{8}{25} = 0.32$

and $P(B) = \frac{1}{4} = 0.25$

∴ since $P(A) > P(B)$, A is more likely to happen.

Exercise 5.4

1. In each of the following change the probabilities into decimals, corrected to two places of decimals and find out which event is more likely to happen.
   (i) $P(A) = \frac{7}{12}$, $P(B) = \frac{5}{9}$ (ii) $P(C) = \frac{5}{13}$, $P(D) = \frac{6}{15}$

2. A bag contains 15 white tiles and 9 black tiles.
   Find the probability of picking a black tile correct to 2 places of decimals.

3. Tickets were sold in a raffle as shown in the table.
   Find the probability that (i) pink wins
   (ii) blue wins (iii) pink or red wins.
   Correct each answer to 2 places of decimals.

yellow	pink	blue	red
32	24	36	12

4. A coin is tossed and a die is rolled.
   What is the total number of outcomes.
   What is the probability of getting a head and an odd number.
   Correct your answer to two places of decimals.

5. Two dice are rolled.
   (i) Using the fundamental principle of counting find out the number of possible outcomes.
   (ii) List the ways in which at least one 2 occurs.
   (iii) Find the probability of at least one 2 occurring.
   Give your answer correct to 2 places of decimals.

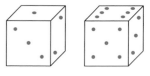

6. Two spinners are spun and their results added.
   (i) How many outcomes are possible.
   (ii) Find the probability getting a total of 8 or greater.
   Give your answer correct to 2 places of decimals.

7. In a class of 24 pupils there are 8 boys.
   Three of the boys and seven girls play basketball.
   If a boy and a girl are chosen at random from the class show that the probability that the girl plays basketball is greater than the probability that the boy plays basketball.

Test yourself 5

1. Write each of these as decimals:

   (i) $\frac{3}{10}$ (ii) $4\frac{7}{10}$ (iii) $\frac{15}{100}$ (iv) $\frac{67}{1000}$ (v) $1\frac{3}{100}$

2. Insert a decimal point in each of these numbers:

   (i) 328 such that the 2 represents *two tenths*

   (ii) 1495 such that the 9 represents *nine hundredths*

   (iii) 932 such that the 9 represents *ninety*

   (iv) 328 such that the 2 represents *two thousandths*.

3. (i) Write 123.6, correct to the nearest whole number.

   (ii) Write 1.476, correct to one decimal place.

   (iii) Write 12.062, correct to two decimal places.

4. Write down the answer to each of these:

   (i) 2.46×10 (ii) 1.34×100 (iii) $12.4 \div 10$ (iv) $412.8 \div 100$

5. Find the missing number in each calculation.

   (i) $\boxed{} \times 10 = 75.3$ (ii) $7321 \div \boxed{} = 73.21$

   (iii) $1000 \times \boxed{} = 45.63$ (iv) $17.3 \times \boxed{} = 17\,300$

6. To what decimal is each arrow pointing?

    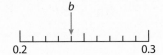 

7. Given that $13.2 \times 5.5 = 72.6$, write down the value of each of these without further calculations:

   (i) 132×5.5 (ii) 1.32×0.55 (iii) 0.132×55

8.

A	B	E	H	I	G	L	N	P	R	T	W
2.0	2.1	2.2	2.3	2.4	2.5	2.6	2.7	2.8	2.9	3.0	3.1

   Round each decimal below to one decimal place and find a letter for each one. Rearrange each set of letters to spell an animal.

   (i) 2.8604, 2.24, 2.138, 2.034

   (ii) 2.609, 2.2561, 2.1901, 1.964, 3.10131

   (iii) 2.51, 2.908, 2.412, 2.98, 2.1984

   (iv) 2.764123, 2.2461, 2.5543, 2.34452, 1.98361, 3.0499, 2.22109, 2.70671

9. Work out the answer to each of these:
  (i) 1.2 × 0.6
  (ii) 1.2 ÷ 0.6

  Use the above examples to write the missing word in each of these sentences:
    (a) Multiplying a positive number by a number between 0 and 1 gives an
        anwer that is _____ than the original number.
    (b) Dividing a positive number by a number between 0 and 1 gives an answer
        that is _____ than the original number.

10. The numbers in the rectangles are written to two decimal places in the loops.
    Find five matching pairs.

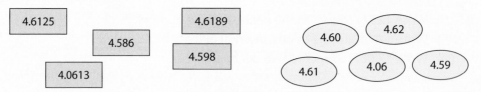

11. Express these decimals as fractions in their lowest terms:
  (i) 0.4   (ii) 0.25   (iii) 0.125   (iv) 0.08   (v) 0.16

12. Kate spent 0.4 of her money in one shop and 0.3 of it in a second shop.
    If she had €21.90 left, how much had she at first?

13. Simplify each of these without using a calculator:
  (i) $\dfrac{2.4 \times 1.2}{0.3}$ (ii) $\dfrac{0.48 \times 2}{0.06 \times 4}$ (iii) $\dfrac{3.1 - 1.9}{0.06 \times 20}$

14.

0.25	2.5
0.9	
	0.8
12.6	1.2

  (i) Which two of these numbers multiply together to give the **smallest** possible
       answer?
  (ii) Which two of these numbers, when multiplied together, give the answer which
       is closest to 1?
  (iii) Find the two numbers such that one divided by the other gives the **largest**
        possible answer.

15. In which of the following lists are the terms **not** increasing?
  A: $\frac{1}{5}$, 0.25, $\frac{3}{10}$, 0.5   B: $\frac{3}{5}$, 0.7, $\frac{4}{5}$, 1.5   C: $\frac{2}{5}$, 0.5, $\frac{7}{10}$, 0.9

  D: $\frac{3}{5}$, 0.5, $\frac{4}{5}$, 0.9   E: $\frac{2}{5}$, 1.5, $\frac{10}{5}$, 2.3

16. Jonathan has to cut a 10.5-metre pole
into 0.5-metre lengths.
How long will it take him if he cuts one length
every 3 minutes?

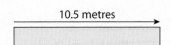

17. Two spinners are spun and there numbers added.
What is the total number of outcomes possible.
Find the chance of getting an odd number?
Correct your answer to 2 places of decimals.

 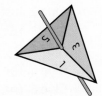

Learning Experience   Unit 5

Assignment 1

A palindrome is a word that reads the same forwards and backwards. E.g. race car.

A palindromic number has the same value when the digits are reversed. E.g. 323

If any number is added to the same number with the digits reversed a palindromic number *may* be formed. E.g. 125 + 521 = 646 a palindrome.

This also applies to decimal numbers. 1.7 + 7.1 = 8.8

Sometimes the reversing procedure might need to be done a number of times before the palindrome is formed. E.g. 6.7 + 7.6 = 14.3 (not a palindrome)

However 14.3 + 3.41 = 17.71 (a palindrome)

Using the decimal 169.21 (and a sheet of paper) show how to find how many reversals need to be done to make a palindromic number from this decimal number.

Problem 1

When Emma bought a train ticket she received €2.50 in change.

She noticed that for each coin in her change, there was exactly one other coin of the same value.

Explain why 5c is the smallest coin in Emma's change.

Problem 2

Using the clues below explain how to find the missing *decimal* number.
Clue 1. It is a four-digit number with the decimal point in the middle.
Clue 2. Just two of the digits are the same.
Clue 3. The tens digit is smaller than the units digit.
Clue 4. The units digit is the same as the tenths digit.
Clue 5. The tens digit is one less than the hundredths digit.
Clue 6. The digits add up to 11.

Chapter 5 review 1

Using the terms from the chapter copy and complete the following sentences:

1. The first digit after the decimal point has _____ as a denominator.

2. A quarter written as a decimal is _____.

3. When adding or subtracting decimals (without using a calculator) always keep the decimal points _____ each other.

4. If a decimal number is multiplied by 100 the decimal point moves _____ places to the _____.

5. If a decimal number is divided by 10 the decimal point moves _____ place to the _____.

6. When rounding a decimal number correct to three places of decimals, if the fourth digit after the decimal point is 4 or less you should _____ the third digit as it is.

7. If an event has a 50-50 chance of occurring then its probability as a decimal number is _____.

8. In the decimal number 4.162 the 2 represents _____.

9. When rounding a decimal number correct to two places of decimals, if the third digit after the decimal point is 5 or more you should increase the _____ digit by 1.

10. Using a calculator the _____ key changes fractions to decimals and decimals to fractions.

11. Decimal numbers such as 42.3333… are called _____ decimals.

12. Decimal numbers such as 42.3333… can be written as _____.

Chapter 5 review 2

You should now be able to:

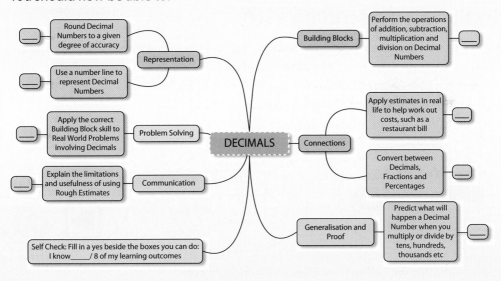

6 Sets

In this chapter, you will learn to:

- define a **set**,
- define an **element**,
- identify a **null set**,
- identify the **universal set**,
- use the symbol, ∈, is an element of,
- use the symbol, ∉, is not an element of,
- use the symbol, ∪, the **union of** sets,
- use the symbol, ∩, the **intersection of** sets,
- identify **equal sets**,
- find **subsets** of a given set,
- draw a **Venn diagram** of a set,
- interpret Venn diagrams,
- find the **cardinal number**, #, of a set,
- find the **complement** of a set.

Section 6.1 Describing a set

If you examine the three collections of items shown below, you will notice that the items in each collection are similar and **clearly defined**.

The first is a collection of cars.

The second is a collection of playing cards.

The third is a collection of road signs.

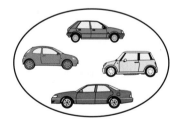  

In mathematics, we call each of these collections a **set**.

The items in a set are called the **elements** of the set.

The elements of a set must be clearly defined, that is, we should be sure whether or not a given object is an element of the set.

For example   (i)   the **days of the week** is a set

(ii)   the **pupils in my class** is also a set.

But **good television programmes** do not form a set as not everybody agrees on what a 'good programme' is.

Listing elements of a set

When it is possible to list the elements of a set, we write down the list inside a pair of chain brackets and separate each element from the next with a comma.
We use **capital letters** to name a set.
If A = the set of whole numbers greater than 4 and less than 10, then
$$A = \{5, 6, 7, 8, 9\}$$

This is a **clearly defined set** as we are in no doubt that each of the elements 5, 6, 7, 8, 9 is greater than 4 and less than 10.

In any set, an element is listed once only.

The letters of the word NAVAN could be listed in set form as {N, A, V}, that is, no letter is repeated.

A change in the order in which the elements are listed does not change the set.
The set {1, 3, 5, 7} could be listed as {3, 7, 5, 1} or {7, 5, 3, 1}.

> Each element of a set must be **listed once only**, separated by **commas** and inside a pair of **chain** brackets.
> The set of letters in the word *mathematics* is
> $$A = \{m, a, t, h, e, i, c, s\}$$

Example 1

(i) List the elements of the set {letters of the word DIVISION}
(ii) Describe in words the elements of the set
     {January, June, July}

(i) The set is {D, I, V, S, O, N}.

(ii) {January, June, July} is the set of months beginning with the letter J.

Exercise 6.1

1. Say whether each of the following could be accurately described as a mathematical set:
   (i) The counties of Leinster
   (ii) The players on my football team
   (iii) The tall pupils in my class
   (iv) The letters of the alphabet
   (v) The dangerous animals in the zoo
   (vi) The vowels in the word OPINION
   (vii) The big counties in Ireland.

2. Describe in words each of these sets:
   A = {Saturday, Sunday}
   B = {1, 2, 3, 4, 5, 6}
   C = {May, June, July}
   D = {v, w, x, y, z}
   E = {Kerry, Cork, Waterford, Tipperary, Limerick, Clare}
   F = {2, 4, 6, 8, 10}
   G = {a, e, i, o, u}

3. List the elements of the following sets using the { } notation:
   A = {The first five letters of the English alphabet}
   B = {The odd numbers between 2 and 14}
   C = {The seasons of the year}
   D = {The days of the week beginning with the letter T}
   E = {The letters of the word SCIENCE}
   F = {Counties in Ireland beginning with C}
   G = {Vowels in the word MATHEMATICS}
   H = {Colours of the rainbow}

4. Describe in words the sets shown below.

   (i)

   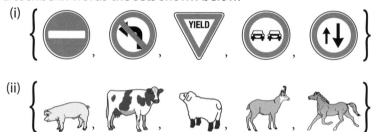

   (ii)

Section 6.2 Elements of a set

We use the symbol ∈ to indicate that an element is a member of a given set.
We use the symbol ∉ to denote **is not an element of**.

For example, if $A = \{$ 🐱, 🐶, 🐰 $\}$ 🐰 $\in A$ but 🦊 $\notin A$.

Similarly, if $B = \{1, 2, 3, 4\}$, $2 \in B$ but $8 \notin B$.

> $B = \{2, 4, 6, 8, 10, 12, 14, 16, 18, 20\}$
> $8 \in B$, 8 is **an element of** B
> $9 \notin B$, 9 is **not an element of** B

A set defined by a Rule

Take, for example, the set $A = \{$Spring, Summer, Autumn, Winter$\}$.

The set A could also be written using a **rule** to describe it as follows:

$A = \{$a season of the year$\}$

Similarly, if $B = \{$a whole number between 1 and 9 inclusive$\}$

then $B = \{1, 2, 3, 4, 5, 6, 7, 8, 9\}$

Sometimes this may be written as, $B = \{x \mid x$ is a whole number between 1 and 9 inclusive$\}$

Which reads as "*B is the set of values of x **such that** x is a whole number between 1 and 9 inclusive*".

The null set Ø or { }

A set that contains no elements is called the **null set** or **empty set**.

The null set is denoted by Ø or **{ }**.

The set of men who are more than 4 metres in height is an example of an empty set.

Do not confuse $\{0\}$ with { }.

$\{0\}$ is a set which has one element i.e. 0.

> The null (or empty) set is denoted by Ø or { }

Number sets

In previous chapters we have defined different sets of numbers.

The **set of** Natural numbers, $N = \{1, 2, 3, 4, 5, \ldots\}$

The **set of** Integers, $Z = \{\ldots -3, -2, -1, 0, 1, 2, 3, \ldots\}$

The **set of** Rational numbers (fractions), e.g. $\{\frac{2}{3}, \frac{-1}{5}, \frac{4}{7}, \frac{11}{23}, \ldots\}$ was denoted by the letter Q.

Example 1

State whether each of the following sentences is True or False.

(a) All Natural numbers are Integers.
(b) All Natural numbers are Rational numbers.
(c) All Rational numbers are Integers.

(a) True; every element of N is also an element of Z.
Natural numbers are also integers.
(b) True; every element of N can be written as a fraction, e.g. $3 = \frac{3}{1}$.
Natural numbers are also rational numbers.
(c) False; the rational number $\frac{2}{5}$ is not a whole number.
All rational numbers are not integers.

Investigation:

In chapter 1 it was stated that **prime numbers** are numbers with two factors only.

Can a negative number be prime?

To what set(s) of numbers do prime numbers belong?

Exercise 6.2

1. State whether each of the following is true or false:
  (i) $3 \in \{1, 3, 5, 7, 9\}$
  (ii) $v \in \{a, e, i, o, u\}$
  (iii) Tuesday $\in \{$The days of the week$\}$
  (iv) Munster $\in \{$The counties of Ireland$\}$
  (v) Metre $\in \{$Units of weight$\}$

2. $A = \{x, y, z\}$, $B = \{3, 6, 9, 12\}$ and $C = \{5, 10, 15, 20\}$ are three sets.
  Copy and insert the symbol $\in$ or $\notin$ in each of the following:
  (i) $3 \dots A$ (ii) $5 \dots C$ (iii) $x \dots A$
  (iv) $y \dots B$ (v) $12 \dots B$ (vi) $z \dots C$
  (vii) $20 \dots C$ (viii) $8 \dots B$.

3. Given $X = \{1, 2, 3, 4, 5\}$, $Y = \{a, b, c, d, e\}$, $Z = \{5, 10, 15\}$.

Say if each of the following is true or false:

(i) $b \in Y$ (ii) $6 \in Z$ (iii) $f \notin Y$

(iv) $5 \in X$ (v) $20 \notin Z$ (vi) $e \in Y$

(vii) $5 \notin X$ (viii) $10 \in Z$.

4. List the elements of each of the following sets:

$A = \{x \mid x$ is a planet beginning with the letter $M\}$

$B = \{x \mid x$ is a vowel of the English language$\}$

$C = \{x \mid x$ is an even number between 1 and 13$\}$

$D = \{x \mid x$ is a number on a clockface$\}$

$E = \{x \mid x$ is a letter of the word PARALLEL$\}$

$F = \{x \mid x$ is an odd whole number between 2 and 14$\}$

5. Write the following sets in the form $\{x \mid x \ldots\}$.

(i) $A = \{1, 2, 3, 4, 5, 6, 7, 8\}$ (ii) $B = \{a, e, i, o, u\}$

(iii) $C = \{2, 4, 6, 8, 10, 12, 14\}$ (iv) $D = \{$Latvia, Lithuania, Luxembourg$\}$

(v) $E = \{1c, 2c, 5c, 10c, 20c, 50c, €1, €2\}$.

6. State whether each of the following is a null set:

(i)   The set of months which begin with the letter T.

(ii)   The set of men who have landed on the moon.

(iii)   The set of pupils in your class who are under 8 years of age.

(iv)   The set of whole numbers between $3\frac{1}{4}$ and $3\frac{3}{4}$.

(v)   The set of women who are more than 100 years old.

(vi)   The set of students in your class who study Nuclear Physics.

(vii) $\{0\}$.

(viii)   The set of months of the year which begin with a vowel.

(ix)   The set of foods that Old Mother Hubbard found in the cupboard.

(x)   The set of odd numbers which are divisible by 2.

7. Can you think of any even numbers that are divisible by 5?

Is the set of even numbers that are divisible by 5 an empty set?

8. Find the set of values of x, given that x is;

a multiple of 5, less than 30 and $\in N$.

9. Find the set of values of x given that, $-5 < x < 2, x \in Z$

10. Find the set of values of x, where x is;

a factor of 120, greater than 10 and $\in N$.

Section 6.3 Equal sets – Subsets

Two sets are **equal** if they contain exactly the same elements.

If $A = \{2, 4, 6, 8, 10\}$ and $B = \{8, 10, 6, 4, 2\}$, then $A = B$ as they both contain exactly the same elements even though they are listed in different ways.

Again, if $C = \{a, b, c\}$ and $D = \{x, y, z\}$
then $C \neq D$ as they do not contain the same elements.

[Note: C and D are **equivalent** sets because they have the same number of elements.]

Subsets

If $A = \{1, 2, 3, 4, 5\}$ and $B = \{3, 4\}$, we notice that all the elements in B are contained in A. We say 'B is a subset of A' and it is written **$B \subset A$**.

The illustration below shows that the first set is a subset of the second set.

We use the symbol $\not\subset$ to denote 'is not a subset of'.

> Set B is a subset of set A if every element of B is also an element of A.

Example 1

If $A = \{a, b, c, d\}$, write down a subset of A containing

(i) 2 elements   (ii) 3 elements.

(i) $\{b, c\}$ is a subset of A containing 2 elements.

(ii) $\{a, b, c\}$ is a subset of A containing 3 elements.

If $A = \{3, 4, 5\}$, then $\{3, 4, 5\}$ is a subset of A
as all the elements in it are contained in A.

> For all sets A,
> $A \subset A$ and $\emptyset \subset A$.

If $X = \{1, 2, 3\}$, then the subsets of X are
$\quad \{1\}, \{2\}, \{3\}, \{1, 2\}, \{2, 3\}, \{1, 3\}, \{1, 2, 3\}, \emptyset$

The set X itself and $\emptyset$ are called **improper** subsets.
All the other subsets are called **proper** subsets.

Investigation:

In mathematics when a pattern forms we can sometimes create a formula for general use. Investigate the following:

   (i) List all of the subsets of the set $A = \{2, 3\}$
  (ii) List all of the subsets of the set $B = \{2, 3, 4\}$
 (iii) List all of the subsets of the set $C = \{2, 3, 4, 5\}$
  (iv) Can you see a pattern in the number of subsets of A, B, C?
   (v) Use this pattern to predict the number of subsets in set $D = \{2, 3, 4, 5, 6\}$
  (vi) How many subsets would a set with 6 elements have?
 (vii) Can you use **indices** to write a rule for the number of subsets in a set with ***n*** elements?

Exercise 6.3

1. $A = \{1, 3, 4, 7, 9\}$ and $B = \{9, 3, 4, 1, 7\}$.
Explain why A and B are equal sets.

2. Which of the following sets are equal?
$A = \{1, 3, 5, 7\}$ $B = \{7, 5, 9\}$ $C = \{5, 7, 9\}$ $D = \{1, 5, 7, 3\}$

3. Given $A = \{a, b, c\}$ and $B = \{x, y, z\}$.
Is $A = B$? Explain your answer.

4. If $X = \{$Letters of the word TITLE$\}$ and $Y = \{$Letters of the word LITTLE$\}$, write down the elements of set X and set Y. Is $X = Y$?

5. $A = \{5, 6, 7, 8, 9\}$ and $B = \{x | x$ is a whole number greater than 5 and less than 10$\}$.
Write down the elements of B and state if $A = B$.

6. $X = \{$Letters of the word PARALLEL$\}$ and $Y = \{$Letters of the word REPEAL$\}$.
Write down the elements of each set and say if they are equal.

7. If $A = \{1, 2, 3, 4, 5, 6, 7, 8, 9, 10, 11, 12\}$, write down the elements of the following subsets:
   (i) The set of 2-digit numbers in A
  (ii) The set of even numbers in A
 (iii) The set of odd numbers less than 6 in A
  (iv) The set of numbers in A which are divisible by 3.

8. $A = \{1, 2, 3, 4, 5, 6\}$, $B = \{3, 4, 5, 6\}$, $C = \{3, 6, 9, 12\}$, $D = \emptyset$.
   State whether each of the following is true or false:
   (i) $B \subset A$ (ii) $B \subset C$ (iii) $D \subset B$ (iv) $C \subset A$ (v) $B \subset B$.

9. Say whether each of the following is true or false:
   (i) $\{6, 7\} \subset \{4, 5, 6, 7\}$ (ii) $\{a, b, c\} \subset \{a, c\}$.   (iii) $\emptyset \subset \{3, 4, 5\}$
   (iv) $\{1, 4, 9\} \subset \emptyset$ (v) $\{x, y, z\} \subset \{x, y, z\}$ (vi) $\{1\} \subset \{0, 1, 2\}$

10. If $A = \{a, b, c, d, e\}$, write down
    (i) two improper subsets of A (ii) three proper subsets of A.

11. Write down all the subsets of
    (i) $\{1, 2\}$ (ii) $\{x, y, z\}$

12. If $A = \{1, 3, 5, 7, 9, 11\}$ and $B = \{5, 7, 8, 9, 14\}$, write down a subset C of A which
    contains three elements such that C is also a subset of B.

13. Which of the following are true?
    (i) $2 \in \{1, 2, 3\}$ (ii) $\{2\} \subset \{4, 6, 8\}$ (iii) $\{p\} \subset \{o, p, q, r\}$
    (iv) $\{a, b, c\} \subset \{c, b, a\}$ (v) $\emptyset \subset \{l, m\}$ (vi) $\{1, 2\} = \{0, 1, 2\}$

14. If $A = \{a, b, c, d, e, f, g\}$, write down three sets B, C and D which are all subsets of A
    such that $C \subset B$ and $D \subset C$.

Section 6.4 Venn diagrams – Intersection and union of sets

A set can be illustrated by a circle with the elements represented by dots inside, each
dot being labelled by a letter or number. This is called a **Venn diagram** in honour of the
English mathematician, John Venn (1834–1923), who first used this type of diagram to
represent sets.

The diagram on the right shows the set
$A = \{a, b, c, d, e\}$ illustrated by a Venn diagram.

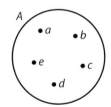

Subsets represented by Venn diagrams

If $A = \{a, b, c, d, e\}$ and $B = \{a, e\}$, then $B \subset A$.
This is shown in the Venn diagram on the right where
the closed curve B is inside the closed curve A.

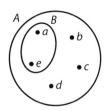

Intersection of two sets

The crosshatched yellow lines in the given diagram
represent the intersection of Main Street and High Street.
It is the part of the street common to both.

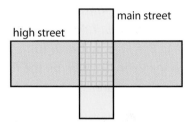

Similarly, the intersection of two sets
is the set of elements common to both.

> The **intersection** of two sets A and
> B is the set of elements that are in
> both A and B.
> A intersection B is written as $\boldsymbol{A \cap B}$.

The Venn diagram on the right shows two sets A and B
with some elements common to both.

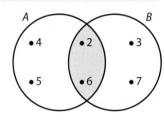

$A = \{2, 4, 5, 6\}$ and $B = \{2, 3, 6, 7\}$

The shaded area common to both sets is the intersection of
the two sets.

From the diagram, $A \cap B = \{2, 6\}$.

Example 1

If $A = \{a, b, c, d, e, f\}$ and $B = \{c, e, x, y\}$, list the elements of $A \cap B$.
Draw a Venn diagram to illustrate the intersection.

$A \cap B = \{c, e\}$.

The Venn diagram is shown on the right.

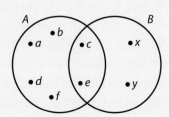

Union of sets

To find the set of elements in two or more sets we must find the **union** of the two sets.

Union of sets

> The **union** of two sets *A* and *B* is found by putting together in a new set all the elements of *A* and of *B* without repeating any element.

A union *B* is written as **A ∪ B**.
If *A* = {1, 3, 5, 7, 9} and *B* = {7, 8, 9, 10}, then
A ∪ *B* = {1, 3, 5, 7, 8, 9, 10}.
In the Venn diagram on the right,
the shaded area represents *A* ∪ *B*.

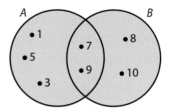

Remember; each element in the set *A* ∪ *B* must be listed once only.

Example 2

If *A* = {2, 4, 6, 8, 10} and *B* = {1, 2, 3, 4, 5}, list the elements of *A* ∪ *B* and illustrate this by a Venn diagram.

A ∪ *B* = {1, 2, 3, 4, 5, 6, 8, 10}.

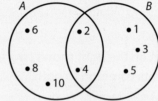

Venn diagram for A ∪ B

Investigation:

In chapter 1 natural numbers were written as the product of prime numbers.
Pamela found the prime factors of 30 as 2 x 3 x 5.
and the prime factors of 48 as 2 x 2 x 2 x 2 x 3.
To find the HCF and LCM she thought of
using a set Venn diagram as over.
She said the HCF was 2 x 3 = 6
and the LCM = 2 x 2 x 2 x 3 x 2 x 5 = 240

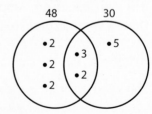

Using the ideas of sets what name did she use for (a) HCF (b) LCM
  (i) Investigate if you would agree with her answers.
 (ii) Explain what is wrong with her method!

The cardinal number of a set (#)

The number of elements in a set is called the **cardinal number** of the set.
The symbol # is used to denote the cardinal number.

From the diagram,
$A = \{1, 3, 4, 5, 6, 7\}$ and $B = \{1, 7, 8, 9, 10, 11\}$
$\quad \therefore \#A = 6 \quad$ and $\quad \#B = 6$
Also $\#(A \cap B) = 2$ and $\#(A \cup B) = 10$

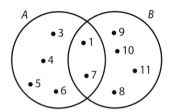

Exercise 6.4

1. What is the diagram on the right called?
Now list the elements of A.
What is #A?

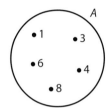

2. From the Venn diagram on the right, list the elements of

   (i)   A   (ii)   B

   (iii) $A \cap B$ (iv) $A \cup B$.

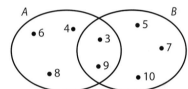

3. On the right are two sets A and B having some
elements in common.

   (i)   List the elements of A.

   (ii)   List the elements of B.

   (iii) Name an element that is in B, but not in A.

   (iv) Name an element that is neither in A nor B.

   (v)   List the elements that are common to A and B.

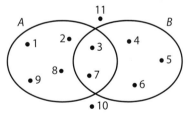

4. Two sets A and B are represented by the Venn diagram
on the right.
List the elements of

   (i)   A   (ii)   B

   (iii) $A \cap B$ (iv) $A \cup B$.

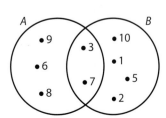

131

5. From the given Venn diagram, list the elements of

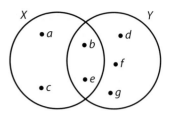

    (i) X (ii) Y

    (iii) $X \cap Y$ (iv) $X \cup Y$.

6. Look at the Venn diagram on the right and say if each of the following is true or false:

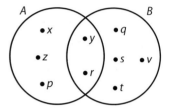

    (i) $p \in A$ (ii) $r \in B$ (iii) $z \in B$

    (iv) $r \in (A \cap B)$ (v) $z \in (A \cup B)$.

7. If $X = \{a, e, i, o, u\}$ and $Y = \{a, b, c, d, e\}$, draw a Venn diagram to illustrate this information.

8. $A = \{1, 2, 3, 4, 5, 6\}$, $B = \{4, 5, 6, 7, 8\}$, $C = \{7, 8, 9, 10\}$

List the elements of each of these sets:

    (i) $A \cap B$ (ii) $B \cup C$ (iii) $B \cap C$ (iv) $A \cap C$.

9. $A = \{$letters in the word SCIENCE$\}$, $B = \{$letters in the word NEARER$\}$

List the elements of   (i) A (ii) B (iii) $A \cap B$ (iv) $A \cup B$

10. From the Venn diagram on the right, list the elements of

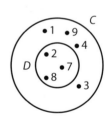

    (i) C (ii) D

    (iii) $C \cap D$ (iv) $C \cup D$.

11. $A = \{0, 1, 2, 4, 8, 12\}$, $B = \{1, 3, 5, 8, 9\}$, $C = \{8, 9, 10, 11, 12\}$

List the elements of each of these:

    (i) $A \cap C$ (ii) $A \cup B$ (iii) $B \cap C$

    (iv) $A \cup C$ (v) $B \cup C$ (vi) $A \cap B$.

12. Using the Venn diagram on the right, write down

    (i) $\#A$ (ii) $\#B$

    (iii) $\#(A \cap B)$ (iv) $\#(A \cup B)$.

13. The Venn diagram on the right shows the elements of two sets X and Y.
Say if each of the following is true or false:

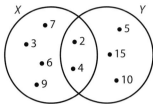

(i) $2 \in Y$ (ii) $15 \in X$ (iii) $4 \in (X \cap Y)$

(iv) $9 \in (X \cup Y)$ (v) $\#Y = 15$ (vi) $\#(X \cap Y) = 2$

(vii) $10 \in (X \cup Y)$ (viii) $\#X = 4$ (ix) $(X \cap Y) \subset X$.

14. Copy the Venn diagram on the right
and insert dots to represent this information:

$\#A = 4$, $\#B = 9$ and $\#(A \cap B) = 2$.

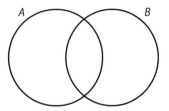

Section 6.5 The universal set – Complement of a set

Consider the following three sets:
$A = \{$pupils in the school over seventeen years of age$\}$
$B = \{$pupils in the school who study French$\}$
$C = \{$pupils in the school who play basketball$\}$

The three sets A, B and C are all based on 'the set of pupils in the school'. This set, from
which all the other sets being considered are taken, is called the **universal set**. Thus,
the universal set may be described as the **background set** necessary when discussing
various subsets.

In a Venn diagram, a rectangle is used to represent
the universal set.
It is denoted by the capital letter **U**.

Complement of a set

The complement of a set A is the set of elements in the
universal set U which are not in A. The complement of A is
denoted by **A'** and is shown by the shaded area in the
Venn diagram on the right.

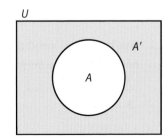

Example 1

If $U = \{a, b, c, d, e, f, g, h, i\}$, $A = \{a, c, e, i\}$ and $B = \{e, f, g, h, i\}$, illustrate these on a Venn diagram and list the elements of

    (i) A' (ii) B' (iii) $(A \cup B)'$ (iv) $(A \cap B)'$

The Venn diagram is shown on the right.

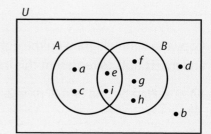

    (i) A' is the set of elements of U which are not in A.

        $\therefore A' = \{b, d, f, g, h\}$

    (ii) $B' = \{a, b, c, d\}$

    (iii) $A \cup B = \{a, c, e, f, g, h, i\}$

        $\therefore (A \cup B)' = \{b, d\}$

    (iv) $(A \cap B) = \{e, i\}$

        $\therefore (A \cap B)' = \{a, b, c, d, f, g, h\}$

Exercise 6.5

1. What set does the shaded region of the given Venn diagram represent?

Use the Venn diagram to list the elements of

    (i) U (ii) A (iii) A'.

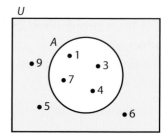

2. Use the given Venn diagram to list the elements of

    (i) B (ii) U (iii) B'.

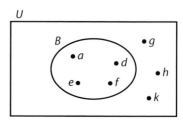

3. Use the given Venn diagram to list the elements of each of these sets:

    (i) A (ii) B (iii) A'

    (iv) B' (v) $A \cup B$ (vi) $(A \cup B)'$.

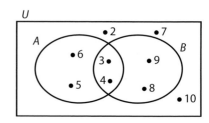

4. Using the Venn diagram on the right,
list the elements of

(i) A' (ii) B' (iii) $A \cup B$

(iv) $(A \cup B)'$ (v) $A \cap B$ (vi) $(A \cap B)'$.

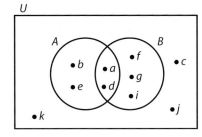

5. In the given Venn diagram, each dot represents an element.
Write down

(i) #A (ii) #A' (iii) #$(A \cap B)$

(iv) #B' (v) #$(A \cup B)'$.

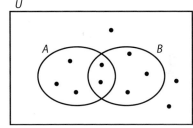

6. If $U = \{1, 2, 3, 4, 5, 6, 7, 8, 9, 10\}$
$A = \{1, 3, 5, 7\}$
$B = \{3, 4, 5, 6\}$, list the elements of

(i) A' (ii) B' (iii) $A \cup B$ (iv) $(A \cup B)'$.

7. Given $U = \{1, 2, 3, 4, 5, 6, 7, 8, 9\}$
$A = \{1, 3, 5, 7\}$
$B = \{5, 6, 7, 8\}$

Copy the Venn diagram on the right and illustrate
the given information on it.

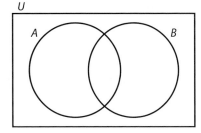

8. By examining the Venn diagram on the right, say whether each of the following
statements is true or false:

(i) $9 \in A'$ (ii) $3 \in (A \cup B)$
(iii) $4 \in B'$ (iv) $2 \in (A \cup B)'$
(v) #$A' = 4$ (vi) #$(A \cup B)' = 3$
(vii) $7 \in U$ (viii) #$U = 10$
(ix) #$(A \cap B) = 6$.

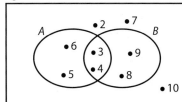

9. Examine the Venn diagram on the right and list the elements of the following sets:

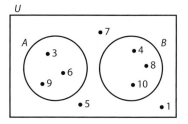

    (i) A' (ii) B'

    (iii) $A \cup B$ (iv) $(A \cup B)'$

    (v) $A \cap B$.

10. What set is represented by the shaded region in each of the diagrams below?

    (i) 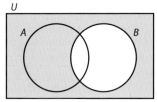   (ii)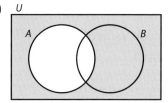

    (iii) 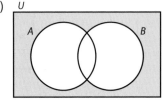   (iv)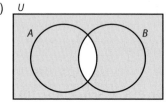

11. Given $U = \{1, 2, 3, 4, 5, 6, 7, 8, 9, 10, 11, 12\}$
           $A = \{2, 3, 5, 7, 11\}$
           $B = \{1, 3, 5, 7, 9, 11\}$

    List the elements of the following sets:

    (i) A' (ii) B' (iii) $A \cup B$ (iv) $(A \cup B)'$ (v) $(A \cap B)'$.

    Investigate if $(A \cap B)' = A' \cup B'$.

Section 6.6 Sets and probability

The probability of an event E has been defined as $P(E) = \dfrac{\text{Number of favourable outcomes}}{\text{Number of possible outcomes}}$

A bag contains discs numbered 1 to 10.
A disc is chosen at random.
What is the probability that it is an even number?
A(even numbers) $= \{2, 4, 6, 8, 10\}$

P(even number) $= \dfrac{5}{10} = \dfrac{1}{2}$

Using sets we have, P(even number) $= \dfrac{\#A}{\#U} = \dfrac{5}{10} = \dfrac{1}{2}$

> Probability $(A) = \dfrac{\#A}{\#U}$

Example 1

List all the 2-letter subsets of the set $A = \{m, s, n, t\}$

What is the probability that a subset chosen at random will contain the letter s?

2-letter subsets $= \{m, s\}, \{m, n\}, \{m, t\}, \{s, n\}, \{s, t\}, \{n, t\}$

2-letter subsets containing $s = \{m, s\}, \{s, n\}, \{s, t\}$

P(subset containing s) $= \frac{3}{6} = \frac{1}{2}$

Example 2

Using the Venn diagram find the following probabilities:

    (i) P(A)   (ii) P(A ∩ B)   (iii) P(A ∪ B)'

From the diagram we have:

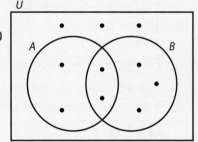

$\#A = 4$, $\#(A \cap B) = 2$, $\#(A \cap B)'$, $\#U = 10$

 (i) P(A) $= \frac{\#A}{\#U} = \frac{4}{10} = \frac{2}{5}$

 (ii) P(A ∩ B) $= \frac{2}{10}$

 (iii) P(A ∪ B)' $= \frac{\#(A \cup B)'}{\#U} = \frac{3}{10}$

Exercise 6.6

1. A letter is chosen at random from the set $A = \{a, b, c, d, e, f, g, h\}$.
   Find the probability that the letter is (i) a vowel (ii) not a vowel.

2. $U = \{1, 2, 3, 4, 5, 6, 7, 8, 10, 15, 20\}$ and $C = \{1, 5, 10, 15, 20\}$
   Draw a Venn diagram of these sets.
   Use the Venn diagram to find the probability of choosing, at random,
   a number from U that is not in C.

3. Let U = {the natural number from 1 to 20}
   T = {multiples of 3}
   F = {multiples of 4}
   (a) Draw a Venn diagram of this information.
   (b) If a number is chosen at random from U, find:
       (i) P(T)   (ii) P(F)   (iii) P(T')   (iv) P(F')   (v) P(T ∩ F)   (vi) P(T ∪ F)

4. Let U = {months of the year}
   R = {months with the letter r in their name}
   Y = {months with the letter y in their name}
   (a) Draw a Venn diagram of this information.
   (b) If a month is chosen at random, use your Venn diagram to find:
       (i) P(R ∪ Y)   (ii) P(R ∩ Y)

5. Copy and complete the Venn diagram over using the following sets.
   U = {1, 2, 3, 4, 5, 6, 7, 8, 9, 10}
   A = {2, 3, 4, 5, 6}
   B = {1, 3, 5, 7, 9}
   (a) Find each of the following

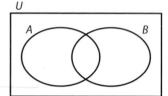

       (i) #A   (ii) #B   (iii) #(A ∩ B)   (iv) #A'
   (b) If a number is chosen at random from U find:
       (i) P(A)   (ii) P(B)   (iii) P((A ∩ B)   (iv) P(A')

6. List all the subsets of the set R = {a, b, c}
   If a subset is chosen at random from the set of subsets find:
   (i) P(the subset contains the letter a).
   (ii) P(of picking an improper subset).

7. The following Venn diagram shows the number of students studying French(F) and German(G) in a school. Use the Venn diagram to find:
   (i) how many students are in the class.
   (ii) how many students study French.
   (iii) how many students study German.
   (iv) how many students study French and German.
   (v) the probability that a student, chosen at random from the class, studies French.
   (v) the probability that a student, chosen at random from the class, does not study French or German.
   (vi) the probability that a student, chosen at random from the class, studies either French or German.

Test yourself 6

1. List the elements of each of these sets:
   - (i) $A = \{$The even numbers between 3 and 11$\}$
   - (ii) $B = \{$The counties in Ireland beginning with W$\}$
   - (iii) $C = \{$The letters of the word COMMITTEE$\}$
   - (iv) $D = \{$Vowels of the word REVISION$\}$
   - (v) $E = \{$The first six multiples of 5$\}$
   - (vi) $F = \{x|x$ is a single digit natural number$\}$

2. (i) If $A = \{m, a, t, h, s\}$ and $B = \{e, x, a, m\}$, list the elements of
   - (a) $A \cup B$ (b) $A \cap B$.

   (ii) If $X = \{3, 4, 5, 6, 7, 8\}$ and $Y = \{1, 2, 7, 8\}$,
   draw a Venn diagram to illustrate these sets.
   Now write down   (a) $\#(X \cap Y)$ (b) $\#(X \cup Y)$

3. Using the Venn diagram on the right, list the
   elements of these sets:
   - (i) X (ii) Y (iii) $X \cap Y$

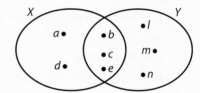

4. $A = \{1, 3, 5, 7, 9\}$, $B = \{1, 2, 3, 4, 5\}$, $C = \{7, 8, 9, 10\}$
   List the elements of these sets:
   - (i) $A \cap B$ (ii) $B \cap C$ (iii) $A \cup C$

5. From the given Venn diagram, list the elements of
   - (i) P (ii) Q
   - (iii) $P \cap Q$ (iv) $P \cup Q$

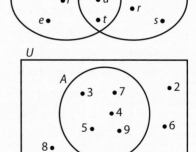

6. Use the given Venn diagram to write down the
   elements of each of these sets:
   - (i) A (ii) U (iii) A'

7. Use the given Venn diagram to list the elements
   of each of these sets:
   - (i) A (ii) B (iii) $A \cap B$
   - (iv) U (v) $A \cup B$ (vi) $(A \cup B)'$

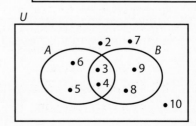

8. Describe the shaded area in each of the Venn diagrams below:

   (i)

   (ii)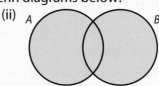

9. $A = \{1, 2, 3\}$, $B = \{a, b, c\}$, $C = \{b, c, d\}$ and $D = \{2, 1, 3\}$.
   Which one of the following is true?

   (i) $A = B$ (ii) $B = C$ (iii) $A = D$ (iv) $A = B = C = D$

10. Explain what is meant by the symbol, $A \subset B$.
    Now copy each of the following and insert $\subset$ or $\not\subset$ in the space provided.

    (i) $\{a, b\} \ldots \{a, b, c, d\}$ (ii) $\{2, 3\} \ldots \{2, 3, 4, 5\}$
    (iii) $\{1\} \ldots \{2, 4, 6, 8\}$ (iv) $\{d, e, f\} \ldots \{a, b, c, d, e\}$

11. From the Venn diagram on the right, write down

    (i) $\#A$ (ii) $\#B$

    (iii) $\#(A \cap B)$ (iv) $\#(A \cup B)$

    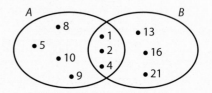

12. $A = \{2, 3, 4, 5\}$ and $B = \{4, 6, 8\}$.
    Say if each of the following is true or false:

    (i) $5 \in A$ (ii) $6 \in (A \cap B)$ (iii) $2 \in (A \cup B)$ (iv) $\#A = 5$

13. Given $U = \{1, 2, 3, 4, 5, 6, 7, 8, 9\}$
    $X = \{1, 2, 3, 7\}$
    $Y = \{2, 4, 7, 8\}$
    Copy the Venn diagram on the right and
    on it illustrate the sets U, X and Y.

    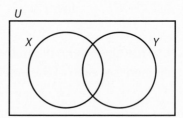

    (i) List the elements of Y'.
    (ii) List the elements of $X \cup Y$.
    (iii) Find $\#(X \cup Y)'$.
    (iv) Find $\#X'$.

14. Copy the following statements, replacing the * sign in each case with the
    appropriate symbol chosen from $\in, \not\in, =, \cup, \cap, \subset, \not\subset$.

    (i) $3 * \{1, 2, 3\}$ (ii) $\{a, b\} * \{a, b, c\}$ (iii) $2 * \{1, 3, 5, 7\}$

    (iv) $\emptyset * \{5, 7, 9\}$ (v) $\{2, 3, 4\} * \{4, 2, 3\}$ (vi) $\{1, 2, 3\} * \{3, 4\} = \{3\}$

15. Two sets of cards are shown.
    A students picks, at random, a card form set *A*
    and then a card form set *B* to form a 2-digit
    number *AB*. E.g., 82.

    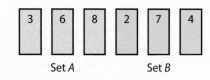

    Set *A*   Set *B*

    (i)   list all the possible outcomes.
    (ii) How many even numbers are possible?
    (iii) How many odd numbers are possible?
    (iv) Find the probability that an odd number is formed.
    (v)   If the order of picking does not matter i.e. *AB* or *BA*, what is the probability of
          forming an even number?

16. Three coins are tossed in the air.
    List all the sets of outcomes
    What is the probability that no head shows?

17. Daragh asked his class of 24 students which
    science subject, Biology or Physics, they preferred.
    He presented his results on a Venn diagram as shown.
    If a student is chosen at random from the class, what is
    the probability of picking a student who;

    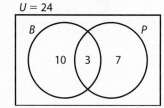

    (i)   preferred Biology
    (ii) liked both Physics and Biology
    (iii) liked neither Biology nor Physics

Learning Experience   *Unit 6*

Assignment 1

(a) Some letters are made using straight lines only (e.g. E)
     Some are made using curved lines only (e.g. C)
     Some are made using both (e.g. D)
     Make a poster placing the following letters into their proper places in the Venn diagram below:

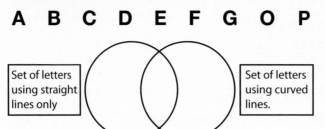

A   B   C   D   E   F   G   O   P

Set of letters using straight lines only

Set of letters using curved lines.

(b) (i)   Using the list of sports below select a set of sports that have something in common.
     (ii) Select a second set of sports that have something else in common.
     (iii) Draw a large Venn diagram of the sets, **naming the sets** carefully.
     (iv) Include the Universal set.
     (v)   Indicate clearly the sports in both sets i.e. in the Intersection of the two sets.

Tennis	Hurling	Swimming	Badminton
Football	Soccer	Rugby	Basketball
Volleyball	Cricket	Boxing	Golf

Problem 1

The set A consists of whole positive numbers, n, such that the difference between $\sqrt{n}$ and 10 is less than 1 and greater than -1.

Explain how to find the number of elements in A.

Problem 2

Describe clearly 5 different possible subsets of a 52 card deck of cards.

Name each subset A, B, C, etc.

If a card is chosen at random from the deck, write down the probability that the card will belong to **each** of your chosen subsets.

Assignment 2

(a) By choosing two (small) sets, A and B, which have some common elements, show that the operations of Union and Intersection **are commutative**.

i.e. show that (i) $A \cup B = B \cup A$ (ii) $A \cap B = B \cap A$

(b) By choosing a third set C which has elements in common with A and B decide whether the operations of Union and Intersection **are associative**.

i.e. (i) Is $A \cup (B \cup C) = (A \cup B) \cup C$?   and (ii) is $A \cap (B \cap C) = (A \cap B) \cap C$?

(c) Draw two **Venn diagram** charts, the first indicating your result for part (a) and the second showing your result for part (b)

(d) Using a Venn diagram of three intersecting sets indicate by shading whether the following is true or false.

$$A \cup (B \cap C) = (A \cup B) \cap C$$

Chapter 6 review 1

Using the terms from the chapter copy and complete the following sentences:

1. The items in a set are called _____.

2. The elements of a set must be _____ _____.

3. Capital letters are used to _____ a set.

4. No element in a set can be repeated more than _____.

5. All the elements are enclosed in _____ _____.

6. Commas are used to _____ elements.

7. Another name for an empty set is a _____ set.

8. The set *B* is a _____ of set *A*, if every element of *B* is also an element of *A*.

9. A set itself and the null set are called _____ subsets.

10. The _____ of two sets *A* and *B* is the set of elements that are in both *A* and *B*.

11. The union of two sets *A* and *B* is the set of all the elements in *A* and *B* without _____ any element.

12. The _____ number of a set is the number of elements in the set.

13. The main set from which all other sets are taken is called the _____ set and is denoted by ____.

14. Given a set *A*, the complement of *A* is the set of all the elements in *U* but ____ __ __ and is denoted by _____.

Chapter 6 review 2

You should now be able to:

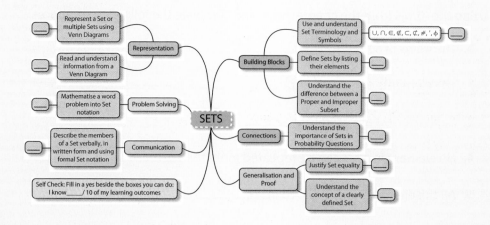

Percentages

In this chapter, you will learn to:

- use **per cent,**
- change fractions to percentages,
- change percentages to fractions,
- change percentages to decimals,
- find the percentage of a quantity,
- find one quantity as a percentage of another quantity,
- increase or decrease a quantity by a percentage,
- find a quantity if you know a percentage of it,
- calculate **VAT,**
- apply **a discount** to price,
- calculate percentage **profit or loss.**

Section 7.1 Percentages – Fractions – Decimals

The words **per cent** mean *per hundred* or *out of every hundred*.

The symbol **%** is used to represent *per cent*.

Thus 10% means 10 out of every 100.

The diagram shows 100 squares.

25 of the squares are coloured red.

The amount of the diagram coloured red is

$$\frac{25}{100} = 25\%.$$

10% of the diagram is coloured green.

Fractions to percentages

$$\frac{1}{5} = \frac{1 \times 20}{5 \times 20} = \frac{20}{100} = 20\%$$

$$\frac{3}{4} = \frac{3 \times 25}{4 \times 25} = \frac{75}{100} = 75\%$$

Here we changed each fraction into an equivalent fraction with 100 as denominator.

This work may be shortened by multiplying each fraction by $\frac{100}{1}\%$.

Thus $\frac{1}{5} = \frac{1}{5} \times \frac{100}{1}\% = \frac{100}{5} = 20\%$

$\frac{3}{4} = \frac{3}{4} \times \frac{100}{1}\% = \frac{300}{4} = 75\%$

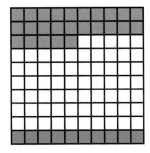

To change a fraction to a percentage, multiply the fraction by $\frac{100}{1}\%$.

$$\frac{2}{5} = \frac{2}{5} \times \frac{100}{1}\% = \frac{200}{5} = \mathbf{40\%}$$

Example 1

Express (i) $\frac{4}{5}$ (ii) $\frac{5}{8}$ as percentages.

(i) $\frac{4}{5} = \frac{4}{5} \times \frac{100}{1}\%$

$= \frac{400}{5} = 80\%$

(ii) $\frac{5}{8} = \frac{5}{8} \times \frac{100}{1}\%$

$= \frac{500}{8} = 62\frac{4}{8}\%$

$= 62\frac{1}{2}\%$

Percentages and decimals

(a) Changing a decimal to a percentage.

(i) $0.25 = \frac{25}{100} = 25\%$

(ii) $0.8 = \frac{8}{10} = \frac{80}{100} = 80\%$

Write the decimal as a fraction with a denominator of 100 and then change the fraction to a percentage.

> To change a decimal to a percentage, multiply by 100%.
> **0.35** $= 0.35 \times 100\% = \textbf{35\%}$

(b) Changing a percentage to a decimal.

(i) $16\% = \frac{16}{100} = 0.16$

(ii) $12\frac{1}{2}\% = \frac{12\frac{1}{2}}{100} = \frac{12.5}{100} = 0.125$

Write the percentage as a fraction with a denominator of 100 and then change the fraction to a decimal.

> To change a percentage to a fraction or a decimal,
> divide the percentage by 100.
> **45%** $= \frac{45}{100} = \textbf{0.45}$

Here are some percentages you should memorise:

Fraction	$\frac{1}{10}$	$\frac{1}{5}$	$\frac{1}{4}$	$\frac{1}{3}$	$\frac{1}{2}$	$\frac{2}{3}$	$\frac{3}{4}$
Percentage	10%	20%	25%	$33\frac{1}{3}\%$	50%	$66\frac{2}{3}\%$	75%

Exercise 7.1

1. Three figures, each with 100 squares, are shown below:

(a) 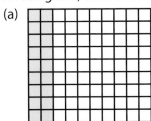   (b) 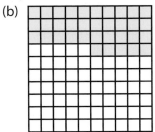   (c)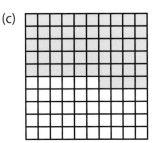

  (i)   What percentage of each figure is coloured yellow?
  (ii)   What percentage of each figure is not coloured yellow?
  (iii)   What fraction of each figure is coloured yellow?
  (iv)   What decimal of each figure is coloured yellow?

2. Copy and complete each of these:

(i) $\dfrac{28}{100} = \square\%$ (ii) $\dfrac{54}{100} = \square\%$ (iii) $\dfrac{\square}{100} = 15\%$

(iv) $\dfrac{9}{10} = \dfrac{\square}{100} = \square\%$ (v) $\dfrac{11}{20} = \dfrac{\square}{100} = \square\%$ (vi) $\dfrac{14}{25} = \dfrac{\square}{100} = \square\%$

3. Express the following percentages as fractions in their simplest form:

  (i)   20%   (ii)   60%   (iii)   70%   (iv)   15%   (v)   25%
  (vi)   75%   (vii)   85%   (viii)   5%   (ix)   2%   (x)   24%.

4. Copy and complete the following:

$$7\tfrac{1}{2}\% = \dfrac{7\tfrac{1}{2}}{100} = \dfrac{7\tfrac{1}{2} \times 2}{100 \times 2} = \dfrac{\square}{200} = \dfrac{3}{\square}$$

5. Change these percentages to fractions and simplify each fraction:

  (i) $33\tfrac{1}{3}\%$ (ii) $12\tfrac{1}{2}\%$ (iii) $2\tfrac{1}{2}\%$ (iv) $8\tfrac{1}{3}\%$ (v) $17\tfrac{1}{2}\%$

6.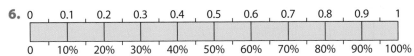

Use the number line above to answer these questions:
  (i)   Write each of these decimals as a percentage:
  (a)   0.5   (b)   0.2   (c)   0.35   (d)   0.8   (e)   0.75
  (ii)   Write each of these percentages as a decimal:
  (a)   20%   (b)   80%   (c)   70%   (d)   65%   (e)   95%

7. Change these fractions to percentages:

  (i) $\dfrac{18}{100}$ (ii) $\dfrac{47}{100}$ (iii) $\dfrac{3}{10}$ (iv) $\dfrac{7}{10}$ (v) $\dfrac{5}{20}$

  (vi) $\dfrac{2}{5}$ (vii) $\dfrac{3}{4}$ (viii) $\dfrac{17}{20}$ (ix) $\dfrac{4}{25}$ (x) $\dfrac{19}{50}$

8. Write these percentages as decimals:

   (i) 50%   (ii) 10%   (iii) 90%   (iv) 35%   (v) 45%

   (vi) 8%   (vii) $12\frac{1}{2}$%   (viii) 24%   (ix) 1%   (x) $24\frac{1}{2}$%

9. Express the following decimals as percentages:

   (i) 0.8   (ii) 0.4   (iii) 0.75   (iv) 0.45   (v) 0.15

   (vi) 0.07   (vii) 0.01   (viii) 0.125   (ix) 0.345   (x) 0.045

10. What percentage of each diagram is shaded?

   (i)   (ii) 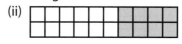   (iii)

11. Put these in three matching groups.

12. Write the following quantities in order, starting with the smallest:

   (i) 50% $\frac{1}{4}$ 20%   0.3 $\frac{2}{5}$

   (ii) $\frac{3}{10}$ 60% $\frac{1}{5}$ $\frac{1}{2}$ $\frac{1}{4}$ 0.45

13. Write these fractions and percentages as decimals:

   (i) $\frac{27}{100}$ (ii) $\frac{7}{100}$ (iii) 54%   (iv) $17\frac{1}{2}$%   (v) $2\frac{1}{2}$%

14. Find four matching pairs.

   What could match the odd one out?

15.

A	E	U	N	R	S	T	M	V
$\frac{1}{2}$	30%	40%	0.8	0.6	0.2	75%	$\frac{1}{4}$	$\frac{7}{10}$

Use this code to find a letter for each fraction, decimal or percentage below.
Rearrange each set of letters to spell a planet.

   (i) $\frac{3}{4}$ 0.5 $\frac{6}{10}$ 20%   80% $\frac{2}{5}$

   (ii) 0.4 $\frac{1}{5}$ 0.7 $\frac{8}{10}$ 0.3

   (iii) $\frac{3}{5}$ 50%   0.4 $\frac{1}{5}$ $\frac{4}{10}$ 80%

16. What percentage of each of the following figures is shaded?

(i)

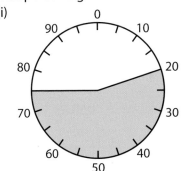

(ii)

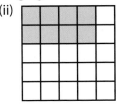

(iii)

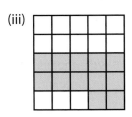

Section 7.2 Working with percentages I

Finding a percentage of a quantity

To find a percentage **of** a quantity, **multiply** the quantity by the percentage.
In the following examples, the percentage is changed to a fraction or a decimal
and then multiplied by the quantity.

Example 1

Find   (i) 8% of 250   (ii) $37\frac{1}{2}$% of €320.

(i) 8% of 250 $= \dfrac{8}{100} \times \dfrac{250}{1} = \dfrac{200}{10} = 20$ ...changing the % to a fraction

(ii) $37\frac{1}{2}\% = \dfrac{37\frac{1}{2}}{100} = \dfrac{37\frac{1}{2} \times 2}{100 \times 2} = \dfrac{75}{200} = \dfrac{15}{40} = \dfrac{3}{8}$

$\dfrac{3}{8}$ of €320 $= \dfrac{3}{8} \times \dfrac{320}{1} = €120$

Example 2

Find   (i) 5% of €250   (ii) 30% of 510 km

(i) 5% = 0.05   ...changing the % to a decimal

$\therefore$ 5% of €250 = 0.05 × €250

          = €12.50

(ii) 30% = 0.3

$\therefore$ 30% of 510 km = 0.3 × 510 km

          = 153 km

Decimal equivalents		
1%	=	0.01
7%	=	0.07
$8\frac{1}{2}$%	=	0.085
16%	=	0.16
$16\frac{1}{2}$%	=	0.165
70%	=	0.7
85%	=	0.85
92.3%	=	0.923

Expressing one quantity as a percentage of another quantity

To express one quantity as a percentage of another quantity:
  (i) make sure both quantities are in the same units,
 (ii) write the first quantity as a fraction of the second quantity,
(iii) multiply by 100%.

> When comparing quantities, make sure both quantities are in the same units.

Example 2

Express (i) 72 as a percentage of 80
         (ii) 15 minutes as a percentage of $1\frac{1}{2}$ hours.

  (i) 72 as a percentage of 80 is $\frac{72}{80} \times \frac{100}{1}\% = \frac{720}{8}\% = 90\%$

 (ii) 15 min as a percentage of $1\frac{1}{2}$ hours is
       15 min as a percentage of 90 min. $\rightarrow \frac{15}{90} \times \frac{100}{1}\% = \frac{150}{9}\% = 16\frac{2}{3}\%$

When using a calculator to express 13 as a percentage of 50, you need to find the value of $\frac{13}{50} \times \frac{100}{1}$.

Key in 13 ÷ 50 × 100 = .

The answer is 26%.

Exercise 7.2

1. Write down the answers to these without written calculations:
  (i) 10% of 50   (ii) 20% of 40   (iii) 25% of 48   (iv) 5% of 300
  (v) 30% of 200   (vi) 40% of 120   (vii) 75% of 16   (viii) 11% of 600

2. Find each of the following:
  (i) 10% of 380   (ii) 40% of 680   (iii) 30% of 1680
  (iv) 15% of €420   (v) 45% of €140   (vi) 80% of €910.

3. To find $17\frac{1}{2}\%$ of 480, copy and complete the calculation on the right.

10% of 480 = 48
5% of 480 = ☐
$2\frac{1}{2}\%$ of 480 = ☐
$17\frac{1}{2}\%$ of 480 = ☐

4. Use the method used in question 3 to find each of these:

(i) 15% of 120 km (ii) $22\frac{1}{2}$% of €450 (iii) $37\frac{1}{2}$% of 800 kg

5. Which is the greater of these sums of money?

$12\frac{1}{2}$% of €160 or $17\frac{1}{2}$% of €120

6. The table on the right gives the marks that a boy got for each subject in a test.
Find the percentage mark that he got in each subject.

Subject	Boy's marks	Total marks
Maths	58	100
Science	60	80
English	48	60
Irish	51	75
History	28	40
Geography	56	70
French	116	200

7. Express the first quantity as a percentage of the second in each of the following:

(i) 12; 48 (ii) 15; 75 (iii) €6; €15
(iv) 25c; €5 (v) 60c; €5.00 (vi) 12 mins; 1 hr 20 mins
(vii) 90 cm; 3 m (viii) 8 days; 2 weeks and 6 days
(ix) 36; 450

8. These labels show the percentage of fat in some foods.

Pizza 10% fat   Chips 15% fat   Croissants 20% fat   Hamburgers 35% fat   Margarine 80% fat   Dry roast peanuts 45% fat

How much fat is there in

(i) a 300 g pizza (ii) 200 g of chips (iii) 120 g of margarine
(iv) a 100 g hamburger (v) a 90 g croissant (vi) 300 g of peanuts?

9. Express each of these percentages as a decimal:

(i) 14% (ii) 27% (iii) 35% (iv) 6% (v) 9%
(vi) $9\frac{1}{2}$% (vii) 30% (viii) 36.5% (ix) 96.3% (x) 20.3%

10. Use your calculator to find each of the following:

(i) 15% of 280 (ii) 12% of 340 (iii) 7% of 84
(iv) 28% of 650 (v) $34\frac{1}{2}$% of 600 (vi) $1\frac{1}{2}$% of 650

11. Which is bigger, 23% of €85 or 48% of €55?

12. Find the sale price of this jumper.

€59   SALE 15% OFF

13. In a school of 1200 pupils, 45% are boys.
  (i) How many are girls?
  (ii) 30% of the girls are under 13.
       How many girls are under 13?

14. A worker with a weekly wage of €750 got an increase of 5%.
Find his new weekly wage.

15. Joan got 248 marks out of 400 in a Science examination.
Express her marks as a percentage of the total.

16. In a French examination, a boy got 336 marks out of 600.
In an English examination, he got 44 marks out of 80.
In which examination did he achieve the higher percentage mark?

17. A worker with a weekly wage of €640 got an increase of €32 a week.
What percentage increase did she get?

18. A theatre has 480 seats. During a certain show, 24 seats were empty.
What percentage of the seats were full?

19. Martin walks $\frac{1}{2}$ km to school and takes the bus for the remaining $4\frac{1}{2}$ km.
What percentage of the total journey does he walk?

20. In a survey, a group of people were asked how they learned to use a computer.
The answers are listed as follows:

Method	Number of people
Self-taught	33
Through work	18
From family or friend	5
At school	21
Other	3

  (i) How many people were asked in the survey in total?
  (ii) What percentage of this total were self-taught?
  (iii) What percentage learned at school?

21. A cake is described as '85% fat-free'.
  (i) What percentage of the cake is fat?
  (ii) If the cake weighs 400 g, how much fat does it contain?

Investigation:

Sugar intake has become an important topic of conversation in the media today.

- Design a chart comparing the **% sugar** in 4 recipes of your choice.

- Comparing your chart with other students, indicate the recipes with the highest percentages. (Make sure that the same definition of sugar is used when comparing).

Investigation:

- Research and explain the word **percentile** and its connection to percentages.

- By means of examples explain how percentiles may be used in sport, in academic examinations and in the development of young infants.

- Find an online height percentile calculator to discover what percentile you are in. Compare the class outcome.

Section 7.3 Working with percentages II

Increasing or decreasing by a given percentage

If a quantity is to be increased or decreased by a percentage it is important to remember that the *original* quantity is 100%.

If the quantity is to be increased by 20% it is now 120% of the *original* quantity.

If the quantity is to be reduced by 20% it is now 80% of the *original* quantity.

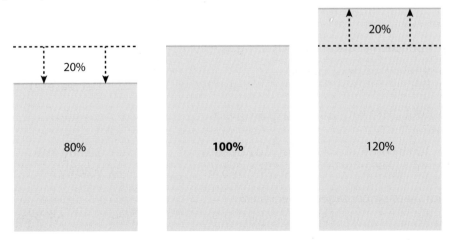

Example 1

(i) Decrease €650 by 12%.
(ii) Increase 440 g by 35%.

(i) Decreasing by 12% means we have (100% − 12%) 88% left of the original.
88% of €650 = 0.88 × €650 = €572

(ii) Increasing by 35% means we have (100% + 35%) 135% of the original.
135% of 440 g = 1.35 × 440 g = 594 g

Finding a quantity when given a percentage of it

If we are given a percentage of a quantity,
we first find 1% and then multiply this
amount by 100 to find the total quantity
which is 100%.

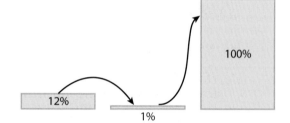

Example 2

If 12% of a number is 72, find the number.

12% = 72
1% = 6 … divide 72 by 12
100% = 6 × 100 = 600.

Exercise 7.3

1. Work out each of these without using a calculator:
   (i) Increase 90 by 10%   (ii) Increase 60 by 20%   (iii) Increase 150 by 30%
   (iv) Decrease 40 by 10%   (v) Decrease 120 by 20%   (vi) Decrease 200 by 5%

2. Work out these without using a calculator:
   Increase
   (i) 100 by 60%   (ii) 300 by 65%   (iii) 320 by 45%
   (iv) 280 by 15%   (v) 480 by 5%   (vi) €80 by 8%

3. Write these percentages as decimals:
   (i) 6%   (ii) 15%   (iii) 35%   (iv) 70%   (v) $7\frac{1}{2}$%.

4. To find 82% of 600, multiply 600 by 0.82 on a calculator.
   Now fill in the missing decimal in each of the following:
   - (i) To find 38% of 700, multiply 700 by ☐
   - (ii) To find 60% of 580, multiply 580 by ☐
   - (iii) To find 13% of 270, multiply 270 by ☐
   - (iv) To find 6% of 300, multiply 300 by ☐
   - (v) To find 120% of 640, multiply 640 by ☐
   - (vi) To find $12\frac{1}{2}$% of 800, multiply 800 by ☐

5. (i) Increase 240 by 10%.   (ii) Increase 150 by 40%.
   (iii) Decrease €140 by 15%.   (iv) Decrease 240 kg by $12\frac{1}{2}$%.
   (v) Increase €90 by 8%.   (vi) Decrease 80 kg by 35%.

6. Find the weight of each of the following after the extra has been added:
   - (i) A 450 g packet of cornflakes with 30% extra
   - (ii) A 750 g container of yogurt with 10% extra
   - (iii) A 250 g pizza with 15% extra.

7. If 11% of a number is 77, find the number.

8. If 20% of a sum of money is €70, find the sum of money.

9. If 15% of the price of a car is €2775, find the price of the car.

10. A bus company plans to increase its prices by 8%. At the moment, the bus fare to town is €1.50. Calculate the new fare.

11. The shop price of a CD is €19.95.
    Calculate the online price if you save $22\frac{1}{2}$%.
    Give your answer to the nearest cent.

12. Deirdre spent 40% of her money in one shop and 35% of it in another.
    If she had €26.80 left, how much had she at first?

13. In a school, there are 336 girls out of a total enrolment of 560 pupils.
    Find the percentage of boys in the school.

14. Dara got a wage increase of 5%.
    If his new wage is €892.50, find his wage before the increase.

15. A car is valued at €26 000. It depreciates in value by 20% in the first year and in the second year, it depreciates by 15% of its value at the beginning of the year.
    Find the value of the car
    - (i) after 1 year
    - (ii) after 2 years.

Section 7.4 Value-added tax (VAT) – Discount

Discount

A 15% discount means the price is reduced by 15%.

If you get a 15% discount on the price of an item, you now pay only 85% of the price.

Example 1

(i) A store offers a discount of 20% on all items during a sale.
Find the sale price of a television set which had a marked price of €780.

(ii) A music shop offered a discount of €4.80 on DVDs with a marked price of €24.
Express this discount as a percentage.

(i) If the discount is 20%, the sale price is 80% of the marked price.
80% = 0.8
€780 × 0.8 = €624
∴ the sale price is €624.

(ii) The percentage discount is

$$\text{Percentage discount} = \frac{€4.80}{€24} \times \frac{100}{1}\%$$

$$= \frac{4.80 \times 100}{24} = 20\%$$

∴ the percentage discount is 20%.

Value-added tax (VAT)

Value-added tax or **VAT** is a government tax that is added to many of the things that we buy. Most receipts for goods bought show how much VAT has been paid on the item.

The shop keeper has set his cash register to calculate the VAT and to add it on to the price of the item to give the total to be paid.

If an article is priced at €280 and the VAT rate is 23%, the price *including* VAT can be worked out as follows:

Using a calculator,

since 100% + 23% = 123%, we need to find 123% **of** the original amount.

123% × €280 = 1.23 × €280 = €344.40

∴ the full price (the price including VAT) = €344.40.

Example 2

The rate of VAT on electrical goods is 20%.
  (i) Find the selling price of a washing machine priced at €650 + VAT.
 (ii) If the selling price of a laptop, including VAT, is €576, find the price of the laptop before VAT is added on.

  (i) VAT at 20% to be added on means 120% of the original price
      ∴ 120% of €650 = 1.20 × €650 = €780

 (ii) €576 represents 100% + 20%, i.e. 120% of the price before VAT is added on.

$$∴ 120\% = 576$$

$$1\% = \frac{576}{120} = €4.80$$

$$100\% = 4.8 × 100 = €480$$

  ∴ the price before VAT is added is €480.

Exercise 7.4

1. Without using a calculator, find the sale price of each of these articles:

Article	Marked price	Percentage discount
DVD recorder	€800	15%
Electric iron	€40	20%
Bicycle	€780	25%
TV set	€950	$12\frac{1}{2}\%$

2. Find the sale price for each of these marked prices:

  (i) Jumper: €45   (ii) Boots: €80

3. The price of a certain car is €27 500.
During the month of December, the garage offers a discount of 15%.
What is the price of the car during December?

4. A man was given a discount of 20% when he bought a suit.
   If he paid €256 for the suit, find the price of the suit before the discount by completing the following:

   80% of the price = €256
   1% of the price =
   100% of the price =
   Price before discount =

5. A woman paid €200 for a coat after a discount of 20% was given.
   Find the price of the coat before the discount was allowed.

6. Find the selling price of each of the following:
   (i) a television set marked €800 + VAT at 20%
   (ii) a bicycle marked €650 + VAT at 20%
   (iii) a games console marked €420 + VAT at 15%
   (iv) a lawn-mower marked €760 + VAT at 10%.

7. Find the cost of hiring a car for 8 days at €75 per day plus VAT at 15%.

8. Find the selling price of a suite of furniture marked €850 + VAT at 20%.

9. A dinner in a restaurant for 4 people cost €148.
   Find the total bill when VAT at $12\frac{1}{2}$% was added on.

10. Without using a calculator, find the total cost, including VAT, of each item.

€180

€700

VAT is 21%

11. A shopkeeper bought 200 pens at €2.40 each + VAT at 20%.
    Find the total cost of the pens.

12. A bill from a garage for a car service consisted of €240 for labour and €360 for parts. VAT, at the rate of 10% for labour and 20% for parts, was added to the bill.
    Find the total cost of the car service.

13. A man sold a house for €420 000.
    The auctioneer charged him fees of 1% of the sale price plus VAT at 21% on these fees.
    Find the amount of the bill from the auctioneer.

14. The price of an article is €33.60 when VAT at 20% is included.
    Find the price of the article before VAT is added on.

15. The price of a meal for 8 people in a restaurant is €264 after VAT at 10% is included. Find the price of the meal before VAT is added.

16. The price of an overhead projector, including VAT at 25%, is €750. Find the price of the overhead projector before VAT is added.

17. Angela bought a bicycle for €744. This price included VAT at 20%. Find the price of the bicycle before VAT was added on.

Investigation:

Jack went to a builder's providers and bought building materials for €3750 plus VAT at 20%.

The providers told him that they would give him a discount of 10%.
Jack considered whether he should take the discount first and then pay VAT on the reduced bill

OR

Pay the VAT first and then get the discount on the total.
Which should he choose to get the cheapest price?

Section 7.5 **Percentage profit and loss**

When a trader buys an item for €8 and sells it for €10, he makes a **profit** of €2.
€8 is called the **cost price** and €10 is the **selling price**.
Traders generally express their profit as a percentage of the cost price.
For example, if an item is bought for €20 and sold for €25, a profit of €5 is made.
This profit, expressed as a percentage of the cost price, is

$\frac{5}{20} \times \frac{100}{1} = \frac{500}{20} = \frac{50}{2} = 25\%$

Terms:
1. **Cost price:** the original price of goods.
2. **Selling price:** the amount of money the trader asks for the goods
3. **Profit:** the amount of money gained by selling the goods. [selling price − cost price > 0]
4. **Loss:** the amount of money lost by selling the goods. [selling price − cost price < 0]

Note: (The selling price usually equals the cost price + profit + VAT).

$$\text{Percentage profit (or loss)} = \frac{\text{Profit (or loss)}}{\text{Cost price}} \times \frac{100}{1}\%$$

Example 1

A shopkeeper buys cameras at €180 and sells them at €216 each.
Find his percentage profit on the cost price.

Profit = €216 − €180 = €36

$$\text{Percentage profit} = \frac{\text{Profit}}{\text{Cost price}} \times \frac{100}{1}\%$$

$$= \frac{36}{180} \times \frac{100}{1}\% = \frac{36 \times 10}{18} = 20\%$$

Example 2

By selling a jacket for €138, a store makes a profit of 15% on the cost price.
Find what the store paid for the jacket.

Since a profit of 15% was made, €138 represents 115% of the cost price.

The cost price is 100%.

$$\therefore \; 115\% = €138$$

$$1\% = \frac{138}{115} = €1.20$$

$$100\% = 1.20 \times 100 = €120$$

∴ the store paid €120 for the jacket

Exercise 7.5

1. Find the selling price in each of the following:
   (i) Cost price €20: sold at a profit of 20%
   (ii) Cost price €32: sold at a profit of 25%
   (iii) Cost price €80: sold at a profit of 15%
   (iv) Cost price €60: sold at a loss of 10%
   (v) Cost price €8.20: sold at a loss of 15%
   (vi) Cost price €120: sold at a profit of $12\frac{1}{2}\%$.

2. Find the percentage profit or loss in each of the following:
  - (i)   Cost price €8:   selling price €10
  - (ii) Cost price €20:   selling price €24
  - (iii) Cost price €60:   selling price €63
  - (iv) Cost price €120:   selling price €96
  - (v)   Cost price €240:   selling price €312
  - (vi) Cost price €16:   selling price €12.80.

3. A shopkeeper buys washing machines at €520 each and sells them at €598.
Find his percentage profit.

4. Find the four matching pairs out of the following:

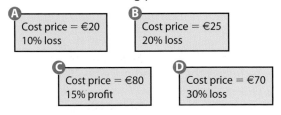

5. Find the cost price for each of these if
  - (i)   the selling price is €10 and there is a 25% profit
  - (ii) the selling price is €8.80 and there is a 10% profit
  - (iii) the selling price is €57.60 and there is a 20% loss
  - (iv) the selling price is €22.80 and there is a 5% loss
  - (v)   the selling price is €1050 and there is a 40% profit.

6. A jeweller bought a gold ring for €550 and sold it at a profit of 40%.
Find the sale price.

7. A dealer purchased a used car for €9000 and sold it for €9900.
Find his percentage profit.

8. An electrical shop buys MP3 docking stations at €360 each.
If they are sold at a profit of 15%, find the selling price.

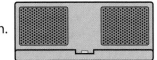

9. A greengrocer buys kiwis in boxes of 50 at €24 per box.
If she sells the kiwis at 60 cent each, find her percentage profit.

10. A fashion shop makes a profit of 30% by selling a coat for €195.
Copy and complete the following to find the cost price of the coat
$$130\% = €195$$
$$1\% = €\frac{195}{130} = €\boxed{}$$
$$100\% = €\boxed{} \times 100 = €\boxed{}$$

11. When an item is sold for €121, a profit of 10% is made.
    Find the cost price of the item.

12. By selling a bicycle for €720, a shopkeeper makes a loss of 10%.
    (i) What did the shopkeeper pay for the bicycle?
    (ii) At what price should he sell the bicycle to make a profit of 15%?

13. A dealer bought television sets at €800
    each and sold them at a profit of 40%.
    During a sale, the selling price was reduced
    by 10%.
    (i) Find the selling price of a television
        during the sale.

    10% off

    (ii) What was the dealer's percentage profit on television sets during the sale?

14. A shopkeeper bought 50 toys at €25 each.
    He sold 40 of them at a marked price of €32.50.
    He sold the remaining 10 toys after reducing the marked price by 20%.
    (i) Find what the shopkeeper paid for the 50 toys.
    (ii) Find the selling price of each of the 10 remaining toys during the sale.
    (iii) Find his total profit on the deal.
    (iv) Work out his percentage profit.

15. During a sale, the price of shirts is reduced by 20%.
    If the sale price of a shirt is €48, what was the marked price before the sale?

16. A trader bought an article for €250 and then added on 20% to get his selling price.
    (i) Find his selling price.
    (ii) During a sale, he reduced his selling price by 15%.
        Find his percentage profit on the article during the sale.

17. A car dealer bought two cars; a Fiat for €8400 and a Ford for €9600.
    He sold the Fiat at a profit of 20% and the Ford at a loss of 5%.
    (i) Find the profit he made on the cars.
    (ii) Find his percentage profit on the whole deal.

Test yourself 7

1. Express each of these as a percentage:

    (i) $\frac{1}{4}$ (ii) $\frac{2}{5}$ (iii) 0.34   (iv) 0.7   (v) $\frac{9}{10}$

2. Write each of these percentages as a fraction in its lowest terms:

    (i) 20%   (ii) 25%   (iii) 45%   (iv) 5%   (v) $87\frac{1}{2}$%

3. Work out these percentages.

    (i) 45 as a percentage of 60   (ii) 15 as a percentage of 75

    (iii) 32 as a percentage of 128   (iv) 42 as a percentage of 112

4.

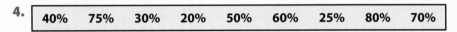

| 40% | 75% | 30% | 20% | 50% | 60% | 25% | 80% | 70% |

Find a percentage from the box for each sentence.

    (i) Seven out of ten people watch the news on TV.

    (ii) One out of every two people who eat at McDonalds is under 12.

    (iii) In a survey, it was found that maths was the favourite subject for three quarters of students.

    (iv) Two out of every five people go abroad for their summer holiday.

    (v) Six out of every twenty students play a musical instrument.

5. Work these out by first writing the percentages as fractions.

    (i) 20% of 60   (ii) 50% of 86   (iii) 25% of 36

    (iv) 10% of 3000   (v) 75% of 140   (vi) 90% of 1200

    (vii) 50% of 65   (viii) 25% of 24   (ix) 60% of 25

6. Copy and complete this table.

Fraction	Decimal	Percentage
$\frac{3}{4}$		
	0.6	
$\frac{7}{10}$		
		40%
	0.9	

7. What percentage of each of these figures is shaded?

    (i)    (ii)   (iii)

8. The pie chart shows how pupils in a class travel to school.
   30 pupils travel by car.
   (i) How many pupils are in the class?
   (ii) How many pupils walk to school?

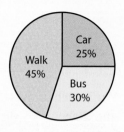

9. Rachel's test scores are given in
   the table to the right.
   Copy and complete the table
   by working out Rachel's
   percentage score for each
   subject.

Subject	Score	Percentage
English	$\frac{35}{40}$	
Maths	$\frac{68}{80}$	
Geography	$\frac{28}{35}$	
History	$\frac{54}{60}$	
Science	$\frac{56}{64}$	

10. Write each of these lists in order of size, starting with the smallest:
    (i) $\frac{1}{4}$ 0.3   20% $\frac{2}{5}$ 10%
    (ii) $\frac{3}{5}$ $\frac{1}{2}$ $\frac{3}{4}$ 40%   0.78

11.

E	G	I	H	L	N	O	P	R	T	Y
$\frac{1}{2}$	20%	0.3	$\frac{1}{4}$	$\frac{2}{5}$	0.7	$\frac{3}{4}$	80%	0.6	90%	0.1

Use this code to find a letter for each fraction, decimal or percentage below.
Rearrange each set of letters to spell an animal.
   (i) 0.75, 30%, $\frac{7}{10}$, 0.4   (ii) $\frac{1}{5}$, 0.9, 60%, $\frac{3}{10}$, 50%

12. (i) If 40% of a number is 96, find the number.
    (ii) In the year 2000, the population of a town was 3840.
         In the year 2010, the population was 4128.
         What percentage increase is this?

13. (i) The price of a lawn-mower is €550 plus VAT at 15%.
        Work out the price when VAT is added on.
    (ii) A bill of €177.60 includes VAT at 20%.
         Find the amount of the bill before VAT was added on.

14. A greengrocer bought 40 punnets of strawberries at
    €3.60 a punnet. He sold 36 punnets at a profit of 40%
    but had to throw away the remaining 4 punnets.
    Find his percentage profit on the whole deal.

Learning Experience   Unit 7

Assignment 1

Research the different VAT rates used
by the government.
Suggest a reason for the different rates.
Using three receipts at home draw a chart
clearly showing, net sales / VAT code
/ VAT amount/total sales.

	Receipt 1	**2**	**3**
Net sales			
VAT code			
VAT			
Total sales			

Assignment 2

Draw a poster of the kettle over.
It is 80% full, then 20% is poured
out leaving 1152 ml of water in it.
Using the information given:

(i) mark in the percentages,
     A and B on the left.
(ii) the volumes, C ml and
     D ml on the right.

Problem 1

S is 25% of 60   60 is 80% of U   80 is M% of 25

Show clearly how to calculate the value of S + U + M.

Problem 2

To make porridge, Goldilocks mixes together 3 bags of oatmeal with 1 bag
containing 20% wheat bran and 80% oats.

All the bags have the same volume.

Describe how to find the
percentage volume of wheat bran
in the porridge.

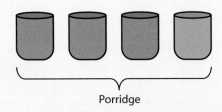

Porridge

Chapter 7 review 1

Using the terms from the chapter copy and complete the following sentences:

1. A percentage is a fraction with _____ as denominator.

2. Percentages can be changed into _____ and _____.

3. _____ % is the same as a half.

4. When comparing quantities make sure that both quantities are in the same _____.

5. If a quantity is decreased by 35% you now have _____% of the original.

6. If a quantity is increased by 45% you now have _____% of the original.

7. If goods are sold at less than cost price a _____ is made.

8. VAT stands for _____ _____ _____.

9. A _____ is a percentage reduction in the selling price.

10. A percentage profit is calculated by dividing the profit by the _____ and then multiplying by 100%.

Chapter 7 review 2

You should now be able to:

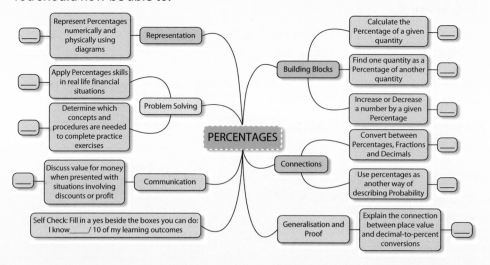

Algebra

In this chapter, you will learn to:

- use **symbols** for **unknown** quantities,
- identify **terms** and **expressions**,
- add and subtract **like terms**,
- use **variables**,
- identify the **coefficients** of different terms,
- multiply out expressions containing **brackets**,
- multiply different terms,
- **substitute** values for variables in an expression,
- find an expression for the area of a rectangle.

Section 8.1 Using symbols

Symbols such as $\blacktriangle$, $\bullet$ or $\blacklozenge$ are often used to stand for numbers.

Sometimes you can work out the value of the symbol.

Look at this example:

$\blacktriangledown + 8 = 12$

We know that $4 + 8 = 12$, so this means that $\blacktriangledown = 4$.

You can also use the value of a symbol in a calculation.

If $\bullet = 7$, then $6 \times \bullet = 42$.

Writing in symbols

'3 more than 5' can be written as $5 + 3$.

'6 less than 14' can be written as $14 - 6$.

'10 increased by 4' can be written as $10 + 4$.

In the same way,

'5 more than $\blacksquare$' can be written as $\blacksquare + 5$.

'7 more than n' can be written as $n + 7$.

'8 less than x' can be written as $x - 8$.

Exercise 8.1

1. Each symbol stands for a number. Write down its value.
   - (i) ▲ + 3 = 5
   - (ii) ■ − 5 = 4
   - (iii) □ × 2 = 12
   - (iv) 3 + ◆ = 15
   - (v) 9 − ● = 2
   - (vi) 5 × ■ = 55
   - (vii) ▼ ÷ 3 = 4
   - (viii) ◆ ÷ 10 = 3

2. Find the value of each of these symbols:
   - (i) 11 − ◄ = 3
   - (ii) 14 + ♣ = 21
   - (iii) ◗ + ◗ = 20
   - (iv) ✳ + ✳ + ✳ = 30
   - (v) □ − 6 = 14
   - (vi) ◆ × ◆ = 16
   - (vii) ▲ × 4 = 20
   - (viii) ✳ ÷ 6 = 5

3. If □ + ▲ = 12, find three pairs of values for □ and ▲.

4. If ● − ◆ = 9, find three pairs of values for ● and ◆.

5. If ● = 5 and ■ = 3, find the value of each of these expressions:
   - (i) ● + 6
   - (ii) ■ × 5
   - (iii) ● − 2
   - (iv) 7 + ■
   - (v) 3 × ●
   - (vi) 6 ÷ ■
   - (vii) 30 ÷ ●
   - (viii) 2 × ■ + ●

6. If ▲ = 18, write down the value of each of these:
   - (i) 6 more than ▲
   - (ii) 3 less than ▲
   - (iii) twice ▲
   - (iv) five times ▲
   - (v) ▲ less 8
   - (vi) twice ▲ + ▲

7. ■ stands for different numbers. Find its value in each of the following:
   - (i) ■ + 6 = 10
   - (ii) ■ − 3 = 5
   - (iii) 7 + ■ = 14
   - (iv) 2 × ■ = 22
   - (v) ■ ÷ 4 = 9
   - (vi) 3 × ■ = 36

8. ▲ stands for a number. Write down each of these using symbols and numbers only:
   - (i) 7 more than ▲
   - (ii) 4 less than ▲
   - (iii) twice ▲
   - (iv) ▲ divided by 2
   - (v) $\frac{1}{3}$ of ▲
   - (vi) ▲ less 6

9. The first line in the table below has been completed.
   Write down what should go in each shaded space in the remaining lines.

	Start number/symbol	Change	Result
	3	Increase by 7	3 + 7 = 10
(i)	9	Increase by 12	
(ii)	12		12 + 6 = 18
(iii)		Increase by 8	21 + 8 = 29
(iv)	□		□ + 5
(v)	▼	Increase by 8	
(vi)	●	Increase by 17	
(vii)		Decrease by 3	16 − 3 = 13
(viii)		Decrease by 12	■ − 12
(ix)	▲	Decrease by 36	
(x)	◗		◗ − 9

10. Each letter stands for a number. What is each number?

(i) $a + 2 = 6$ (ii) $b + 3 = 12$ (iii) $c - 4 = 5$ (iv) $d - 2 = 9$

(v) $9 - e = 3$ (vi) $2 \times f = 16$ (vii) $g + g = 12$ (viii) $h \div 3 = 6$

(ix) $i + i + i = 12$

11. Write down what should be written in each of the shaded boxes below. The first one is done for you.

	Start letter	Change	Result
	x	Increase by 6	$x + 6$
(i)	a	Increase by 8	
(ii)	b	Decrease by 7	
(iii)	c	Double	
(iv)	d		$d + 9$
(v)	e		$e - 10$
(vi)	f	Multiply by 5	
(vii)	g		$3g$
(viii)	h		$h + k$

Section 8.2 Using letters

If we do not know a quantity, for example, how many computer games Ethan has, we can use a letter to represent that quantity.

We could say that Ethan has **x** computer games.

If Ethan buys 3 more games, he now has **x + 3** games.

x + 3 is an **expression**.

x stands for an unknown number.

The expression $x + x + 2 + 5$ has four **terms**.

The expression can be simplified to $2x + 7$ which has 2 terms.

Notice that $x + x$ can be added to get $2x$.

$x + x$ can be added because they are **like terms**.

Consider the cars and vans below:

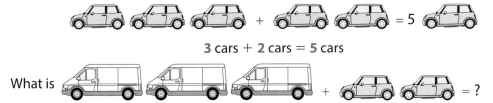

3 **cars** + 2 **cars** = 5 **cars**

What is

Three vans and two cars cannot be added as they are not like terms. In algebra, terms with the same letter such as $2x$ and $3x$ can be added as they are **like terms**.

Thus, $2x + 3x = 5x$ and $2y + 4y = 6y$.

However, $5x$ and $7y$ are **unlike terms** and cannot be added.

Variables

In the expression, $2x + 3y + 4$, we do not know the values of x and y.

Until we are given more information to find x and y, their values are **variable**.

Letters of the alphabet are used as variables e.g. x, y, a, b, c etc.

The number 4 does not change. Since it is fixed, we call it a **constant**.

In $2x$, the number 2 tells us how many xs there are.

We call 2 the **coefficient** of x. Similarly, 3 is the coefficient of y.

Notation

In algebra, the symbols $\times$ and $\div$ are not normally used.

Instead of writing $2 \times k$, we just write $2k$.

We write $\dfrac{a}{b}$ instead of $a \div b$.

Also   (i) $x + x + x = 3x$

            (ii) $2 \times a \times b = 2ab$

            (iii) $4 \times x \times y \times 3 = 4 \times 3 \times x \times y = 12xy$

            (iv) $2 \times a \times b \times c = 2abc$

> **Remember:**
>
> x ... variable
> $3x$ ... term
> $3x - 2y + 5$ ... expression
> $3x, 6x$ ... like terms
> $3x, 6y$ ... unlike terms
> 5 ... constant
> $3x$, 3 is the coefficient of x.
> $1x$ is written as x
> $1x + 1y$ is written as $x + y$.

Example 1

Simplify each of these by adding like terms:
   (i) $x + 2x + 3y + 5y$ (ii) $3a + 4b - a + 2b + 2a$

   (i) $x + 2x + 3y + 5y = 3x + 8y$

   (ii) $3a + 4b - a + 2b + 2a = \underline{3a - a} + 2a + 4b + 2b$
                                     $= 2a + 2a + 6b$
                                     $= 4a + 6b$

Exercise 8.2

1. Write each of the following without using the multiplication sign:

     (i) $5 \times a$ (ii) $4 \times b$ (iii) $4 \times 2 \times x$ (iv) $3 \times 4 \times y$

     (v) $4 \times 2c$ (vi) $5a \times 3$ (vii) $a \times b$ (viii) $4 \times a \times b$

2. Write these without the multiplication sign:

(i) $2a \times 4b$　　　　(ii) $3x \times 7y$　　　　(iii) $3 \times ab$　　　　　(iv) $a \times b \times c$

(v) $3xy \times 2$　　　　(vi) $ab \times c$　　　　(vii) $3xy \times 4z$　　　(viii) $2ab \times 5c$

3. Simplify each of the following by adding like terms:

(i) $x + x + x$　　　　　(ii) $x + 2x + 3x$　　　　(iii) $a + 2a + 3 + 4$

(iv) $2b + 4 + 5b + 2$　　(v) $3x + 4 + 2x + 6$　　(vi) $x + y + 3x + 2y$

4. Simplify these by adding like terms:

(i) $5x - 2x$　　　　　(ii) $3a - a$　　　　　(iii) $5x - 2x - 10x$

(iv) $3a + 2 - a + 5$　　(v) $6b - 2 + b - 4$　　(vi) $3a - 2b + 2a + 4b$

5. Simplify each of these:

(i) $12a + b + 3a + 5b$　　　　　(ii) $3x + 2y + 3 + 4x + 3y + 1$

(iii) $5x - 4 + 2x + 8$　　　　　(iv) $7x - 4 - 3x + 7$

(v) $6a + b + 3 + 2a + 2b - 1$　　(vi) $3x + 4 + 2x - 6 + x + 3$

6. Simplify each of these expressions:

(i) $ab + ab$　　　　　(ii) $3ab + 2ab$　　　　(iii) $4xy - 2xy$

(iv) $4cd + 5cd - 2cd$　(v) $2ab - 5ab + 4ab$　(vi) $5xy + 6xy - 7xy$

7. Simplify these expressions:

(i) $2p + 3q - r + p - 4q + 2r$　　(ii) $5k + 3 - 4k + 6 + k - 4$

(iii) $2ab + c + 5ab - 4c$　　　　(iv) $3xy + 2z + xy + 9z$

(v) $6ab + 2cd - ab + 3cd$　　　(vi) $6x - xy + 5x - 7xy$

8. Find and simplify an expression for the perimeter (length all round) of each of the following figures:

(i)　　　　　　　　　(ii)　　　　　　　(iii)

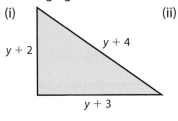
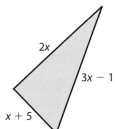
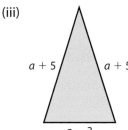

9. The number in each box is found by adding the numbers in the two boxes below it. Write an expression for the blue box as simply as possible.

(i)　　　　　　　　　　　　　　(ii)

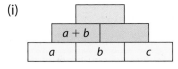
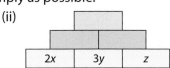

(iii)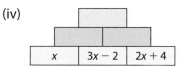

(iv)

10. Here are six cards containing expressions:

A $x + 3$ **B** $3x + 1$ **C** $2x - 4$ **D** $7 - x$ **E** $2x - 6$ **F** $3 - 2x$

  (i) Which two cards total $5x - 5$?

  (ii) Which two cards total $2x + 8$?

  (iii) Which two cards total $x + 3$?

  (iv) Which two cards total $10 - 3x$?

  (v) What is the total of all the expressions on the cards?

11. $3x + 5y - 8$ is an expression.

  (i) Name the two variables in this expression.

  (ii) Why are they called variables?

  (iii) Write down the coefficient of x.

  (iv) Write down the constant in the expression.

  (v) Are there any like terms in the expression?

12. An expression contains three terms.
The variable in one term is c; the variable in another term is d; there is also a term which is a constant.
What is the expression if

  (i) the coefficient of c is 4

  (ii) the coefficient of d is -3

  (iii) the constant term is a prime number between 6 and 10?

Section 8.3 Substituting numbers for letters ───────

When a calculation contains more than one operation, remember to do them in the correct order.

Here are some examples:

  (i) $3 + 4 \times 6 = 3 + 24 = 27$ ... multiply and divide before you add and subtract

  (ii) $27 \div (7 - 4) = 27 \div 3 = 9$ ... do what is inside the brackets first

The rules for the order of operations in an **expression** are the same as the rules for arithmetic.

When $x = 3$, the value of $5x$ is $5 \times 3 = 15$.

When $x = 4$, the value of $3x + 7$ is $3 \times 4 + 7 = 12 + 7 = 19$.

When $x = 6$, the value of $3x \div (x - 3) = 3 \times 6 \div (6 - 3)$

$$= 18 \div 3$$

$$= 6$$

Example 1

If $x = 3$ and $y = 4$, find the value of

  (i) $3x$ (ii) $2x - y$ (iii) $2x + 3y - 6$ (iv) $2xy$

  (i) $3x = 3 \times 3 = 9$ (ii) $2x - y = 2 \times 3 - 4 = 6 - 4 = 2$

  (iii) $2x + 3y - 6 = 2 \times 3 + 3 \times 4 - 6$

$$= 6 + 12 - 6 = 12$$

  (iv) $2xy = 2 \times x \times y$

$$= 2 \times 3 \times 4 = 24$$

Exercise 8.3

1. If $x = 2$ and $y = 3$, find the value of each of these:

  (i) $x + 2$ (ii) $3x$ (iii) $4y$ (iv) $6y - 8$

  (v) $2x + y$ (vi) $3x + 2y$ (vii) xy (viii) $5xy$

2. Find the value of each expression when $x = 5$.

  (i) $x + 3$ (ii) $5x$ (iii) $4x + 5$ (iv) $3x - 7$

  (v) $12 - x$ (vi) $15 - 2x$ (vii) $-3x + 20$ (viii) $9 - 3x$

3. If $a = 4$ and $b = 2$, find the value of

  (i) $a - b$ (ii) $6a + 3b$ (iii) $5a - 2b$ (iv) ab

  (v) $6ab - 2a$ (vi) $6a - 2ab$ (vii) $3ab + 6b$ (viii) $2a - b + 4ab$

4. Find the value of each expression when $y = 2$:

  (i) $6y$ (ii) $3(y + 4)$ (iii) $4(2y - 1)$

  (iv) $3(5y - 4)$ (v) $y(y + 3)$ (vi) $6y \times (2y + 1)$

5. If $a = 1, b = 2$ and $c = 3$, find the value of

  (i) $2a + b$ (ii) $3ab - c$ (iii) $4abc + 3c$

  (iv) $3bc - 4ab$ (v) $3abc - 2ac$ (vi) $5bc - 2ab$

6. Find the value of each expression when $x = 9$:

  (i) $\dfrac{x}{3}$ (ii) $\dfrac{x + 5}{2}$ (iii) $\dfrac{5x}{3}$

  (iv) $\dfrac{3x + 3}{10}$ (v) $\dfrac{2x - 6}{3}$ (vi) $\dfrac{18}{x}$

7. If $x = 1\frac{1}{2}$ and $y = \frac{1}{2}$, find the value of

    (i) $4x + 2y$ (ii) $3x + y$ (iii) $2x - 4y$

    (iv) $4x - 2y$ (v) $5x - 6y$ (vi) $8xy$

8. If $x = -2$, find the value of these expressions:

    (i) $x + 4$ (ii) $2x$ (iii) $2x + 8$ (iv) $x - 6$

    (v) $3x - 2$ (vi) $-2x$ (vii) $-2x + 5$ (viii) $6 - 2x$

9. Match these expressions to their answers when $p = -3$.

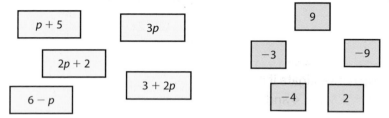

10.

A	B	C	D	E	F	G	L	N	R
−8	4	−9	3	−6	−10	−12	−2	−17	−7

Find the value of each expression in the boxes below when $x = -5$.

Use the code above to change your answers to letters.

Rearrange the letters to spell the name of a country.

$4x + 3$	$x - 1$	$x - 3$	$2x$	$-4 + x$	$2x + 3$

11. Find the perimeter of the given figure when $h = 4$.

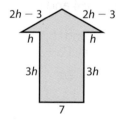

12.

$4t$	$t + 6$	$2t$	$4t - 5$	$2t - 2$	$-5 - t$	$5t - 2$

Find the value of each of the expressions in the boxes above when $t = -3$.

Use the code in question 10 above to find a letter for each answer.

Rearrange the letters to spell the name of another country.

13. The expression $3d + 2$ gives the **total** number of dots needed to make a row with d blue dots.

    (i) Show that $3d + 2$ gives the correct total of dots for 5 blue dots.

    (ii) How many dots in total are needed to make a row with 15 blue dots?

14. In a magic square, each row, column and diagonal add up to the same number.

    (i) Show that this is a magic square if
       $a = 7, b = 2$ and $c = 3$.

    (ii) Now investigate if it is a magic square when
       $a = -2, b = 4$ and $c = -3$.

$a - b$	$a + b - c$	$a + c$
$a + b + c$	a	$a - b - c$
$a - c$	$a - b + c$	$a + b$

Section 8.4 Removing brackets

The expression $4(3 + 2) = 4(5) = 4 \times 5 = 20$.

$4(3 + 2)$ is a short method of writing $(3 + 2)$ multiplied by 4.

The multiplication sign is not visible.

We would get the same result to the question above if we multiplied each term inside the brackets by 4 and then added the results, i.e.,

$$4(3 + 2) = 4 \times 3 + 4 \times 2$$
$$= 12 + 8 = 20$$

Similarly   (i) $3(x + 5) = 3 \times x + 3 \times 5 = 3x + 15$

        (ii) $5(2x + 4) = 5 \times 2x + 5 \times 4 = 10x + 20$

        (iii) $4(2a - 3b) = 4 \times 2a + 4 \times (-3b) = 8a - 12b$

If there is a minus sign outside the bracket, the sign of each term inside the bracket is changed when the bracket is removed.

$$5(2x - 4) = 10x - 20$$
$$-5(2x - 4) = -10x + 20$$

Examples   (i) $-(2x + 3y) = -2x - 3y$

        (ii) $-(5x - 4) = -5x + 4$

        (iii) $2(x + 4) - (x - 3) = 2x + 8 - x + 3 = x + 11$

        (iv) $-3(2x + 5) = -6x - 15$

        (v) $-5(x - 3y) = -5x + 15y$

Example 1

Remove the brackets and simplify:

$$2(3x + 2y - 4) - 3(x - 3y + 2)$$

$$\begin{aligned}
2(3x + 2y - 4) - 3(x - 3y + 2) &= 6x + 4y - 8 - 3x + 9y - 6 \\
&= 6x - 3x + 4y + 9y - 8 - 6 \\
&= 3x + 13y - 14
\end{aligned}$$

We have seen above that $3(x + 7) = 3x + 21$.

Look at the large rectangle here.

The length of the large rectangle is $(x + 7)$ and its width is 3.

Area $= 3(x + 7) = 3x + 21$ ... the area of a rectangle is given by: Area = Length × Width

The area of the yellow rectangle is $3x$.

The area of the green rectangle is 21.

The sum of the two areas is $3x + 21$, as found above.

Exercise 8.4

Remove the brackets in each of the following:

1. $4(x + 2)$ **2.** $3(a + 6)$ **3.** $4(2a + 7)$

4. $3(x + y)$ **5.** $5(2x + y)$ **6.** $4(2x + 3y)$

7. $6(2x - y)$ **8.** $3(x + 2y + 1)$ **9.** $6(2a + b + 3)$

Remove the brackets in each of these and simplify:

10. $6(a + 4) + 2(2a + 3)$ **11.** $7(x + y) + 3(2x - 3y)$

12. $5(2a + 3) - a + 4$ **13.** $5(a - b) + 2(2a + 3b)$

14. $5(x + 2y) - 3x + 2y$ **15.** $6(a + b) - 3a + b$

16. $2(3x - 2y) + 3x + 5y$ **17.** $3(a - 2) - 4(2a - 3)$

18. $8(a + b) - 4(2a + 3b)$ **19.** $3(x + 2y) - 2(2x - y)$

20. $4(2a - 3) - 2(a - 5)$ **21.** $3(2c + d) - 3(3c - 2d)$

22. $3(x + 2y + 1) + 2(2x + y - 3)$ **23.** $4(a + 3b + 1) + 2(a - 2b - 1)$

24. $3(2x - y + 4) + 2(x + y - 3)$

25. $3(a + b) + 4(2a - b) + 3a - b$

26. $4(x + y) + x - y + 2(x - y)$

27. $3(a - 2b) - 4(a - 2b) + 3a - b$

28. Find and simplify an expression for the perimeter of each of these figures:

(i)

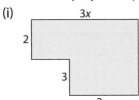

(ii)

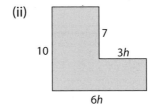

Section 8.5 Multiplication involving indices

You will have already learned that 5×5 can be written as $\mathbf{5^2}$.

Similarly, (i) $a \times a$ can be written as a^2 (ii) $a \times a \times a$ can be written as a^3.

In the term a^2, **2** is called the **power** or **index**.

Now $a^2 \times a^2 = a \times a \times a \times a = a^4$

and $a^2 \times a^3 = (a \times a) \times (a \times a \times a)$

$\qquad = a \times a \times a \times a \times a = a^5$

To multiply $2x$ by $3x$,

first multiply 2×3 and then multiply x by x.

$\qquad \therefore 2x \times 3x = 2 \times 3 \times x \times x$

$\qquad\qquad = 6x^2$

Similarly, $\quad 3a \times 4b = 3 \times 4 \times a \times b = 12ab$

> $x \times x = x^2$
>
> $2x \times 4x = 8x^2$
>
> $3x^3 \times 5x^2 = 15x^5$
>
> $x \times y = xy$
>
> $2x \times 6y = 12xy$

Example 1

Remove the brackets and simplify each of these:

(i) $2x(x + 4) + 5x(2x - 1)$ \qquad (ii) $x(x + y) + 3x(4x - 3y) + 2xy$

(i) $2x(x + 4) + 5x(2x - 1) = 2x^2 + 8x + 10x^2 - 5x$

$\qquad\qquad\qquad\qquad = 2x^2 + 10x^2 + 8x - 5x$

$\qquad\qquad\qquad\qquad = 12x^2 + 3x$

(ii) $x(x + y) + 3x(4x - 3y) + 2xy = x^2 + xy + 12x^2 - 9xy + 2xy$

$\qquad\qquad\qquad\qquad\qquad = x^2 + 12x^2 + xy - 9xy + 2xy$

$\qquad\qquad\qquad\qquad\qquad = 13x^2 - 9xy + 3xy$

$\qquad\qquad\qquad\qquad\qquad = 13x^2 - 6xy$

Evaluating expressions containing x^2

If $x = 3$, then $x^2 = 3 \times 3 = 9$.

If $x = 3$, then $4x^2 = 4 \times 3^2$

$$= 4 \times 9 = 36$$

Work out the powers before multiplication

Example 2

Find the value of $2x^2 - 6x + 7$ when $x = 3$.

$$2x^2 - 6x + 7 = 2(3)^2 - 6(3) + 7$$
$$= 2(9) - 18 + 7$$
$$= 18 - 18 + 7 = 7$$

Exercise 8.5

Write each of the following as a single term to a power, without using the multiplication sign:

1. 5×5

2. $4 \times 4 \times 4$

3. $a \times a$

4. $b \times b \times b$

5. $2 \times a \times a$

6. $3 \times x \times x$

7. $4 \times b \times b$

8. $a \times a^2$

9. $x^2 \times x^2$

10. $4 \times a \times a^2$

11. $2 \times 3 \times a \times a$

12. $4 \times x \times x^2 \times 5$

Remove the brackets and simplify each of the following:

13. $2(x^2 + 4) + 3(2x^2 + 5)$

14. $3(x^2 - 2) + 4(x^2 + 6)$

15. $x(x + 4) + 2x(x + 6)$

16. $2x(x + 2) + 3x(x - 1)$

17. $3x(2x + 1) + 4x(x - 3)$

18. $a(3a - 4) + 3a(2a - 3)$

19. $2x(2x - 6) - 3x(x + 5)$

20. $5a(a - 3) - 2a(a + 4)$

21. $3x(2x - 7) - 3x(2x - 4)$

22. $2a(3a - 4) - 3a(a - 7)$

23. $3(x^2 + 2x + 4) + 2(x^2 - 3x - 2)$

24. $4(a^2 + 2a - 1) - 2(2a^2 - 3a + 4)$

25. Evaluate each of the following when $x = 2$:

    (i) $2x$ (ii) x^2 (iii) $2x^2$ (iv) $5x^2$ (v) $4x^2 + 2x$

26. If $x = 2$ and $y = 3$, evaluate each of these:

    (i) $x^2 + y^2$ (ii) $3x^2 + y^2$ (iii) $2y^2 - x^2$ (iv) $x^2 + 3xy$

    (v) $2x^2 + 3y^2$ (vi) $4y^2 - 2x^2$ (vii) $3y^2 - 2xy$ (viii) $5xy - 2x^2$

27. (i) If $x = 2$, find the value of $x^2 - 3x + 5$.

   (ii) If $x = -3$, find the value of $x^2 - 4x - 6$.

28. If $a = 2$ and $b = -3$, find the value of each of these:

(i) b^2	(ii) $4a^2$	(iii) $a^2 + 2b^2$	(iv) $3a^2 + 2b$
(v) $2ab$	(vi) $2a^2b$	(vii) $2ab^2$	(viii) $b^2 - 4ab$

29. The area of a rectangle is the length multiplied by the breadth.

Find the area of this rectangle when $x = 3$.

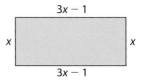

30. Match these expressions to the answers on the cards when $n = -3$.

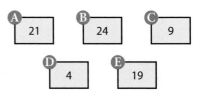

   (i) n^2 (ii) $n^2 - 5$

   (iii) $3n^2 - 8$ (iv) $2(n^2 + 3)$

   (v) $n^2 - 2n + 6$

Section 8.6 Multiplying two expressions

What is $(2 + 3)(4 + 5)$?

Here we simplify what is inside each bracket and multiply the results.

Thus $(2 + 3)(4 + 5) = (5)(9) = 45$.

Here is another way to work out the answer.

$(2 + 3)(4 + 5)$ is twice $(4 + 5)$ + three times $(4 + 5)$

Thus $(2 + 3)(4 + 5) = 2(4 + 5) + 3(4 + 5)$

$= 2(9) + 3(9)$

$= 18 + 27 = 45$ ... as found above

Since algebra follows the same rules as arithmetic, we multiply $(x + 2)(x + 3)$ as follows:

$$(x + 2)(x + 3) = x(x + 3) + 2(x + 3)$$
$$= x^2 + 3x + 2x + 6$$
$$= x^2 + 5x + 6$$

179

Array models

Consider $(x + 2)$ as a side of a rectangle and $(x + 3)$ as the second side.

The product $(x + 2)(x + 3)$ is the area of the rectangle.

By getting the area of each smaller rectangle, we find that $(x + 2)(x + 3) = x^2 + 3x + 2x + 6$
$$= x^2 + 5x + 6.$$

	x	3	
x	x^2	$3x$	x
2	$2x$	6	

Similarly $(x + 4)(x - 1) = x^2 + 4x - x - 4$
$$= x^2 + 3x - 4.$$

	x	4
x	x^2	$4x$
-1	$-x$	-4

Example 1

Multiply (i) $(2x - 3)(3x + 4)$ (ii) $(2a + b)(a - 3b)$

(i) $(2x - 3)(3x + 4) = 2x(3x + 4) - 3(3x + 4)$
$$= 6x^2 + 8x - 9x - 12$$
$$= 6x^2 - x - 12$$

(ii) $(2a + b)(a - 3b) =$

	a	$-3b$
$2a$	$2a^2$	$-6ab$
$+b$	$+ab$	$-3b^2$

$2a^2 - 6ab + ab - 3b^2 = 2a^2 - 5ab - 3b^2$

Exercise 8.6

Multiply each of the following and simplify your answers. Use the array method in questions 1. – 15.

1. $(x + 2)(x + 1)$

2. $(x + 1)(x + 3)$

3. $(x + 4)(x + 2)$

4. $(x + 5)(x + 2)$

5. $(x + 3)(x + 4)$

6. $(2x + 1)(x + 4)$

7. $(3x + 2)(x + 6)$

8. $(x + 5)(2x + 1)$

9. $(3x + 4)(2x + 1)$

10. $(x + 4)(x - 2)$

11. $(x - 3)(x + 5)$

12. $(x - 2)(2x + 1)$

13. $(3x + 2)(x - 3)$

14. $(3x - 1)(x + 4)$

15. $(5x + 2)(x - 4)$

16. $(x - 4)(x - 5)$

17. $(2x - 1)(3x - 2)$

18. $(4x - 3)(2x - 4)$

19. $(3x + 5)(2x - 1)$

20. $(5x - 2)(4x + 3)$

21. $(4x + 2)(2x - 3)$

22. $(2a + 3)(3a - 2)$

23. $(2a - 1)(5a + 2)$

24. $(4a + 1)(2a - 3)$

25. $(a + b)(c + d)$

26. $(x + y)(a + b)$

27. $(a + 2b)(c + 2d)$

28. $(2a - 3c)(3b - d)$

29. $(2a - 3b)(5a + 4b)$

30. $(x - 2y)(x + 3y)$

31. $(x + 2y)(x - 2y)$

32. $(3x + 2y)(3x - 2y)$

33. Copy and complete the array model to show that $(x + 2)^2 = x^2 + 4x + 4$

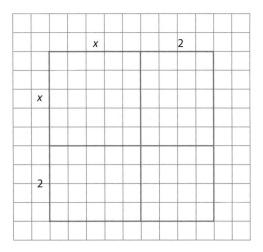

34. By copying and completing the array model over simplify $(2x + y)^2$

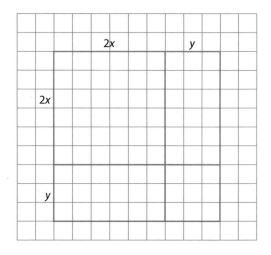

35. $(2x + y)^2$ **36.** $(x + 3y)^2$ **37.** $(2a - b)^2$ **38.** $(3x - 2y)^2$

39. Use the four smaller rectangles on the right to show that $(3x + 4)(2x + 3) = 6x^2 + 17x + 12$.

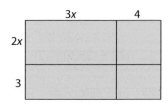

Investigation:

A: Match the expressions below with the array models over:
   (a) $4xy$
   (b) $2xz + 2xc$
   (c) $x^2 + 2xz$

B: Draw array models for
   (d) $2x(z + c)$ and (e) $x(x + 2z)$ and compare them to the array models over.

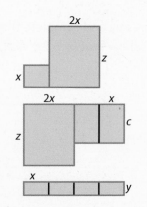

C: Pick any 2 algebraic expressions and build your own array model to represent them.

Test yourself 8

1. Simplify each of these expressions:
   (i) $5x + 3x - 4x$
   (ii) $4x + 5 + 6x - 3$
   (iii) $6x^2 - 2x + x^2 - 5x$
   (iv) $3a + 4b + a - 3b$
   (v) $2p - 3q + 3p + 5q$
   (vi) $a^2 - 4a + 6a + 5a^2$

2. If $x = 3$ and $y = 2$, find the value of each of these:
   (i) $6x$
   (ii) $2x + 3y$
   (iii) $6x - 2y$
   (iv) $x^2 + 2y^2$

3. (i) Express the perimeter of the given figure in its simplest form.
   (ii) Now find the length of the perimeter when $p = 5$ and $q = 1$.

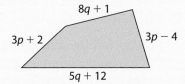

4. Write each of the following using index notation.
   (i) $a \times a$
   (ii) $b \times b \times b$
   (iii) $a \times a \times b$
   (iv) $a \times a \times a \times 4$

5. In number walls, each brick is made by adding the two bricks underneath it. Copy the walls below and fill in the missing expressions:
   (i)
   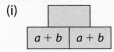
   (ii)
   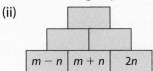
   (iii)
   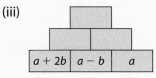

6. Expand the brackets and simplify each of these:
   (i) $3(2x + 1) + 4(x - 3)$
   (ii) $5x(2x - 3) + 2x(3x - 1)$

7. Work out the value of each of these expressions when $a = -6$.
   (i) $a + 10$
   (ii) $5a$
   (iii) $-7 + a$
   (iv) $3a - 4$

8. Write down an expression for each of these statements:
   (i) 4 more than x
   (ii) 5 less than x
   (iii) twice x plus 4
   (iv) 6 more than three times x

9. Work out an expression for each length marked **?**.
   (i)
   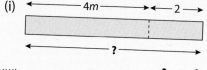
   (ii)
   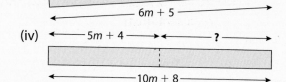
   (iii)
   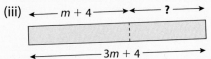
   (iv)

10. One Saturday a shop starts with x games.
    It bought a further 20 games and sold y games.
    Write an expression for the number of games left in the shop.

11. Remove the brackets and simplify each of these:
    (i) $(2x + 3)(x + 4)$ (ii) $(3x - 1)(2x + 5)$

12.

A	B	C	E	G	H	I	M	O	P	R	S	T	U	W
−2	−5	8	3	−3	0	−6	2	−1	5	1	−4	7	6	−9

Work out the value of the expressions in each list.
Change the numbers to letters using the code above.
Rearrange the letters to spell an animal.

(i)
$a - 1$ when $a = -2$
$b - 2$ when $b = -4$
$2 - c$ when $c = -3$

(ii)
$x + 9$ when $x = -2$
$y - 4$ when $y = 3$
$2z$ when $z = -1$
$2w + 1$ when $w = -2$

(iii)
$2a$ when $a = -2$
$b + 5$ when $b = -5$
$5 + 3c$ when $c = -2$
$2d + 5$ when $d = -1$
$-4 + e$ when $e = 5$

13. Use an array model to simplify (i) $(2x + 4)^2$ (ii) $(y - 4)^2$.

Learning Experience   Unit 8

Assignment 1

In chapter 5 we came across recurring decimals e.g. 1.727272…where the decimal digits keep repeating. Algebra can be used to change a recurring decimal into a fraction.

The method is shown in the following 2 cases (a) 4.2222…. and (b) 1.2626… .

Using your knowledge of algebra copy and explain each line of the procedure by filling in the brackets.

(a) to change 4.22222… to a fraction

$4.2222… = x$ (Let……………………)

$42.2222 … = 10x$ (…………………………)

$\underline{4.2222… = x}$ (…………………………)

$38.0 \quad = 9x$ (…………………………)

$\therefore x = \frac{38}{9}$ (…………………………)

$\therefore \frac{38}{9} = 4.2222 …$

(b) to change 1.262626… to a fraction

$1.2626… = x$ (Let……………………)

$126.2626 … = 100x$ (…………………)

$\underline{1.2626… = x}$ (…………………………)

$125.0 \quad = 99x$ (…………………………)

$\therefore x = \frac{125}{99}$ (…………………………)

$\therefore \frac{125}{99} = 1.262626 …$

Now try to change the recurring decimal 1.666… into a fraction using algebra.

Assignment 2

Algebra is very central to the study and operation of mathematics, just like the skeleton is central to the working of the body.

Many mathematicians used and helped to develop algebra.

Research each of the following mathematicians and write a note on each stating one connection they had to the development of mathematics.

(a) Hamilton   (b) Einstein   (c) al-Khwarizmi

Problem 1

Show that the expression $x^2 - x + 11$ when evaluated using the following values of x, produces a **prime** number in all **except one**.

Find the odd one out.

(i) $x = 2$ (ii) $x = 3$ (iii) $x = 5$ (iv) $x = 7$ (v) $x = 9$ (vi) $x = 11$

List 4 other even values which result in primes.

Problem 2

a, b, c and x are numbers connected by the following lines of algebra.

(i) $a + b = c \ldots$ (which also means that $c = a + b$)
(ii) $a \quad\quad = b + x$
(iii) $a + a + b = c + x + x.$

Show how to find how many $xs = b$

Chapter 8 review 1

Using the terms from the chapter copy and complete the following sentences:

1. An _____ is a collection of terms.

2. When simplifying expressions, we can add _____ terms.

3. Since the values of x and y are not known and since they can change value they are called _____.

4. The _____ of x is the number of xs in an expression.

5. A term which has a fixed value is called a _____ term.

6. To _____ an expression, substitute numbers for variables.

7. To multiply brackets an _____ model can be used.

Chapter 8 review 2

You should now be able to;

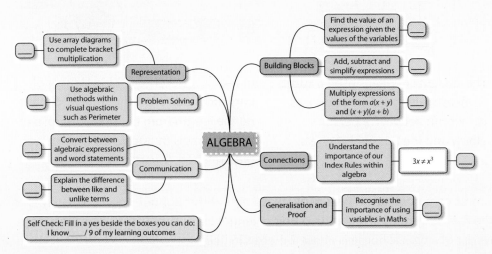

Area – Perimeter – Volume

In this chapter, you will learn to:

- use the **metric system**,
- convert **units of length**,
- calculate the length of a **perimeter**,
- calculate **area** of a square,
- change the **units of area**,
- identify **length and width**,
- measure the area of **triangles** and **rectangles**,
- measure the area of **compound shapes**,
- measure **perpendicular height**,
- measure the **volume** of a solid,
- measure the **surface area** of a solid,
- use **nets** to calculate surface area.

Section 9.1 The metric system – Units of length

Down through the ages, different civilisations have used various ways to measure length and distances.

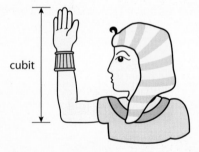

The ancient Egyptians used a **cubit** to measure length. One cubit was the length between a person's elbow and the tips of his fingers.

In the twelfth century, King Henry I of England made a law that the **yard** was to be the length from the tip of his nose to the end of his thumb when his arm was outstretched. (1 yard = 3 feet)

The most commonly-used system of measurement throughout the world today is known as the **metric system**. The standard unit of length in the metric system is the **metre**. The door of a typical house is about 2 metres in height.

The part of the ruler shown below is 10 cm in length. Each **centimetre** is divided into 10 units called **millimetres**. There are 100 centimetres in a metre.

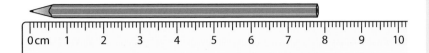

This pencil is 7 cm and 8 mm in length.

We use the **kilometre** (1000 metres) to measure long distances.

The distance between Dublin and Cork is about 260 kilometres.

The main units of length and their abbreviations are given in the table below:

> 1000 metres = 1 kilometre   1000 m = 1 km
> 1 metre = 100 centimetres   1 m = 100 cm
> 1 metre = 1000 millimetres   1 m = 1000 mm
> 1 centimetre = 10 millimetres 1 cm = 10 mm

When converting from one metric unit to another, the following two rules should prove useful.

Rules for converting

1. When changing to a larger unit, you will have fewer of them, so divide.
2. When changing to a smaller unit, you will have more of them, so multiply.

Example 1

Convert   (i) 37 mm to cm   (ii) 420 cm to m   (iii) 3.8 km to m

(i) 10 mm = 1 cm, so to convert mm to cm, divide by 10.
    ∴   37 mm = (37 ÷ 10) cm = 3.7 cm
(ii) 100 cm = 1 m, so to convert cm to m, divide by 100.
    ∴   420 cm = (420 ÷ 100) m = 4.2 m
(iii) 1 km = 1000 m, so to convert km to m, multiply by 1000.
    ∴   3.8 km = (3.8 × 1000) m = 3800 m

Exercise 9.1

1. Which unit would you use to measure each of these lengths?
   Choose from millimetres, centimetres or metres.
   (i)   the length of a pen
   (ii) the length of a football pitch
   (iii) the thickness of a bathroom tile
   (iv) the height of a giraffe
   (v)   the thickness of an exercise book
   (vi) the perimeter of a basketball court.

2. Measure the lengths of these lines and give your answer in centimetres and millimetres:
   (i) _____
   (ii) _____

3. Use a ruler to draw lines of lengths:
   (i) 6 cm   (ii) 75 mm   (iii) 6.4 cm   (iv) 6 cm 8 mm   (v) 84 mm

4. What reading, in mm,
   is given by each pointer?

   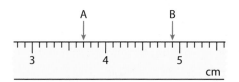

5. Copy and complete each of the following:
   (i)   5 cm = ☐ mm   (ii) 6.8 cm = ☐ mm   (iii) 40 mm = ☐ cm
   (iv) 200 mm = ☐ cm   (v)   145 mm = ☐ cm   (vi) 16.4 cm = ☐ mm

6. Maria only had a broken ruler.
   Find the length of this strip in
   centimetres and millimetres.

   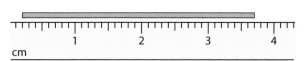

7. Copy and complete each of the following:
   (i)   100 cm = 1 ☐   (ii) 1 km = ☐ m   (iii) 2.5 km = ☐ m
   (iv) 300 cm = ☐ m   (v)   850 cm = ☐ m   (vi) 55 m = ☐ cm

8. What length does the pointer show
   (i) in metres
   (ii) metres and centimetres?

9. Express each of the following in metres:
   (i) 600 cm   (ii) 8 km   (iii) 2.8 km   (iv) 480 cm   (v) 3.28 km

10. Express each of these in centimetres:
    (i) 15 m   (ii) 2.8 m   (iii) 40 mm   (iv) 124 mm   (v) 8 m 64 cm

11. Convert each of the following to kilometres:
   (i) 4000 m   (ii) 12800 m   (iii) 750 m   (iv) 3 km 450 m   (v) 90 m

12. Change each of the following to metres:
   (i) $\frac{3}{5}$ km   (ii) 0.63 km   (iii) 60 m 90 cm   (iv) 6500 cm

13. What are the readings on the scale below
   (i) in cm   (ii) in mm?

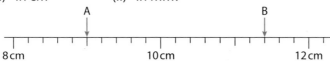

14. Which of the following is most likely to be the length of a biro?
   (i) 30 mm   (ii) 13 cm   (iii) 1.3 m   (iv) 0.8 m

15. Write these lengths in order of size, starting with the shortest:
   12 cm   80 mm   10.8 cm   1.2 m   0.8 m

16. The Eiffel Tower is about 300 metres in height.
How long would it take a lift travelling at
120 cm per second to reach the top?

17. A tortoise moves 8 mm every second.
How many metres will it travel in one hour?

18. Susan's bedroom wall is 3 metres long.
Can she fit all of these units along the wall?
Give a reason for your answer.

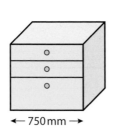
← 750 mm →

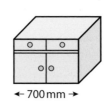
← 700 mm →

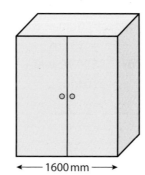
←——— 1600 mm ———→

Section 9.2 Perimeter

The **perimeter** of a shape is the distance around the edge of the shape.

The perimeter of this **rectangle** is

$$5 + 3 + 5 + 3 = 16 \text{ cm}$$

Since the opposite sides of a rectangle are equal in length, the perimeter can be written as

$$2 \times 5 + 2 \times 3 \quad \text{or} \quad 2(5 + 3) \text{ cm}.$$

For any rectangle,

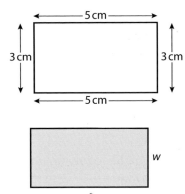

> Perimeter $= 2(\ell + w)$
> where $\ell =$ length and $w =$ width.

Since the four sides of a **square** are equal in length,

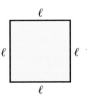

> Perimeter of a square $= 4 \times \ell$
> where ℓ is the length of a side.

Example 1

Find the perimeter of this figure in
(i) centimetres
(ii) millimetres.

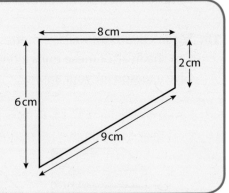

(i) Perimeter $= 6 \text{ cm} + 8 \text{ cm} + 2 \text{ cm} + 9 \text{ cm}$
$\qquad\qquad\quad = 25 \text{ cm}$

(ii) $25 \text{ cm} = 25 \times 10 \text{ mm}$
$\qquad\qquad = 250 \text{ mm}$

Exercise 9.2

1. Find the answer to each of the following:

(i) $2 \text{ mm} + 3 \text{ mm} + 24 \text{ mm}$

(ii) $69 \text{ cm} + 23 \text{ cm} + 92 \text{ cm}$

(iii) $7.9 \text{ m} - 65 \text{ cm}$

(iv) $54 \text{ cm} + 130 \text{ mm}$

(v) $93 \text{ m} - 783 \text{ cm}$

(vi) $736 \text{ m} - 0.234 \text{ km}$

2. Anna cut the following lengths of tape from a roll containing 2.5 m.
   How much tape was left on the roll:

   (i) 28 cm 5 mm   (ii) 360 mm   (iii) 76 mm   (iv) 1.5 m

3. A 10 m roll of fabric has the following lengths cut from it. Find how much fabric is left on the roll.

   (i) 3 m   (ii) 3.6 m   (iii) 0.7 m   (iv) 0.53 m

4. Copy and complete these:

   (i) 5 cm = ☐ mm   (ii) 45 mm = ☐ cm   (iii) 6.5 cm = ☐ mm
   (iv) 280 mm = ☐ cm   (v) 2.4 m = ☐ cm   (vi) 0.75 m = ☐ cm

5. Add each of the following measurements giving your answers in centimetres.

   (i) 25 cm + 80 mm   (ii) 8.5 cm + 90 mm   (iii) 24 cm + 0.25 m

6. What is meant by the perimeter of a shape?
   Use your ruler to measure the perimeter of each of these figures.
   Give each answer in centimetres and millimetres, e.g. 20 cm 8 mm.

   (i)   (ii)   (iii)

7. These rectangles have been drawn on 1 cm squared paper.
   Find the perimeter of each figure in cm.

   (i)   (ii)   (iii)

8. Work out the perimeter of each of these rectangles:

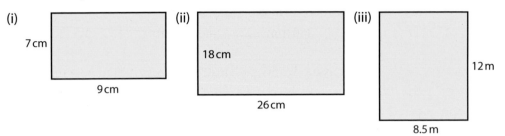

(i) 7 cm, 9 cm

(ii) 18 cm, 26 cm

(iii) 12 m, 8.5 m

9. Find the perimeters of these shapes.

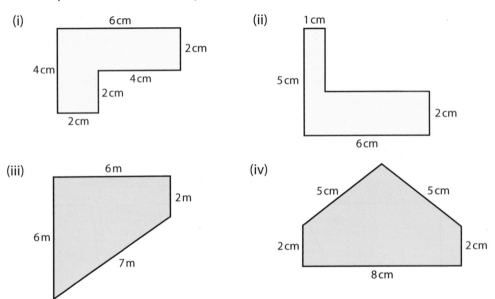

(i) 6 cm, 2 cm, 4 cm, 2 cm, 2 cm, 4 cm

(ii) 1 cm, 5 cm, 6 cm, 2 cm

(iii) 6 m, 2 m, 6 m, 7 m

(iv) 5 cm, 5 cm, 2 cm, 2 cm, 8 cm

10. Work out the perimeter of these shapes:

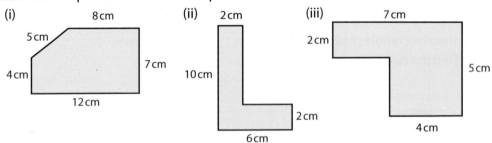

(i) 8 cm, 5 cm, 7 cm, 4 cm, 12 cm

(ii) 2 cm, 10 cm, 2 cm, 6 cm

(iii) 7 cm, 2 cm, 5 cm, 4 cm

11. Work out the perimeter of each square.

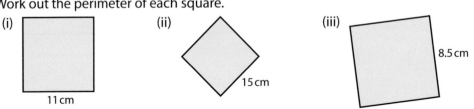

(i) 11 cm

(ii) 15 cm

(iii) 8.5 cm

12. Work out the perimeter of each of these:

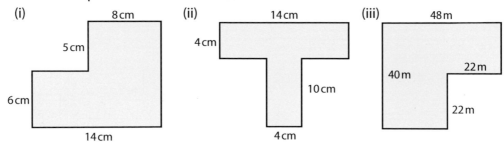

(i)   8 cm   5 cm   6 cm   14 cm

(ii)   14 cm   4 cm   10 cm   4 cm

(iii)   48 m   40 m   22 m   22 m

13. (i) Work out the perimeter of this shape.

(ii) Show that the perimeter can be worked out by adding two of the lengths shown and doubling the answer.

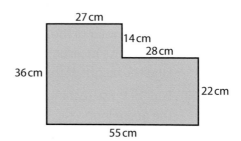

27 cm   14 cm   28 cm   36 cm   22 cm   55 cm

14. Some of the dimensions are missing in these figures but it is still possible to work out the perimeters. Try them.

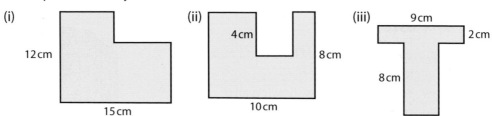

(i)   12 cm   15 cm

(ii)   4 cm   8 cm   10 cm

(iii)   9 cm   2 cm   8 cm

15. Find the perimeter of each shape. Explain your method.

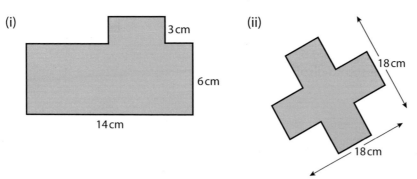

(i)   3 cm   6 cm   14 cm

(ii)   18 cm   18 cm

16. In each of these figures, the perimeter is given.
Find the dimension marked **?** in each figure.

(i)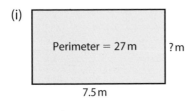

(ii)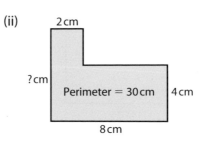

17. (i) The perimeter of the yellow rectangle is 24 cm
and its base measures 4 cm.
Find the height of the rectangle.

(ii) Four of these rectangles are used to make
the green logo.
Find the perimeter of this logo.

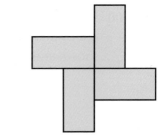

Investigation:

A farmer has 20 meters of fencing to make
an enclosure for his sheep.
Draw rectangular shapes showing all of
the possible sized enclosures he could make
using all of the fencing each time. (Note; each side
must be a whole number of metres)

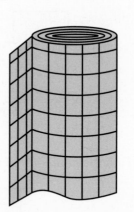

(i) What is the area of the largest enclosure
he could make?

(ii) What type of shape is this enclosure?

(iii) Make a poster to display your work.

Section 9.3 Area of rectangle and triangle

Area is the amount of surface covered by a shape.

In the grid below, each square has side of length 1 cm.

The area of each square is **1 cm²**.

It is pronounced *1 square centimetre*.

By counting the squares, we can write down the area of each figure.

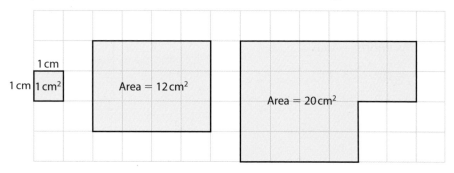

The **rectangle** on the right is 5 cm long and 3 cm wide.

Its area = 5 cm × 3 cm

$\quad\quad\quad$ = 15 cm²

> The area of a rectangle = length × width.

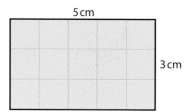

The area of a triangle

Since a diagonal bisects the area of a rectangle, it can be seen from the given diagram that the area of the biggest shaded triangle is half the area of the biggest rectangle.

Since the area of this rectangle is *b* × *h*, the area of the triangle is half of *b* × *h*.

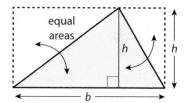

Area of triangle = $\frac{1}{2}$ × base × height

In these triangles, *b* is the base and *h* is the **perpendicular height**.

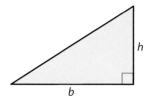
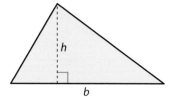
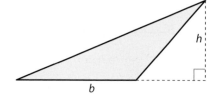

Finding the length or width

The area of the given rectangle is 28 cm² and its length is 7 cm.
If the width of the rectangle is w cm,
using the ideas in algebra we can write;

Length × Width = Area

$\therefore$ 7 cm × w cm = 28 cm²

$7w$ cm² = 28 cm²

$\therefore$ the width, w = 28 ÷ 7 = 4 cm

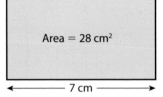

Area = 28 cm²

7 cm

Example 1

Find the area of the given figure.

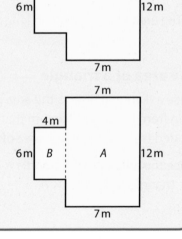

7 m

4 m

6 m

12 m

7 m

The broken line divides the figure into two
rectangles A and B.

Area of A = 12 m × 7 m = 84 m²

Area of B = 6 m × 4 m = 24 m²

Total area = (84 + 24) m²
= 108 m²

7 m

4 m

6 m B A 12 m

7 m

Example 2

Find the area of each of the triangles given below:

(i)

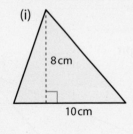

8 cm

10 cm

(ii)

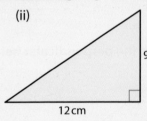

9 cm

12 cm

(iii)

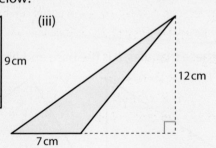

12 cm

7 cm

(i) Area $= \frac{1}{2}$ base $\times$ perpendicular height

$\quad = \frac{1}{2} \times 10 \times 8$

$\quad = 40 \, cm^2$

(ii) Area $= \frac{1}{2} \times 12 \times 9$

$\quad = 54 \, cm^2$

(iii) Area $= \frac{1}{2} \times 7 \times 12$

$\quad = 42 \, cm^2$

Example 3

The triangle POQ has an area of 14cm².

If the length of the base is 7 cm, find the height of the triangle.

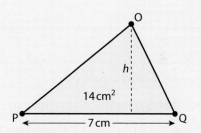

Area of triangle $= \frac{1}{2} \times base \times height$

$\therefore 14 \, cm^2 = \frac{1}{2} \times 7 \, cm \times h$

$\therefore 28 \, cm^2 = 7h$ ...multiplying both sides by 2

$\therefore h = \frac{28}{7} = 4 \, cm.$

The area of a square

The area of this square is 9 cm² when you count the small squares.

You get the same result if you multiply the length by the width, i.e.,

$\quad 3 \, cm \times 3 \, cm = 9 \, cm^2$

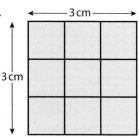

> Thus, the area of a square is (length of side)²

Conversely, if we know area of a square we can find the length of the side as follows:

Length $\times$ Width $= 25 \, cm^2$

$\quad x \times x = 25 \, cm^2$

$\quad \therefore x^2 = 25 \, cm^2$

and $x = \sqrt{25 \, cm^2} = 5 \, cm$

Example 4

(i) Find the area of the square with perimeter 40 cm.
(ii) Find the perimeter of the square with area 81 cm².

(i) If the perimeter is 40 cm, then each side is $\frac{40}{4} = 10$ cm.
   Area $= 10$ cm $\times 10$ cm $= 100$ cm²

(ii) Area $= 81$ cm²
   ∴ (side)² $= 81$ cm²
   ∴ length of side $= \sqrt{81 \text{ cm}^2} = 9$ cm
   Perimeter is length of side $\times 4 = 9 \times 4$
   $= 36$ cm

Investigation:

Investigate the diagram over:

A: Find the area of the square **ABCD**.

B: Describe 2 ways of finding the area of **EFGH**.

C: Describe how to find the % of ABCD **not** covered by EFGH.

D: Explain the significance of 0.625 in the diagram.

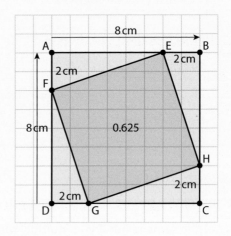

Investigation:

Measure the length and width of each room on the ground-floor of your house.

On squared paper draw a large diagram of the ground-floor using an appropriate scale.

Exercise 9.3

1. Find the area of each shape. Each square on the grid represents 1 cm².

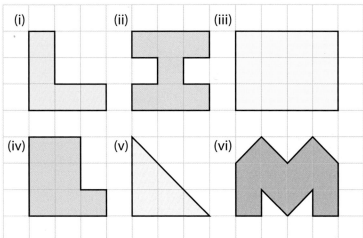

2. Estimate the area of this island.

   Each square represents 1 km².

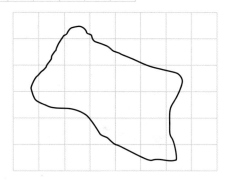

3. Find the area of each rectangle shown below:

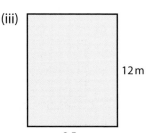

   (i) 7 cm, 9 cm

   (ii) 18 cm, 26 cm

   (iii) 12 m, 8.5 m

4. Work out the area of each of these rectangles:

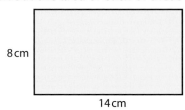
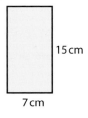
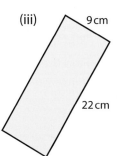

   (i) 8 cm, 14 cm

   (ii) 15 cm, 7 cm

   (iii) 9 cm, 22 cm

5. Find the area of each square.

(i)

(ii)

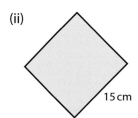

7 m

15 cm

(iii)

22 mm

6. The area of the square shown is 25 m².

Find   (i) the length of its side
        (ii) the perimeter of the square.

Area = 25 m²

7. Find the length of the side of each square shown below:

(i)

Area = 81 cm²

(ii)

Area = 144 cm²

(iii)

Area = 400 m²

8. Find the length (or width) of each of these rectangles:

(i)   12 cm

Area = 96 cm²

(ii)   12 m

Area = 240 m²

(iii)   18 mm

Area = 216 mm²

9. (i) Find the perimeter of the given figure.
    (ii) Find the area of the figure by dividing
          it into 2 rectangles.

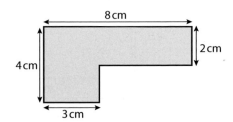

8 cm

2 cm

4 cm

3 cm

10. Find the area of each of these figures.

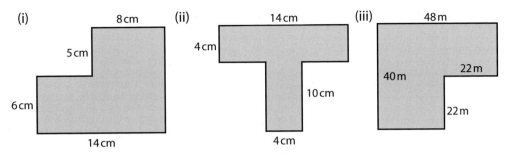

(i) 8 cm, 5 cm, 6 cm, 14 cm

(ii) 14 cm, 4 cm, 10 cm, 4 cm

(iii) 48 m, 40 m, 22 m, 22 m

11. Work out the area of each of these floors.

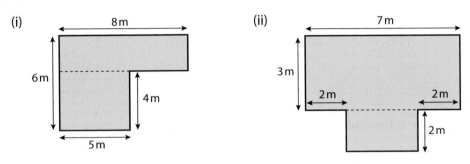

(i) 8 m, 6 m, 4 m, 5 m

(ii) 7 m, 3 m, 2 m, 2 m, 2 m

12. Find the area of each of these triangles:

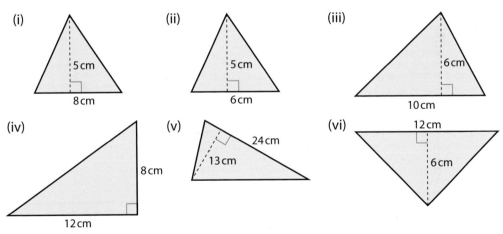

(i) 5 cm, 8 cm

(ii) 5 cm, 6 cm

(iii) 6 cm, 10 cm

(iv) 8 cm, 12 cm

(v) 24 cm, 13 cm

(vi) 12 cm, 6 cm

13. Work out the areas of these triangles:

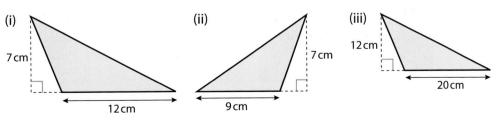

(i) 7 cm, 12 cm

(ii) 7 cm, 9 cm

(iii) 12 cm, 20 cm

14. Find the area of each of the four triangles A, B, C and D drawn on the centimetre grid:

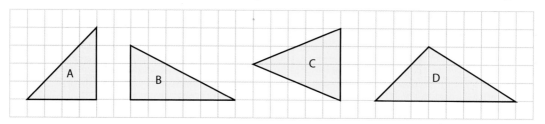

Verify your answer to triangle A by counting squares.

15. Find the value of x in each of these triangles:

(i)   (ii)   (iii)

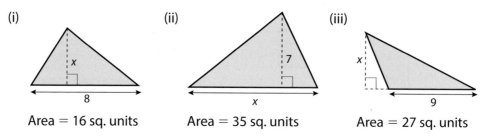

Area = 16 sq. units   Area = 35 sq. units   Area = 27 sq. units

16. Find the areas of the following shapes which are comprised of rectangles and triangles:

(i)   (ii)   (iii)

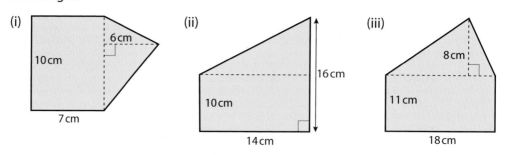

17. Find the area that needs painting on each of these walls.

(i)   (ii)

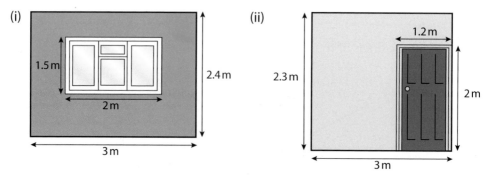

18. Find the area of the blue region in this flag.

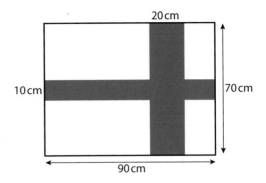

19. Work out the area of each of these shapes:

(i)

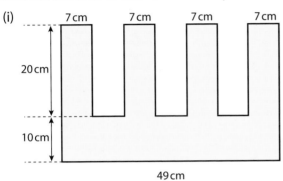

(ii)

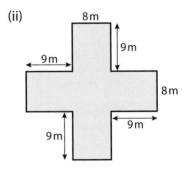

20. The diagram shows a square ABCD with a green square drawn inside.

ABCD has area 100 cm².

Calculate the area of the green square and explain how you found your answer.

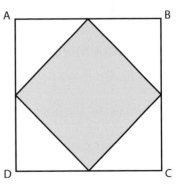

21. Find the area of the shaded border in each of these rectangles:

(i)

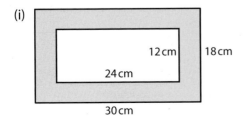

(ii)

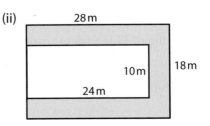

This is the floor plan of an apartment.

Use it to answer questions **22–25.**

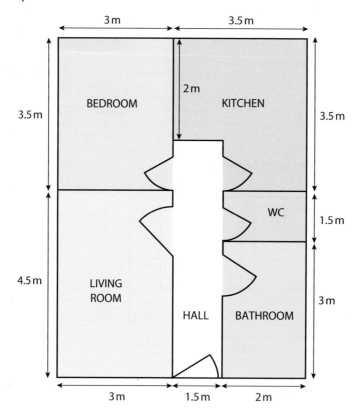

22. Find the floor area of

    (i) the living room   (ii) the hall.

23. Work out the floor area of the kitchen.

24. Find the cost of cleaning the bedroom carpet at €8 per square metre.

25. Find the cost of tiling the hall and WC if the cost of each square metre is €65.

Section 9.4 Rectangular solids

The figure on the right is a **rectangular solid**
(or **cuboid**).

The space occupied by this solid is called
its **volume**.

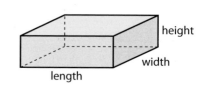

The solid on the right is called a **cube** because its length, width and height are all equal.

Its volume is **1 cm³**, pronounced **one cubic centimetre**.

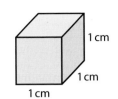

The figure on the right is made up of three layers of cubes.
In each layer there are 24 cubes.
In the three layers there are 72 cubes altogether.
From this we can see that the volume is found by multiplying the length by the width by the height.

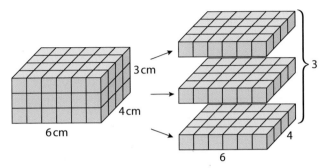

$$\text{Volume} = 6 \text{ cm} \times 4 \text{ cm} \times 3 \text{ cm} = 72 \text{ cm}^3$$

> Volume of rectangular solid = length × width × height

Surface area of rectangular solid

The given solid shows three faces A, B and C.
The three faces that we cannot see are also A, B and C.

Area of A = 5 cm × 4 cm = 20 cm²
Area of B = 3 cm × 4 cm = 12 cm²
Area of C = 5 cm × 3 cm = 15 cm²
$\therefore$ Surface area of solid = (2 × 20 cm²) + (2 × 12 cm²) + (2 × 15 cm²)
= 40 cm² + 24 cm² + 30 cm² = 94 cm²

Surface area of rectangular solid	The surface area of a rectangular solid of length ℓ, width w and height h is $$2\ell w + 2\ell h + 2wh$$

Volume and surface area of a cube	Volume = $\ell \times \ell \times \ell = \ell^3$ Surface area = $6\ell^2$

Example 1

Find (i) the volume   (ii) the surface area
of the given rectangular solid.

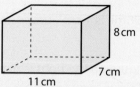

(i) Volume $= \ell \times w \times h$

$\qquad = 11 \text{ cm} \times 7 \text{ cm} \times 8 \text{ cm} = 616 \text{ cm}^3$

(ii) Surface area $= 2\ell w + 2\ell h + 2wh$

$\qquad\qquad = 2(11 \text{ cm} \times 7\text{cm}) + 2(11 \text{ cm} \times 8 \text{ cm}) + 2(7 \text{ cm} \times 8 \text{ cm})$

$\qquad\qquad = 154 \text{ cm}^2 + 176 \text{ cm}^2 + 112 \text{ cm}^2 = 442 \text{ cm}^2$

Example 2

The volume of the rectangular box shown is
2156 cm^3.
Find the length of the side marked x.

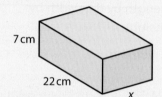

$\qquad$ Volume $=$ length $\times$ width $\times$ height

$\therefore \quad 2156 \text{ cm}^3 = 22 \text{ cm} \times x \times 7 \text{ cm}$

$\quad\ 2156 \text{ cm}^3 = 154x \text{ cm}^3$

$\qquad 154x = 2156$

$\qquad\quad x = \dfrac{2156}{154} = 14$

The side marked x is 14 cm.

Exercise 9.4

1. Find the volume of each of these rectangular solids:

(i) 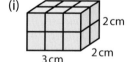   (ii) 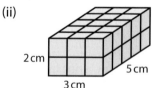   (iii)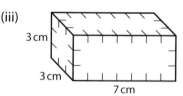

2. Find the surface area of each of the solids in Question **1.** above.

3. Find   (a) the volume   (b) the surface area of these solid cuboids:

(i) 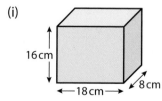   (ii) 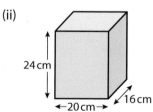   (iii)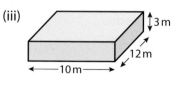

4. Find the surface area of each of these solids:

(i)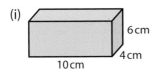

6 cm
4 cm
10 cm

(ii)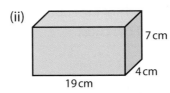

7 cm
4 cm
19 cm

(iii)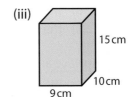

15 cm
10 cm
9 cm

5. The diagram shows a rectangular box partly filled with cubes of side 1 cm.
How many more of these cubes are required to fill the box?

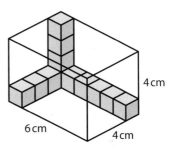

4 cm
6 cm
4 cm

6. Five cubes of side 2 cm are joined to make the solid shown. Which of the following is the surface area of the solid?

(i) 68 cm²   (ii) 72 cm²   (iii) 20 cm²   (iv) 88 cm²

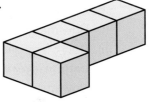

7. Find (i) the volume and (ii) the surface area of the given cube.

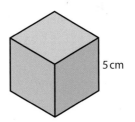

5 cm

8. The volume of each of the following rectangular solids is given. Find the length of the side marked with a letter.

(i)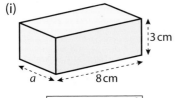

3 cm
a
8 cm

Volume = 120 cm³

(ii)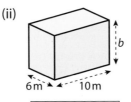

b
6 m
10 m

Volume = 420 m³

(iii)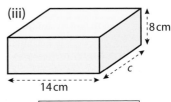

8 cm
c
14 cm

Volume = 2240 cm³

9. The volume of a cube is 64 cm³.
    Find (i) the length of the side of the cube
          (ii) the surface area of the cube.

10. The surface area of this cube is 150 cm².
    Find (i) the length of the side of the cube
          (ii) the volume of the cube.

11. The figure on the right shows a stack of cubes of
    side 3 cm.
    (i) How many cubes are there in the stack?
    (ii) Find the volume of the stack.

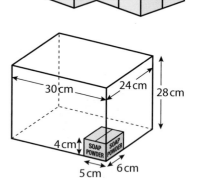

12. Hannah is packing packets of soap powder into
    a box, as shown.
    (i) How many will fit along one 30 cm side?
    (ii) How many packets will there be in the
          bottom layer when the box is full?
    (iii) How many layers will there be when the
          box is full?
    (iv) How many packets of soap powder will
          fit in the box altogether?

13. A hotel buys washing powder in boxes which are
    20 cm long, 12 cm wide and 16 cm high.
    (i) Calculate the volume of powder in the box.

    The hotel puts the powder into smaller boxes
    which are cubes of side 4 cm.
    (ii) How many smaller boxes can be filled from
          one of the large boxes?

14. A box has dimensions 10 cm by 8 cm by 6 cm.
    Dice like these are to be packed into this box.
    What is the largest number of dice the box will hold?

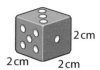

Investigation:

A: In the top diagram eight blocks were stacked to form a cube.

If the outside of the cube was painted, how many sides (faces) of each block were painted.

What % of the surface area of all the blocks was painted.

B: Investigate the second cube.

How many blocks were needed to make this cube?

This cube was also painted.

Write down the number of blocks that had
  (i) 3 faces   (ii) 2 faces
(iii) 1 face, painted.

C: Design a chart which shows the number faces painted (3), (2), (1) and the number of blocks needed if there are
(a) 2 blocks   (b) 3 blocks   (c) 4 blocks, along each side.

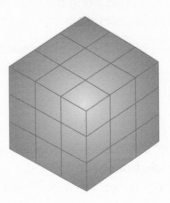

Investigation:

Barry has a large box measuring 1 m × 1 m × 1 m.

He wants to fill the box with sugar cubes measuring 1 cm × 1 cm × 1 cm.

What is the volume of the
(i) box (ii) sugar cube.

Investigate:
(a) How many sugar cubes fit in a row in the box?

(b) How many sugar cubes fit in a layer in the box?

(c) How many sugar cubes fit in the box.

Draw a chart of your results finishing with the line
   (   ) cm³ = ( ) m³

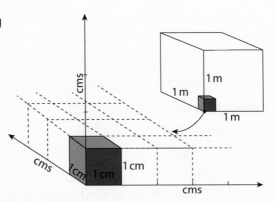

Section 9.5 Nets of solids

To measure the surface area of a solid it is helpful to be able to draw a **net** of the solid.

Consider each edge of a solid a hinge, then each surface can be opened out and laid flat in many different ways.

The surface of the solid then becomes a series of connected rectangles.

Conversely, if we are given the net, it can be folded along the edges(hinges) to form the solid again.

On the right is the net of a **closed** rectangular box. It has a base, a top and four sides.

The net of an **open** rectangular box has a base, four sides but no top.

There are 11 different nets for a cube. Two of them are shown here.

Investigation:

A: On squared paper draw two different nets of a cube other than the three shown above.

B: On the right is a cardboard cube folded flat.
If it is refolded to make a cube, which *two* corners will touch corner *b*?

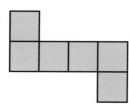
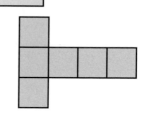
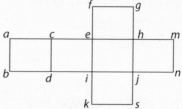

Example 1

By drawing a net of this closed rectangular box, find its total surface area.

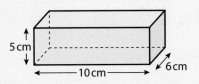

The net for the box is shown below.

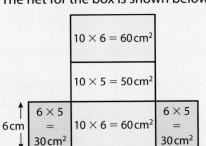

Total surface area

= 60 + 60 + 50 + 50 + 30 + 30

= 280 cm²

Exercise 9.5

1. This is the net of a cube. The length of each side is 4 cm.

   (i) Find the volume of the cube.

   (ii) Find the surface area of the cube.

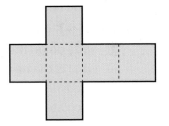

2. The net shown is folded to make a rectangular box. The pink rectangle will be the base of the box.

   (i) Write down the height of the box.

   (ii) Is the box open or closed?

   (iii) Find the volume of the box.

   (iv) Work out the surface area of the box.

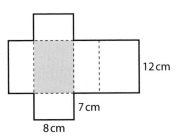

3. The diagram shows a net of a cube with a different letter on each face. When the cube is assembled, which letter is opposite the letter:

   (i) A   (ii) E   (iii) D?

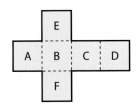

4. When the given net is formed into a cube, which
   letter is opposite the letter:

   (i) A   (ii) E   (iii) D?

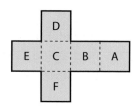

5. This is the net of a rectangular box.
   Draw a rough sketch of the assembled box and
   then calculate

   (i) the volume of the box,
   (ii) the surface area of the box.

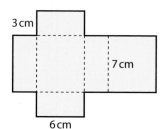

6. Shown on the right is the net of a dice.
   Make a copy of this net and label the faces from 1 to 6
   so that when it is folded to form a dice, the numbers on
   the opposite faces add up to 7.

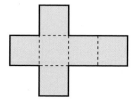

7. This is the net of a rectangular box.
   When it is folded to make a box,

   (i)   write down the dimensions of the base.
   (ii) what is the height of the box?
   (iii) calculate the volume of the box.
   (iv) calculate the external surface area of
         the box.

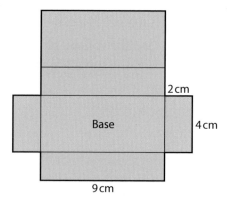

8. The dimensions of a closed rectangular box
   are shown on the right.
   Draw an accurate sketch of the net for this box.

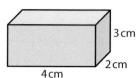

9. A square sheet of metal has a side of length 30 cm. Four identical squares of side 4 cm are cut away from the corners, as shown.

The remaining shape is folded to form a box.

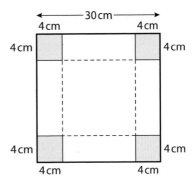

(i)   Is the box an open or closed box?

(ii) Find the volume of the box.

(iii) Find the outer surface area of the box.

Test yourself 9

1. Here are three rectangles and one square. Find the perimeter of each shape.

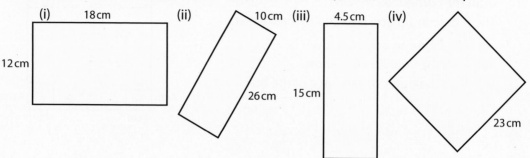

2. Work out the area of each figure in question **1.** above.

3. Measure these shapes and then find their perimeters.
   Give each answer in centimetres and millimetres.

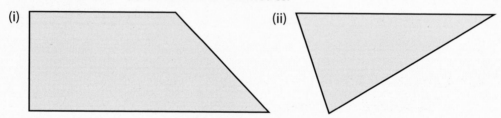

4. Work out the area of each of these shapes.

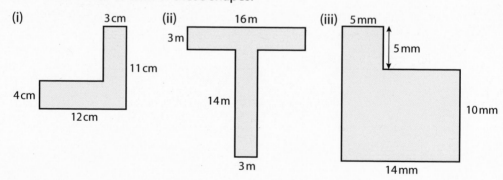

5. Triangles X, Y and Z are drawn on a centimetre grid.
   Work out the area of each triangle.

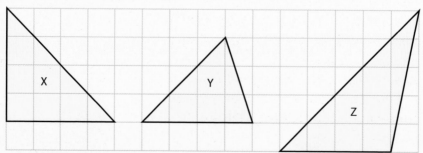

6. Find the areas of the following shapes which are composed of rectangles and triangles.

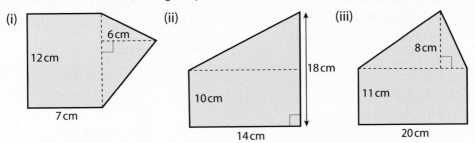

(i)   (ii)   (iii)

7. Work out the coloured areas of these diagrams.

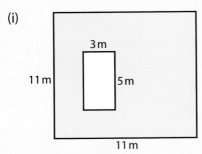

(i)   (ii)

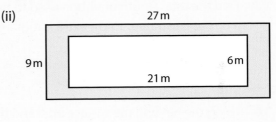

8. The area of the given triangle is 40 cm².

Find the perpendicular height, h cm.

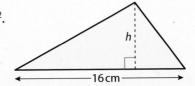

9. Find (i) the perimeter

(ii) the area of this figure.

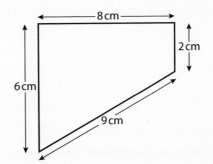

10. (i) Copy and complete the table showing how the area of a rectangle changes, even though its perimeter is fixed at 28 cm.

(ii) What can you say about the shape when it has the largest area?

(iii) A farmer has 100 m of fence and wants to construct a rectangular enclosure with the largest possible area. What is this area?

Length (cm)	Width (cm)	Area (cm²)
13	1	
12		
11		
10		
9		
8		
7		

11. Find (i) the volume
  (ii) the total surface area
of the given rectangular solid.

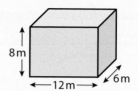

12. The volume of the given solid is 1080 cm³.
Find the height h of the solid.

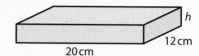

13. Find the total length of ribbon used to tie
a box as illustrated. 15 cm extra is required
for the knot and bow.

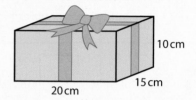

14. Using the net find the surface area and the volume
of the figure shown.

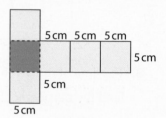

15. A closed rectangular box has a net as shown.
Find (i) the volume   (ii) the surface of the box
correct to one decimal place.

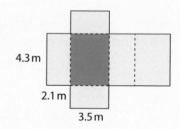

16. A pink triangle is drawn inside a
blue rectangle on squared paper
(1 cm × 1 cm) as part of a design.
Find:
  (i) Area of rectangle,
  (ii) Area of triangle,
  (iii) The percentage of blue left in
    the rectangle

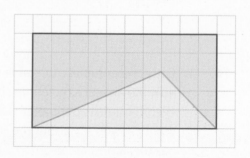

17. At a carnival darts are thrown at a coloured board as above.

Find the area of (i) orange (ii) green
(iii) blue if each square measures
4 cm × 4cm.

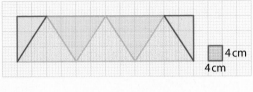

Assuming a dart hits the board
at random, find in percentage terms:
  (i)   the probability of hitting an orange triangle
  (ii) the probability of hitting a green triangle,
  (iii) the probability of hitting a blue triangle.

18. (a) The diagram shows a square ABCD with a
green square drawn inside made by joining
the midpoints of the sides of ABCD.

Given that the area of ABCD = 100 cm²,
calculate the area of the green square
as a percentage of ABCD.

Explain how you found the area of the
green section.

(b) The midpoints of the green square
are now joined forming a blue square.
A dart hits ABCD at random.

Find the probability that the dart hits
  (i)   the blue area
  (ii) the green area.

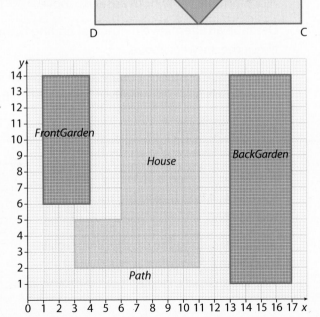

19. The plan of Ruth's house
is drawn on a grid as shown.
Find as a percentage of the
total plot:
  (i)   the area of her garden
        (front and back), correct
        to 2 places of decimals,
  (ii) the area of her house,
Find also the cost of tiling the
Path (the grid is measured
in metres) given that;
  (a) the tiles cost €6 per m²
        and VAT is charged at 23%
  (b) labour costs are €450
        (VAT is charged at 13.5%)

Learning Experience

Unit 9

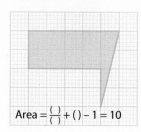

$$\text{Area} = \frac{b}{2} + c - 1$$

$$= \frac{10}{2} + 3 - 1 = 7$$

To find the area of a many sided shape a close friend of Einstein, Gorg Pick, devised a formula based on the number of (whole number) points (●) on the boundary and the number of interior points (◯).

b = the number of boundary points.

c = the number of interior points.

Assignment 1

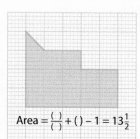

$$\text{Area} = \frac{(\;)}{(\;)} + (\;) - 1 = 10$$

$$\text{Area} = \frac{(\;)}{(\;)} + (\;) - 1 = 13\frac{1}{2}$$

Mark in the boundary and interior points on the two examples above. Using Pick's formula verify both answers above.

Describe an alternative method of finding the areas and use this method to check the answers above.

Make a large poster of a many-sided shape on squared paper. Using Pick's formula and one other method, show how to find the area of the shape.

Assignment 2

A line is drawn parallel to the base AB.

A point on the line, L, is joined to the points A and B, forming the triangle LAB.

As L moves along the parallel line explain (using the information in the chapter) why the shaded triangles have the same areas.

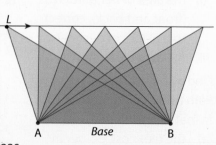

Problem 1

Four rectangular strips, each measuring
10 cm × 1 cm, are laid on a flat table as shown.
Each strip is at right angles to two other strips.

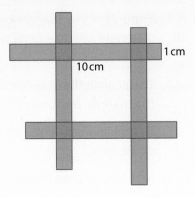

Explain why the area of the table covered by
the strips is 36 cm².

Problem 2

Five identical rectangles fit
together as shown.
By studying the diagram,
complete the following lines of
algebra.

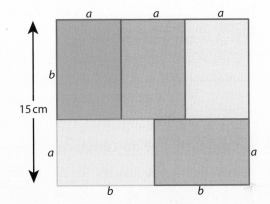

(i) $a + b =$ ……….
(ii) $2b =$ …………
(iii) $\therefore b =$ ………..
(iv) $\therefore a + (\ \ ) =$ ……. using (i)
(v) $\therefore a =$
(vi) $\therefore b =$

Hence calculate the total area, in cm², covered by the rectangles.

Chapter 9 review 1

Using the terms from the chapter, copy and complete the following sentences:

1. The perimeter of a rectangle can be described by "twice the sum of the
   length and the _____ " of the rectangle.

2. The distance around a shape is called the _____ of a shape.

3. Units of length are _____ , centimetres, _____
   and kilometres.

4. The amount of surface covered by a shape is the _____ of the shape.

5. The area of any triangle can be described as "half the area of a rectangle with the same perpendicular height standing on the same _____."

6. To calculate the area of a triangle the _____ height of the triangle must be used.

7. To find the length of a side of a square we get the _____ _____ of the area.

8. Area is measured in cm _____.

9. Volume is measured in cm _____.

10. A _____ of a solid can be used to calculate its surface area.

11. A rectangular solid has _____ sides(faces), _____ edges and _____ vertices.

Chapter 9 review 2

You should now be able to;

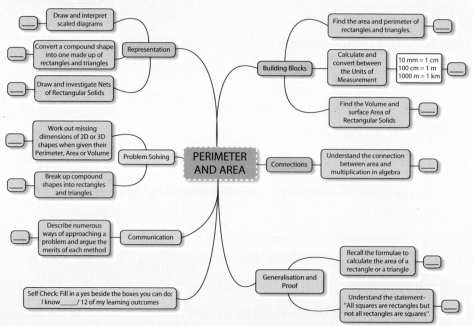

Geometry 1

In this chapter, you will learn to:

- recognise **lines** and **line segments,**
- name lines and line segments,
- understand **angles** as **measures of rotation** about a point,
- recognise **acute** and **obtuse** angles,
- recognise **right angles** and **reflex angles,**
- find **supplementary angles,**
- recognise **vertically opposite** angles,
- recognise **alternate** angles,
- recognise **corresponding** angles,
- use a **protractor** to measure angles,
- use a protractor to draw an angle,
- recognise **collinear** points,
- understand **parallel** lines,
- draw parallel and **perpendicular** lines,
- use **transversal** lines.

Introduction to Geometry

Think of ancient man-made structures such as the Pyramids of Egypt, the Tombs of Newgrange, Stonehenge in England and the Colosseum in Rome. All were built thousands of years ago and were designed by people who understood shapes, lines, triangles, circles and space. In a word, they were built by people who understood Geometry.

Around 600 BC–100 BC, the ancient Greeks took geometry to a whole new plane. They studied it, came up with proofs, and most importantly they wrote it down. The most famous book was called *Elements*, written by a very famous mathematician called Euclid.

Most of his Maths is still used today – just ask any architect. Our Geometry course is based on his work.

Section 10.1 Points – Lines – Line segments

On the right are 2 points, labelled A and B.

There is only one straight line that passes through the points A and B.
We call that the line **AB**.
The line AB goes on forever, in both directions.

We can also name the line with a single lowercase letter such as ℓ, m or n.

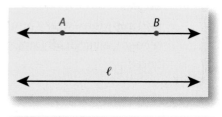

A line beginning at the point A and ending at the point B is called the **line segment** AB.
It is written as **[AB]**.

On the right we have a line segment [AB] which is 4 cm in length.
This is written as $|AB| = 4$ cm.

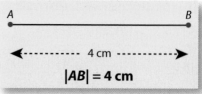

The triangle on the right is made up of three line segments.
They are [AB], [AC] and [BC].

Rays

A line that starts at the point A and continues on through B is called the **ray [AB**.
Rays are sometimes referred to as **half-lines**.

Collinear points

If three points are in the same straight line, then the points are said to be **collinear**.
This is illustrated on the right.
The points A, B and C are collinear.

The plane

The flat surface on which points and lines are shown is called a **plane**. A plane contains an infinite number of points.

The given diagram shows five points A, B, C, D and E drawn on the **plane** of the page.

The points C, E and B are **collinear**.

The points A, B and D are not collinear. (Why?)

Unlike the page, a plane has no boundaries i.e. the page is part of a plane.

The ceiling of the classroom is part of a different plane.

A ●   ● B
       ● E
         ● D
    C ●

Exercise 10.1

1. Measure the length of each line in centimetres:

   (i) ————————————————————————

   (ii) ——————————————————

   (iii) ————————————————————

2. Use your ruler to draw line segments having the following lengths:

   (i) 5 cm   (ii) $6\frac{1}{2}$ cm   (iii) 75 mm   (iv) 46 mm

3. Describe in words each of the following diagrams:

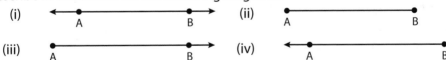

4. If X and Y are two distinct points, draw a separate diagram to represent each of the following:

   (i) [XY]   (ii) XY   (iii) [XY   (iv) [YX

5. Write down the length of each of the four line segments shown below:

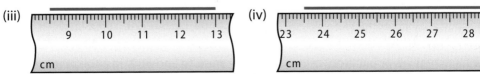

6. In the diagram below, C and D are two points in the line segment [AB].

A   C   D   B

Name a line segment equal in length to

   (i) $|AC| + |CD|$ (ii) $|CD| + |DB|$ (iii) $|AD| - |CD|$

7. The Colosseum in Rome is shown.
   (i) Use your ruler to measure [AB] in centimetres.
   (ii) If the real Colosseum is roughly 1600 times this height, what is the estimated height of the building?
      Give your answer in metres.
      [1 metre = 100 cm]

Section 10.2 Angles

The angle on the right is formed by rotating the line segment [OB] as indicated.
We use the symbol $\angle$ to denote an angle.
Thus $\angle AOB$ is the angle on the right.
It is a measure of the rotation from [OB] to [OA].

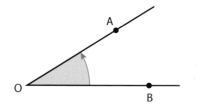

When the hand of a clock moves from one position to another, we say that it has made or generated an **angle**.

When the hand of a clock starts at 12 and does a complete turn and stops again at 12, ...we say that the rotation done is **one complete revolution.**

One complete revolution is divided into 360 parts.

Each part is called a **degree** (written **1°**).

360 degrees is written as 360°.

The Babylonians (2000 BC–1000 BC) loved the number 60 because it had so many factors. They also loved multiples of 60, i.e. 60, 120, 180 240, ...
That is why there are 60 seconds in a minute and 360° in a full revolution.

Naming angles

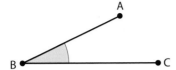

The shaded angle above can be named in three ways, namely

(i) ∠ABC   (ii) ∠CBA   (iii) ∠B

Right angle

A quarter of a revolution is called a **right angle.**
Therefore a right angle is 90°.

We use the symbol ⌐ to denote a right angle.

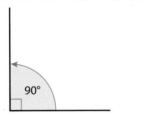

Straight angle

A half a revolution makes a **straight angle** or
two right angles.
A straight angle is 180°.

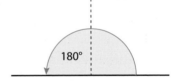

Other angles

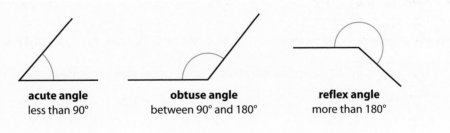

| **acute angle** | **obtuse angle** | **reflex angle** |
| less than 90° | between 90° and 180° | more than 180° |

Ordinary angle

The given diagram shows two angles that can be called ∠AOB.

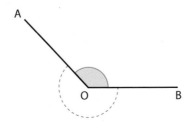

The shaded angle, which is less than 180°, is generally referred to as an **ordinary angle**.

Exercise 10.2

1. Use three letters to name each shaded angle below:

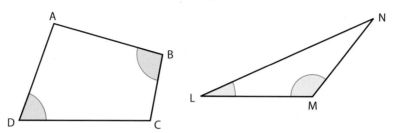

2. Use a single letter to name each shaded angle in the figures above.

3. Use a single letter to name these angles.
   The letters you write down can be arranged to name an important river.
   What is it?

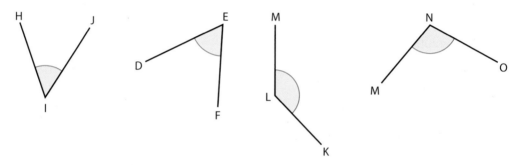

4.

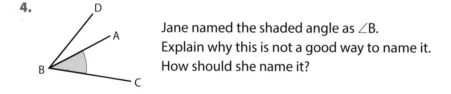

   Jane named the shaded angle as ∠B.
   Explain why this is not a good way to name it.
   How should she name it?

5. Copy and complete the name of each shaded angle in the box below.
   The first letter is done for you. What sentence do they spell?

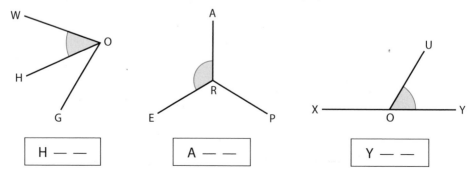

| H — — | | A — — | | Y — — |

6. Describe each of the angles shown below:

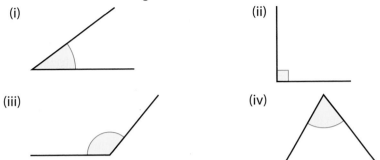

(i)   (ii)

(iii)   (iv)

7. Say if each of the following angles is acute, obtuse or reflex:

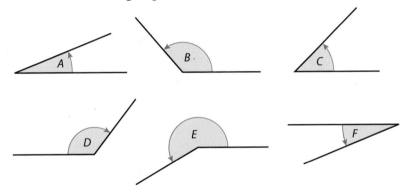

8. If one full turn is 360°, copy and complete the following table:

Fraction of turn	1	$\frac{1}{2}$	$\frac{1}{4}$	$\frac{1}{3}$	$\frac{1}{6}$	$\frac{1}{12}$
Angle (degrees)	360°					

9. What fraction of a complete revolution has the hand of the clock done in each of the following?

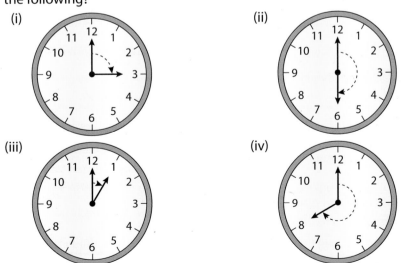

(i)   (ii)

(iii)   (iv)

229

10. How many degrees are there in the indicated angle between the two hands of the clocks in question 9 above?

11. How many degrees does the hand of a clock turn through when it goes from
  (i)   12 to 4
  (ii) 12 to 2
  (iii) 3 to 9
  (iv) 4 to 7
  (v) 5 to 9
  (vi) 2 to 6
  (vii) 2 to 9
  (viii) 3 to 11 ?

12. How many degrees are there in the indicated angle between the two hands in each of these clocks?

(i)

(ii)

(iii)
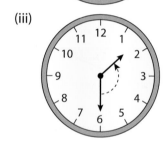

(iv)
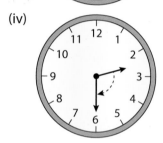

Section 10.3 Calculating angles

Angles on a straight line

Angles on one side of a straight line add up to **180 degrees**.

From the diagram we note:

A, B and D are collinear and so form a straight line. $\therefore \angle ABD = 180°$ $\ldots \therefore =$ therefore

$\Rightarrow x° + 60° = 180°$

then $x° = 180° - 60° = 120°$.

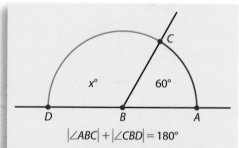

$|\angle ABC| + |\angle CBD| = 180°$

Two angles which add up to 180° are called **supplementary** angles

Any combination of angles on one side of a straight line add up to 180°.

$|\angle A| + |\angle B| + |\angle C| = 180°$

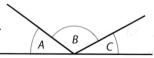

$\ldots |\angle A| =$ **size** of angle A

Angles at a point

Angles at a point form a full rotation (1 revolution) and so add up to 360°.

$$|\angle A| + |\angle B| + |\angle C| + |\angle D| + |\angle E| = 360°$$

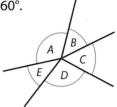

In this diagram, the three given angles add up to 266°.

$$x = 360° - 266°$$
$$\therefore \quad x = 94°$$

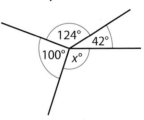

Vertically opposite angles

When two lines intersect, four angles are formed, two pairs of **vertically opposite angles**.
Vertically opposite angles are equal in measure,
$$\angle \boldsymbol{a} = \angle \boldsymbol{b}.$$

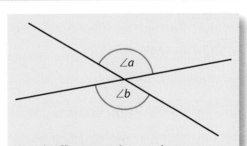

Vertically opposite angles are equal in measure.
$$|\angle a| = |\angle b|$$

Investigation:

Proofs play an important role in geometry.

To prove that,
"Vertically opposite angles are equal".

Complete the following lines using the information in the preceding sections:

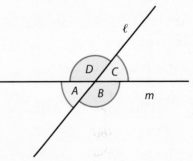

1. $|\angle C| + |\angle D| = 180°$ *because* ....

2. $|\angle A| + |\angle D| = 180°$ *because* ....

3. $\therefore$ ...... = ...

4. $\therefore$ Vertically opposite angles are equal in measure.
Similarly, $|\angle B| = |\angle D|$.

In the given figure,

$|\angle b| = 54°$ ... vertically opposite angles

$|\angle a| = 180° - 54°$ ... angles in a straight line

$\quad\quad = 126°$

$|\angle c| = 126°$ ... vertically opposite angles

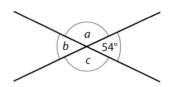

Measuring angles using a protractor

The instrument shown opposite is called a **protractor**.

We use it to measure angles and draw angles of given sizes.

The diagram shows that the size of the angle is 50°.

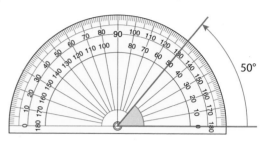

Drawing angles

Draw an angle of 74°.

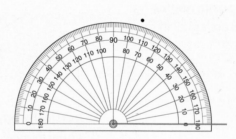

Draw a line.
Mark the vertex of the angle.

Position the protractor as if you were measuring an angle.
Mark a dot at 74°.

Draw a line from the vertex through the dot.

Exercise 10.3

1. Find the size of the angle A in each of the following diagrams:

(i)

(ii)

(iii)

(iv)

2. Find the measure of the angle marked with a letter in each of the following diagrams:

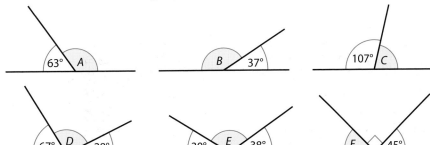

3. Find the value of x in each of the following diagrams:

(i)　　　　　　　　　(ii)　　　　　　　　　(iii)

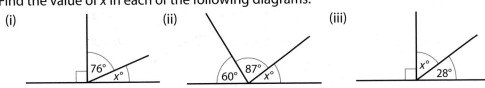

4. Find the size of the angle marked with a letter in each of the following:

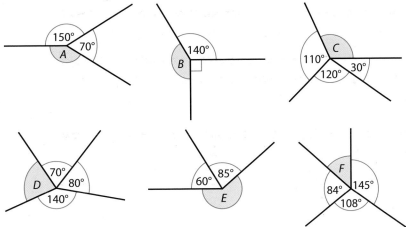

5. Find the value of x in each of the following diagrams:

(i)　　　　　　　　　(ii)　　　　　　　　　(iii)

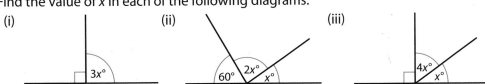

6. Write down the size of the angle marked with a capital letter in each of the following diagrams.

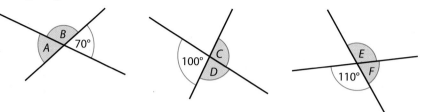

7. In each of the following diagrams, write down the sizes of the angles marked with a letter.

   Give a reason for your answer in each case.

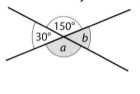
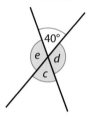
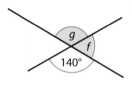

8. Find the value of y in each of the following figures:

   (i)   (ii)   (iii)

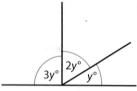
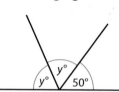
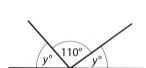

9. Find the value of x in each of these diagrams:

   (i)   (ii)   (iii)

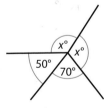
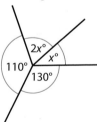
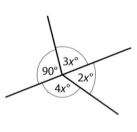

10. Use your protractor to measure these angles:

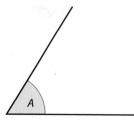

11. Use your protractor to draw angles of measure
    (i) 30°   (ii) 45°   (iii) 75°   (iv) 110°

12. Find the values of
    the angles marked
    A, B and C in the
    given diagram.

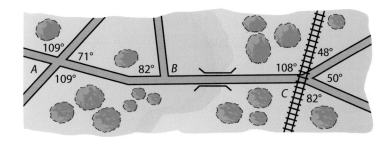

13. Work out the size of the unknown angles.
    Give a reason for each of your answers.

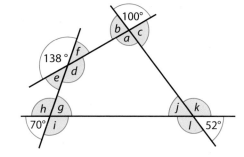

14. A designer is looking at folding stools.

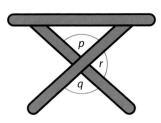

    (i) If angle *p* is 100°, what is angle   (a) *q*   (b) *r*?
    (ii) For safety reasons, angle *p* must be greater than 120°.
         Which one of these statements must be true for
         angle *r*?
         A: The angle *r* must be greater than 60°.
         B: The angle *r* must be less than 60°.
         C: The angle *r* must be equal to 60°.

         Give a reason for your answer.

Section 10.4 Angles and parallel lines _____

The two rails on a railway track are always the same distance apart.

The rail lines are **parallel**.

The lines ℓ and *m* are parallel.

It is written as **ℓ∥m**.

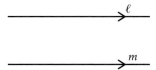

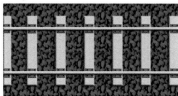

Corresponding angles

The diagram opposite shows a line
m and four other lines parallel to it.

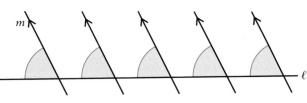

The line *ℓ* crosses each of these lines.

The line *ℓ* is called a **transversal**.

All the pink shaded angles are in
corresponding positions.

These angles are known as **corresponding
angles**.

If you measure these angles, you will find
that they are all equal.

Here are some more corresponding angles.

Each pair is equal in measure.

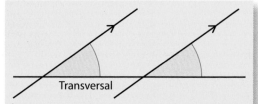

Corresponding angles are equal in
measure.

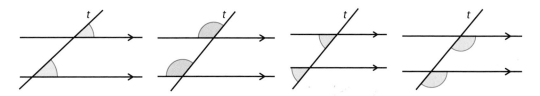

Note: on a diagram parallel lines are indicated by arrows on the lines.

Alternate angles

The diagram on the right shows a line *ℓ* intersecting two
parallel lines *m* and *n*.

The shaded angles are between the parallel lines and on
alternate sides of the line *ℓ*.

These shaded angles are called **alternate angles** and
are equal in size.

Another pair of alternate angles are
shown in the diagram over.

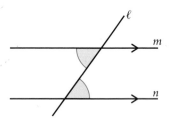

Note: It is also true that if a line *ℓ* crosses two
lines and the alternate angles are equal then
the lines are parallel.

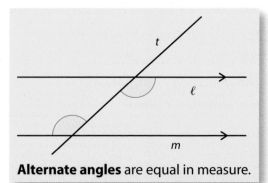

Alternate angles are equal in measure.

In the given diagram, the transversal ℓ intersects the two lines m and n.

The equal alternate angles are marked.

The lines m and n are parallel because the alternate angles are equal.

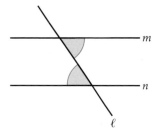

Interior angles

In the given figure, the lines ℓ and m are parallel.

The line t is a transversal.

The shaded angles shown are called **interior angles**.

These angles add to 180°.

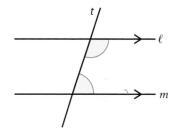

Investigation:

The diagram shows parallel lines ℓ and m with a transversal t.

Investigate why **interior angles** (angles between parallel lines on the same side of a transversal) add up to 180°, by completing the following lines.

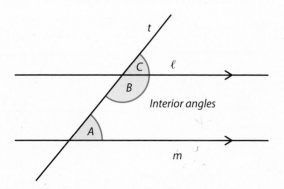

Interior angles

1. $|\angle A| = |\angle C|$ *because.....................................*

2. $|\angle B| + |\angle C| = 180°$ *because ....*

3. $\therefore$ ....= 180°

4. $\therefore$ interior angles add up to 180°.

Example 1

Write down the size of the angles marked with letters.

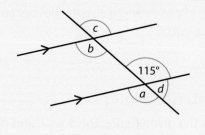

$|\angle a| = 115°$ ... vertically opposite angles

$|\angle b| = 115°$ ... alternate angles

$|\angle c| = 115°$ ... corresponding angles

$|\angle d| + 115° = 180°$ ... angles in a straight line

$|\angle d| = 180° - 115°$

$|\angle d| = 65°$

Exercise 10.4

1. In each of the following diagrams, write down the number of the angle that **corresponds** to the shaded angle:

(i)

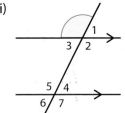

(ii)

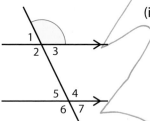

(iii)

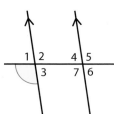

(iv)

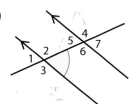

(v)   (vi)

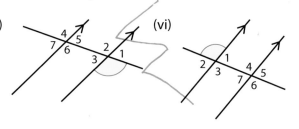

2. Write down the size of the angle marked with a letter in each of the following diagrams:

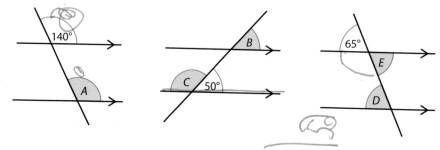

3. In each of the following figures, write down the number of the angle which is **alternate** to the shaded angle:

(i)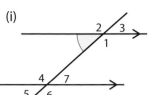

(ii)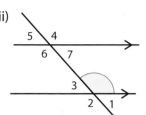

(iii)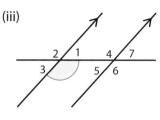

4. ℓ and m are parallel lines. Name

   (i) four pairs of vertically opposite angles

  (ii) two pairs of corresponding angles

 (iii) two pairs of alternate angles.

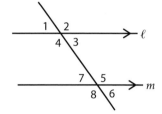

5. Write down the size of the angles marked with letters in the following diagrams:

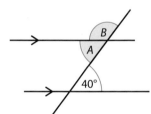

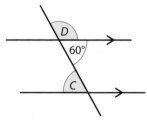

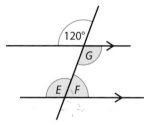

6. Find the size of the lettered angles. Give a reason for each answer.

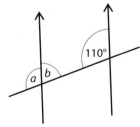

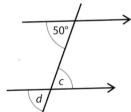

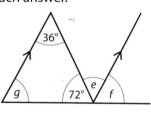

7. In this mechanism, the two bars h and k stay parallel.

Find angles x and y.

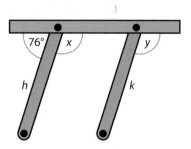

8. Find the size of the angles marked with letters in each of these diagrams:

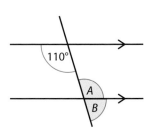
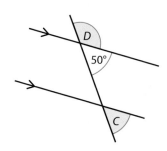
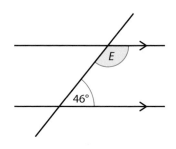

9. This diagram shows a lifting platform.
The top always remains parallel to the base.
  (i) Angle c must not go above 35°.
     Which one of these statements about angle b is true?
     (a) Angle b must be equal to 35°.
     (b) Angle b must be greater than 35°.
     (c) Angle b must be less than or equal to 35°.

 (ii) If angle c must not go above 35°, what can you say about angle a?

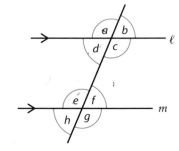

10. In the given diagram, ℓ and m are parallel lines.
Copy and complete these statements to make them true.
  (i) h and ..a.. are corresponding angles.
  (ii) e and ..g.. are vertically opposite angles.
 (iii) e and ..... are alternate angles.
  (iv) e and ..d.. are interior angles.
  (v) b and ..f.. are corresponding angles.
  (vi) b and ..d.. are vertically opposite angles.
 (vii) d and ..c.. are interior angles.
(viii) a and ..e.. are corresponding angles.
  (ix) f and ..h.. are vertically opposite angles.
  (x) d and ..... are alternate angles.

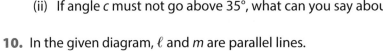

11. A snooker table is shown.

The ball follows a path from A to D.

AB is parallel to CD.

Find the size of the angles marked
V, W, X, Y, and Z.

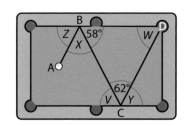

12. The pictures show a gate and a shed door.
Find the angles marked with letters.

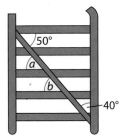

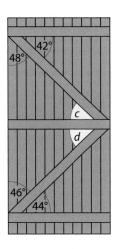

Section 10.5 Drawing parallel and perpendicular lines —

How to draw a line parallel to a given line ————

We use a ruler and set square to draw a line parallel to a given line.
The diagrams below show the steps to be followed.

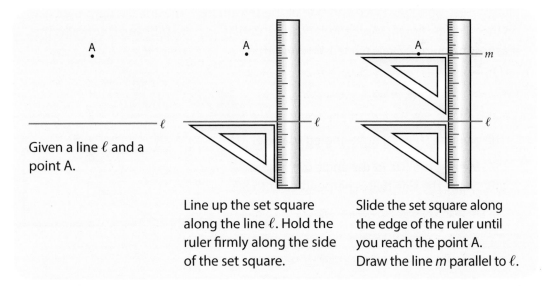

Given a line ℓ and a
point A.

Line up the set square
along the line ℓ. Hold the
ruler firmly along the side
of the set square.

Slide the set square along
the edge of the ruler until
you reach the point A.
Draw the line *m* parallel to ℓ.

ℓ is parallel to *m* is written as ℓ ∥ *m*

Perpendicular lines

The lines ℓ and m intersect to form 4 right angles.

They are said to be **perpendicular** to each other.

It is written $\ell \perp m$.

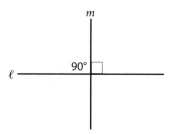

Drawing a line perpendicular to a given line through a given point

Given the line segment [AB] and a point P.

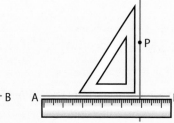

Place a ruler along AB. Place one side of the set square on the ruler, as shown. Move the set square until it reaches the point P. Draw a line ℓ through P.

The line ℓ is perpendicular to [AB] and it contains the point P.

Exercise 10.5

1. The diagram shows a right-angled triangle.

    (i) What is the size of the angle C?

    (ii) Name the side that is perpendicular to BC.

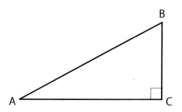

2. (i) Which line is perpendicular to SP?

    (ii) Which lines are perpendicular to PQ?

    (iii) Which line is parallel to QR?

Arrows indicate parallel lines.

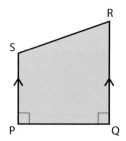

3. The diagram shows a rectangular box.

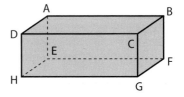

    (i) Name two edges parallel to [AB].

    (ii) Name two edges perpendicular to [HG].

    (iii) How many edges are parallel to [DH]?

    (iv) Name three edges perpendicular to [BF].

4. Examine the diagram on the right and say if
each of the following is true or false:

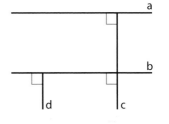

    (i) $a \perp c$ (ii) $b \parallel c$

    (iii) $b \perp d$ (iv) $a \parallel d$

    (v) $d \parallel c$ (vi) $b \perp c$

5. Use a ruler and set square to draw three lines
perpendicular to the line ℓ shown on the right.

6. Copy the following diagrams and draw a line perpendicular to ℓ through the point
P in each case:

7. Copy the diagrams in Question 6 and use your ruler and set square to draw a line
through P parallel to ℓ in each case.

8. The diagram shows the shape ABCDE.

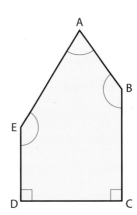

    (i) Name two right angles.

    (ii) What line is perpendicular to [BC]?

    (iii) Name an acute angle.

    (iv) Name an obtuse angle.

    (v) Name two parallel lines.

9. The diagram below shows some local roads near a village.

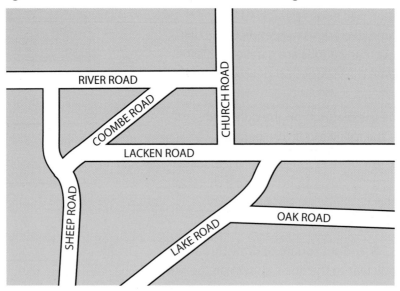

  (i) Which road is parallel to Lacken Road?

  (ii) Which road is perpendicular to River Road?

  (iii) Name two roads perpendicular to Church Road.

10. (i) In each of the following write down one line of algebra connecting the unknown to the information given.

  (ii) Use algebra to find the value of x.

(i)   (ii)   (iii)

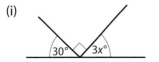   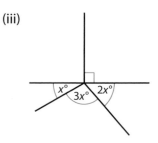

11. Using the information in the diagram write down an equation:

  (i) in terms of y.

  (ii) in terms of x.

      Using the equations in part (i) and (ii) find the value of x and the value of y.

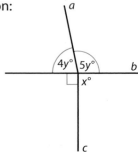

Test yourself 10

1. Name the shaded angles.

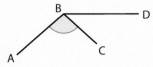 

2. Find the values of *x*, *y* and *z* in these diagrams.

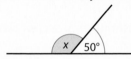 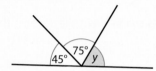

3. Find the size of each angle marked with a letter in the figures below, where the arrows indicate parallel lines:

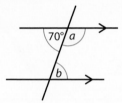 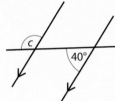 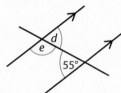

4. Name the parallel lines in this shape.
   Name the perpendicular lines.

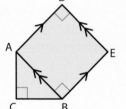

5. How many degrees are there between the two hands of the clock in each of the following?

   (a) 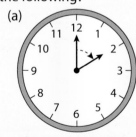 (b) 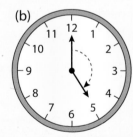 (c)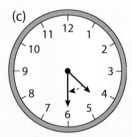

6. Write down the size of the angle marked with a letter in each of the following diagrams, where the arrows indicate parallel lines:

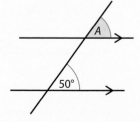 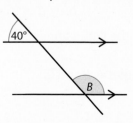 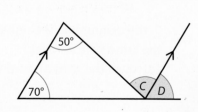

7. Find the values of *a*, *b* and *c* in the following figures:

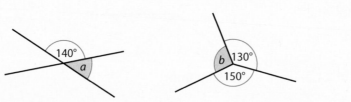

8. Calculate the angles marked with letters on this cot, fishing stool and workbench.

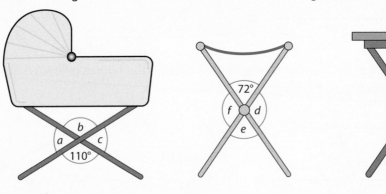

9. In the diagram on the right, the arrows
indicate that the lines are parallel.
Calculate the measures of the
angles *A* and *B*.

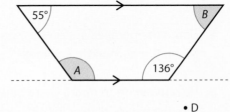

10. Make a copy of this diagram.
Use your ruler and set square to draw
(a) a line through C that is perpendicular to AB
(b) a line through D that is parallel to AB.

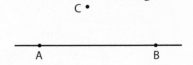

11. Calculate the angles marked with letters in these diagrams:

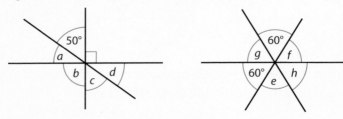

12. In the diagram on the right, the lines containing
the arrows are parallel.
Calculate the sizes of the angles *A*, *B* and *C*.

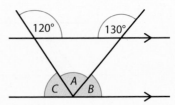

13. Examining the diagram below copy and complete the chart.

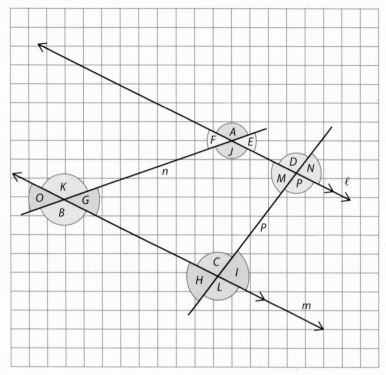

	Pair 1	**Pair 2**
1 pair of parallel lines		
2 pairs of alternate angles		
2 pairs of corresponding angles		
2 pairs of interior angles		
2 pairs of supplementary angles		
2 pairs of vertically opposite angles		

Learning Experience   Unit 10

Assignment 1

At the beginning of the chapter we stated that "there is only one straight line passing through 2 points".

Make a large chart containing the following sets of points. Show on the chart the number of lines that can be drawn through sets of 2, 3, 4 points.

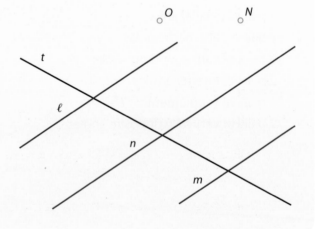

Number of lines = 1   Number of lines = ?   Number of lines = ?

Explain how the patterns of numbers   (i) 1   (ii) $2 + 1$ (iii) $3 + 2 + 1$ are connected to your answers.

Use the pattern of numbers to find the number of lines that can be drawn through 5 points.

Assignment 2

Three parallel lines ℓ, n and m are crossed by a transversal t.

Draw a poster size diagram of these lines and colour code all angles that are equal.

Problem 1

ABCD is a rectangle.

AC is a diagonal line.

If ∠BAĈ = 34°, using your knowledge of parallel and perpendicular lines, explain clearly how to find the size of all the other angles in the diagram.

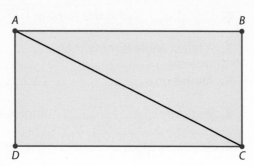

Problem 2

Given AB ‖ CD and AC ‖ BD, copy this diagram and colour code the angles at B, C and D.

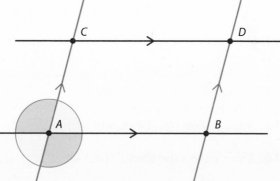

(i)   Using a protractor measure ∠CAB.

(ii) Using your knowledge of interior angles explain how to calculate the size of the angle ∠ACD.

(iii) Using a protractor again check the size of ∠ACD. Explain any inaccuracy that may have occurred.

Chapter 10 review 1

Using the terms from the chapter, copy and complete the following sentences:

1. A line beginning at a point A and ending at a point B is called the
    _____ – _____ [AB].

2. Three points on a straight line are said to be _____.

3. An angle is a measure of _____.

4. A full _____ is also called a complete _____ and
    equals _____ degrees.

5. A 90° angle is called a _____ angle.

6. _____° is the same as half a rotation.

7. A reflex angle is more than _____°.

8. Angles on a _____ _____ add up to 180°.

9. Vertically _____ angles are equal in measure.

10. A _____ is used to measure angles.

11. Parallel lines are always the _____ _____ apart.

12. A line crossing parallel lines is called a _____.

13. A line crossing parallel lines makes alternate and _____ angles.

14. To draw a line parallel to a given line you need a _____ _____ and a _____.

15. If $C \parallel D$ then the lines C and D are_____.

16. If $E \perp F$ then the lines E and F are _____.

Chapter 10 review 2

You should now be able to:

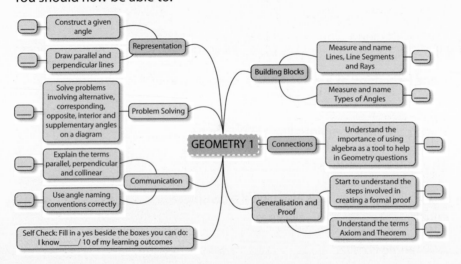

Ratio and Proportion

In this chapter, you will learn to:

- use **ratio**,
- simplify ratios,
- use ratio notation,
- divide in **proportion**,

- recognise **direct proportion**,
- use the **unitary method**,
- recognise **inverse proportion**,
- check for **value for money**.

Section 11.1 Introducing ratio

Below we have one glass of concentrated orange squash and three glasses of water.

They are mixed together to make a diluted orange squash.

We say that the ratio of squash to water is 1 is to 3.

This is written as **1 : 3**.

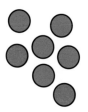

The ratio of blue discs to red discs is 5 : 2.

The ratio of red discs to blue discs is 2 : 5.

From these two statements, you can see that a **ratio** is used to compare one amount with another.

There are 12 boys and 18 girls in a class.

The ratio of boys to girls is 12 : 18.

We can simplify this ratio by dividing each part by 6.

Thus, 12 : 18 simplifies to 2 : 3.

> 12 : 18 = 2 : 3
> .... divide ratio by 6

When you compare two or more quantities, they must be expressed in the same units.

$$4 \text{ days} : 2 \text{ weeks} = 4 \text{ days} : 14 \text{ days}$$
$$= 4 : 14$$
$$= 2 : 7 \quad \text{... 2 is a common factor}$$

> **Important:** the quantities in a ratio must have the same units

---

Example 1

Express the following ratios in their simplest form:
  (i) $21:28$ (ii) $80\,cm:2\,m$ (iii) $€1.25:€5$ (iv) $\frac{1}{2}:\frac{3}{4}$

  (i) $21:28 = 3:4$ ... divide both terms by 7
  (ii) $80\,cm:2\,m = 80:200 = 8:20 = 2:5$
  (iii) $€1.25:€5 = 125:500 = 25:100 = 1:4$
  (iv) $\frac{1}{2}:\frac{3}{4}$ ... Here multiply each term by 4 to make whole numbers

  $$\therefore \quad \frac{1}{2}:\frac{3}{4} = \frac{4}{2}:\frac{3\times 4}{4} = 2:3$$

Exercise 11.1

1. For the tile pattern on the right, find
   (i) the fraction of the pattern that is purple
   (ii) the ratio of purple tiles to white tiles
   (iii) the ratio of white tiles to the total
     number of tiles.

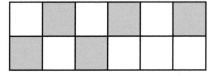

2. Express the shaded area as a ratio of the total area in each of the following diagrams:
   (i) 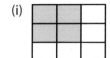   (ii) 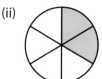   (iii)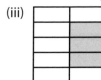

3. In the given group of 10 faces,
   there are 6 SMILERS and 4 GLUMS.
   Write down the missing numbers
   in each of the following:

   (i) For every 3 SMILERS there are ☐ GLUMS.
   (ii) For every 12 SMILERS there are ☐ GLUMS.
   (iii) For every 2 GLUMS there are ☐ SMILERS.
   (iv) For every 6 GLUMS there are ☐ SMILERS.
   (v) For every 20 faces there are ☐ GLUMS.

4. Express each of these ratios in its simplest form:
   (i) $4:2$ (ii) $15:5$ (iii) $2:10$ (iv) $8:24$ (v) $14:21$

5. Write down these ratios in their simplest form:
   (i) $24:16$ (ii) $25:40$ (iii) $30:70$ (iv) $44:110$ (v) $35:63$

6. The recipe on the right gives the ingredients required for
   6 servings of *Lemon Ice Cream*.

   > **Lemon Ice Cream**
   > (makes 6 servings)
   > 10 egg yolks
   > 200 g caster sugar
   > 50 ml lemon juice
   > 400 ml double cream

   (i)   How many egg yolks would be needed for 9 servings?
   (ii) How many ml of lemon juice would be needed for
         3 servings?
   (iii) How many grams of caster sugar would be needed
         for 18 servings?
   (iv) How many ml of double cream would be needed for 9 servings?
   (v)   If 25 eggs yolks were used, how many servings could be made?

7.
   > **Fish Pie**
   > (serves 4)
   > 500 g haddock
   > 400 ml milk
   > 60 g butter
   > 200 ml single cream
   > 2 eggs
   > 800 g potatoes

   The recipe on the left will make a fish pie to serve 4 people.
   (i)   How many grams of haddock are needed to make a fish
         pie for 6 people?
   (ii) How many eggs are needed to make a fish pie for
         12 people?
   (iii) How many grams of potato are needed to make a fish
         pie for 10 people?
   (iv) If a fish pie contains 150 g of butter, how many people
         would it serve?

8. Fill in the missing number in each of these boxes:
   (i) $2:3 = 4:\square$
   (ii) $3:5 = \square:10$
   (iii) $3:\square = 9:12$
   (iv) $2:7 = 6:\square$
   (v) $5:15 = \square:3$
   (vi) $7:\square = 21:9$

9. Express each of the following ratios in its simplest form.
   Change both sides to the same units where necessary.
   (i) $10\,c:50\,c$
   (ii) 5 days : 2 weeks
   (iii) 30 minutes : 2 hours
   (iv) $20\,c:\text{€}1$
   (v)   30 mins : $1\frac{1}{2}$ hours
   (vi) 3 weeks : 7 days

10. In a mixed class, there are 12 girls and 8 boys.
    What is each of the following ratios in its simplest form?
    (i) the number of boys to the number of girls.
    (ii) the number of girls to the total number in the class.

11. A pets' home has 18 dogs, 12 cats, 9 rabbits and 3 mice.
    What is each ratio in its simplest form?
    (i)   mice to cats
    (ii) mice to dogs
    (iii) rabbits to mice
    (iv) cats to the total number of pets.

12. Express each of the following ratios as whole numbers:
    (i) $\frac{1}{2}:2$
    (ii) $\frac{1}{2}:\frac{1}{4}$
    (iii) $\frac{1}{4}:\frac{3}{4}$
    (iv) $\frac{1}{3}:\frac{2}{3}$
    (v) $\frac{3}{4}:1\frac{1}{2}$
    (vi) $1\frac{1}{4}:2$
    (vii) $\frac{3}{5}:\frac{7}{10}$
    (viii) $\frac{2}{5}:\frac{1}{2}$

13. A mortar mix is made by adding sand and cement in the ratio $4:1$.

   (i) If 6 buckets of cement are used, how many buckets of sand are needed?

  (ii) If 10 buckets of sand are used, how many buckets of cement are needed?

 (iii) In a mortar mix, 15 buckets in total were used. How many of these buckets contained cement?

Section 11.2 Dividing in a given ratio

Alan and Barbara share €60 between them in the ratio $2:3$.
How much do they each receive?
The number of shares is $2 + 3 = 5$.
Each share is worth €60 $\div$ 5 = €12.

Alan receives $2 \times$ €12 = €24
Barbara receives $3 \times$ €12 = €36

Alan gets $\frac{2}{5}$ and Barbara gets $\frac{3}{5}$.

$2:5$ is a ratio, $\frac{2}{5}, \frac{3}{5}$ are proportions.

$$2:3 = \frac{2}{2+3}, \frac{3}{2+3} = \frac{2}{5}, \frac{3}{5}$$
Ratio $\longrightarrow$ **Proportion**

Example 1

Divide €900 between A, B and C in the ratio $4:3:2$.

$4 + 3 + 2 = 9$, so we make 9 divisions of the money.   Each division is $\frac{1}{9}$ of the total.

A gets $\frac{4}{9}$ of €900 $= \frac{4}{9} \times \frac{900}{1} =$ €400

B gets $\frac{3}{9}$ of €900 $= \frac{3}{9} \times \frac{900}{1} =$ €300

C gets $\frac{2}{9}$ of €900 $= \frac{2}{9} \times \frac{900}{1} =$ €200 $\therefore$ A gets €400; B gets €300; C gets €200.

Example 2

In a school, the ratio of boys to girls is $6:5$.
If there are 325 girls in the school, find the number of pupils in the school.

Boys : Girls $= 6:5$, so $\frac{6}{11}$ of the total are boys and $\frac{5}{11}$ are girls

$\therefore$ $\frac{5}{11} = 325$

    $\frac{1}{11} = 65$

    $\frac{11}{11} = 715$ $\therefore$ there are 715 pupils in the school.

Exercise 11.2

1. Anna and Billy share €90 between them in the ratio 2:3.
   (i) What fraction of the €90 does Anna get?
   (ii) What fraction of the €90 does Billy get?
   (iii) How much money does each of them get?

2. Divide a prize of €400 between Claire and Dara in the ratio 5:3.

3. A box of 40 chocolates had milk and dark chocolates in the ratio 2:3. How many were milk chocolates?

4. Pat is 6 years old and Emer is 3 years old. Divide 36 sweets between them in the ratio of their ages.

5. (i) Divide €120 in the ratio 3:1 (ii) Divide €714 in the ratio 3:4.
   (iii) Divide €121 in the ratio 6:5 (iv) Divide €106.50 in the ratio 7:3.
   (v) Divide €864 in the ratio 5:4 (vi) Divide 1 hour 30 mins in the ratio 9:1.

6. Divide €1400 between three people in the ratio 4:2:1.

7. There are 90 pupils in first-year. The ratio of girls to boys is 5:4. How many boys are there in first-year?

8. A farmer had all his farm under two crops, beet and barley, in the ratio 3:4. If his farm consisted of 91 acres, how many acres were under each crop?

9. A prize is divided between A and B in the ratio 5:2. If A gets €165, find the total prize fund.

10. The ratio of nurses to doctors in a hospital is 7:1. If there are 91 nurses on the staff, find the number of doctors.

11. In a rectangle, the ratio of length to width is 5:2.

28 cm

If the width is 28 cm, find the length.

12. The ratio of males to females in the crowd at a rock concert is 5:4. There are 360 males in the crowd. How many females are there?

13. The ratio of girls to boys on a school trip is 5 : 4.
Find the numbers of girls when there are these numbers of pupils:
- (i) 56 boys
- (ii) 72 boys
- (iii) 189 pupils altogether

14. Mortar that is used for interior walls is a mixture of sand,
lime and cement in the ratio of 6 : 2 : 1.

- (i) How much sand is needed to make 60 kg of mortar?
- (ii) How much lime is needed to make 45 kg of mortar?
- (iii) To mix an amount of mortar, Tom uses 6 bucketfuls
  of lime. How many bucketfuls of sand will he need?

15. On a Saturday, the football results gave a ratio of home wins to away wins to draws
of 6 : 2 : 1. If there were 10 away wins, how many home wins were there and how
many draws were there?

16. A prize fund is divided between *A*, *B* and *C* in the ratio 7 : 4 : 1.
If *B* receives €960, find the value of the total prize fund.

17. For a football team, the ratio of goals scored at home games to goals scored at
away games was 3 : 2.
- (i) If the team scored 45 goals, how many of them did they score at home?
- (ii) In a full season, the team scored 24 goals in away games.
  How many goals did they score at home?

18. Sally makes breakfast cereal by mixing bran, currants and wheatgerm in the ratio
8 : 3 : 1 by mass.
- (i) How much bran does she use to make 600 g of the cereal?
- (ii) One day she only has 20 g of currants.
  How much cereal can she make? She has plenty of bran and wheatgerm.

19. Alan is 12 years old and Emer is 8 years old.
€5400 is divided between them in the ratio of their ages.
How much does each receive?
In eight years time, another €5400 will be divided between them in the ratio of
their ages at that time. How much will they each receive then?

20. Two squares and their perimeters are shown.

- (i) Write down the ratio of the lengths of their sides.
- (ii) Work out the ratio of their areas.

Perimeter
= 20 cm

Perimeter
= 28 cm

21. Three quarters of the junior members of a tennis club are boys and the rest are girls.
What is the ratio of boys to girls among the members?

22. First-year and second-year pupils are in an assembly.

The given table shows some facts about these pupils.

Year	boys : girls	Pupil data
1	4 : 5	84 boys
2	2 : 3	150 pupils

Work out the total number of girls in the assembly.

Section 11.3 Proportion

As stated in the last two sections **ratio** compares **part to part**, while **proportion** compares **part to whole**.

In the given figure, there are 4 red squares and 5 blue squares

The ratio of red to blue squares is written as 4 : 5.

The total number of squares is 9.

The proportion of red squares is $\frac{4}{9}$.

The proportion of blue squares is $\frac{5}{9}$.

> You can write a proportion as a fraction, decimal or percentage.

Example 1

In a football match, *Rovers* had 25 shots at goal with 17 on target.
City had 20 shots at goal with 13 on target.
  (i)   Write the proportion of shots on target for each team as a fraction and as a decimal.
 (ii)   Which team seems to be more accurate?
(iii)   Which did you find more useful, fraction or decimal, when answering part (ii)?

 (i) *Rovers*:   fraction $= \frac{17}{25}$; decimal $= \frac{17 \times 4}{25 \times 4} = \frac{68}{100} = 0.68$

     City: fraction $= \frac{13}{20}$; decimal $= \frac{13 \times 5}{20 \times 5} = \frac{65}{100} = 0.65$

 (ii) As 0.68 is greater than 0.65, *Rovers* seem to be more accurate.
(iii) Decimals are more useful as it is usually much easier to compare decimals than compare fractions.

Direct proportion

If   1 apple costs 80 cent,
     2 apples cost €1.60,
     3 apples cost €2.40.

Apples
80c each

Here we can see that the number of apples and the prices increase in the same ratio, that is, they are **directly proportional**.

Similarly, if   9 kg of potatoes cost €5.67,

  1 kg costs €5.67 ÷ 9 = €0.63,

  5 kg cost €0.63 × 5 = €3.15.

In this example, we found the cost of 1 kg first and then found the cost of 5 kg.
This method is generally called **the unitary method**.

Example 2

If a car travels 120 km on 9 litres of petrol, find
  (i) how far it will travel on 15 litres at the same rate of consumption
  (ii) how many litres will be required for a journey of 280 km.

(i) 9 litres do 120 km

  1 litre does $\dfrac{120}{9}$ km

  15 litres do $\dfrac{120}{\cancel{9}_{3}} \times \dfrac{\cancel{15}^{5}}{1} = \dfrac{120 \times 5}{3} = 200$ km

  ∴   the car travels 200 km on 15 litres

> Here we require km in our answer, so we keep km last.

(ii) 120 km require 9 litres

  1 km requires $\dfrac{9}{120}$ litres

  280 km require $\dfrac{9}{120} \times \dfrac{280}{1} = \dfrac{9 \times 280}{120} = 21$ litres

  ∴   21 litres are required for 280 km.

> Here we require litres, so litres are last.

Example 3

The number of pages in a magazine increased from 54 to 72.
The price increased in the same ratio.
If the old price was €3.60, what is the new price?

Here we are looking for 'price', so we keep price last.

  54 pages cost   €3.60

  1 page costs $\dfrac{€3.60}{54}$

  72 pages cost $\dfrac{3.60 \times \cancel{72}^{8}}{\cancel{54}_{6}} = \dfrac{3.60 \times \cancel{8}^{4}}{\cancel{6}_{3}} = \dfrac{14.40}{3} = €4.80$

  ∴   the new price is €4.80.

Remember proportions can be read in two directions.

e.g. **A**: Eoin earns €55 for 5 hours work, can also be read as,
    B: for 5 hours work Eoin earns €55 (the first line reversed).

When answering questions using proportion it is good practice to keep the quantity required, last on the line as follows:

A: Eoin earns €55 for 5 hours work.

Question: **How many hours** does he need to work to earn €100?

For **€55** Eoin needs to work 5 hours

For **€1** Eoin needs to work $\frac{5}{55}$ hours

For **€100** Eoin needs to work $100 \times \frac{5}{55}$ h

$$= 9\frac{1}{11} \text{ hours}$$

B: For 5 hours work Eoin earns €55.

Question: **How much money** would Eoin earn if he worked 9 hours?

For **5 hours** of work he earns €55.

for **1 hour** of work he earns $\frac{55}{5} = €11$

for **9 hours** of work he earns $9 \times €11$

$$= €99$$

Exercise 11.3

1. (i) What is the ratio of blue discs to red discs?
   (ii) What proportion of the discs are red?
        Give the answer as a fraction.
   (iii) What proportion of the discs are blue? Give the answer as a percentage.

2. There were 10 accidents on a busy road last month.
   7 were car accidents and 3 were cycle accidents.

   (i) Give the proportion of car accidents as a fraction.
   (ii) Give the proportion of cycle accidents as a percentage.
   (iii) What is the ratio of car to cycle accidents?

3. The table shows the choices made by a class of 30 pupils going on a school trip.

   (i) Copy and complete the table.
   (ii) What proportion of boys want to go bowling?
   (iii) What proportion of girls want to go bowling?
   (iv) What proportion of pupils want to go bowling?

	Boys	Girls	Total
Bowling	9	12	
Cinema	3	6	
Total			30

(v) What proportion of pupils going bowling are girls?

(vi) Is bowling more popular among boys or girls?

4. The bar chart shows the number of A-grades achieved by a class of 24 pupils.

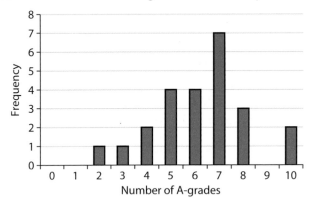

(i) What proportion of the pupils achieved exactly 5 A-grades?
Give your answer as a fraction in its simplest form.

(ii) What proportion of the pupils achieved 5 or more A-grades?
Give your answer as a fraction in its simplest form.

(iii) What is the ratio of pupils achieving 5 A-grades to pupils achieving other results?

5. The tables below show pairs of values of x and y.
Which tables show x and y in direct proportion?

(i)

x	1	2	3
y	3	6	9

(ii)

x	1	3	5
y	7	9	12

(iii)

x	4	12	20
y	2	6	10

6. Copy and complete these tables so that x and y are in direct proportion.

(i)

x	5	7	9
y	10		

(ii)

x	8	9	
y	24		33

(iii)

x	10	18	
y		9	15

7. If seven books cost €55.30, find the cost of nine books.

8. If 8 litres of milk cost €7.36, find the cost of 11 litres.

9. If 3 m of cloth cost €23.55, find the cost of 7 m.

10. If 12 m² of carpet cost €516, find the cost of 16 m².

11. A car travels 100 km on 8 litres of petrol. How far will it travel on 20 litres?

12. A recipe for making 12 scones requires 360 g of flour.
How many grams of flour are needed for 9 scones?

13. Lilian earns €45 for 5 hours work.
   (i)   What would she earn in 18 hours?
   (ii) How many hours would she have to work to earn €207?

14. A car can travel 80 km on 6 litres of petrol.
   How far can it travel on (i) 21 litres and (ii) 9 litres ?

15. Franco uses this recipe to make pizzas for 4 people.
   He wants to make pizzas for 10 people.
   (i)   What quantity of cheese does he need?
   (ii) How many tomatoes does he need?
   (iii) What quantity of bacon does he require?

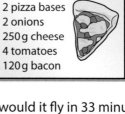

Pizza
2 pizza bases
2 onions
250 g cheese
4 tomatoes
120 g bacon

16. A small plane flies 80 km in 15 minutes.
   (i)   How long will it take to fly 400 km?   (ii)   How far would it fly in 33 minutes?

17. A vehicle can travel 100 km on €12 worth of petrol.
   (i)   How much would the petrol cost for a journey of 350 km?
   (ii) How many km would the vehicle travel on €30?

18. A model car is made to a scale of 1 : 50.
   (i)   The model has a length of 10 cm.
         Calculate the length of the real car.
         Give your answer in metres.
   (ii) The real car has a height of 1.75 m. Calculate the height of the model car.

19. A secretary can type 320 words in 8 minutes.
   (i)   At the same rate, how many words would she type in 10 minutes?
   (ii) How long would it take her to type 180 words?

Section 11.4 **Conversion graphs**

A conversion graph is used to change one quantity into an equivalent quantity.

For example (i) kilometres to miles (ii) degrees Celsius to degrees Fahrenheit
          (iii) US dollars to euro.
Some conversions are examples of **direct proportion** and if plotted produce straight
line graphs through (0, 0).

Example 1

The graph shows the relationship between degrees Celsius and degrees Fahrenheit.

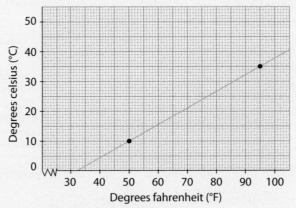

Use the graph to convert approximately:

(i) 35°C to °Fahrenheit   (ii) 50°F to °Celsius

If the temperature in New York on a particular day ranges between 55° F and 99°F, express this range in °C.

(i) 35°C = 95°F   (ii) 50°F = 10°C

Range of 55°F to 99°F = 13°C to 37°C

Exercise 11.4

1. The graph below shows the relationship between kilometres and miles.

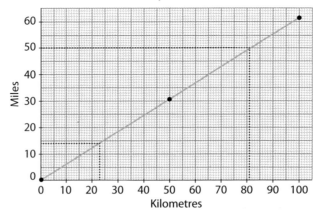

Use the graph to convert (approximately) (i) 60 km to miles   (ii) 30 miles to km

(a) If the speed limit in Northern Ireland is 40 miles per hour (mph), express this in kilometres per hour (km/h)

(b) If a car was travelling at 100 mph use the graph to covert this speed to km/h.

2. You can use this conversion graph to change measurements from inches to centimetres.

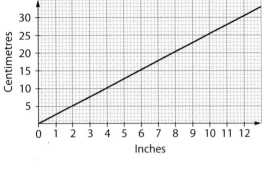

(i) Change 7 inches to centimetres.

(ii) How many inches are there in 25 centimetres?

(iii) Use information from the graph to change 36 inches to centimetres.

(iv) Use the information from the graph to change 80 centimetres to inches.

3. Shown here is the conversion graph between gallons and litres.

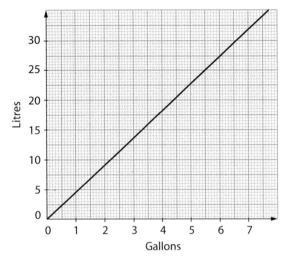

(i) How many litres are equivalent to 6 gallons?

(ii) How many gallons are equivalent to 20 litres?

(iii) Use the information from the graph to express 18 gallons in litres.

4. A graph of the charges made for units of electricity used in the home is shown.

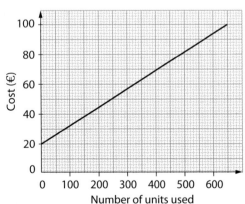

(i) What is the cost of using 400 units of electricity?

(ii) What is the cost of using 540 units of electricity?

(iii) How many units are used if the bill is €60?

(iv) How many units are used if the bill is €100?

(v) Why do you think the graph starts at €20 on the cost axis?

5. The following is a conversion graph between kilograms (kg) and pounds (lb).

Use the graph to convert:
  (i)   20 lb to kilograms
  (ii) 10 lb to kilograms
  (iii) 4 kg to pounds
  (iv) $6\frac{1}{2}$ kg to pounds.

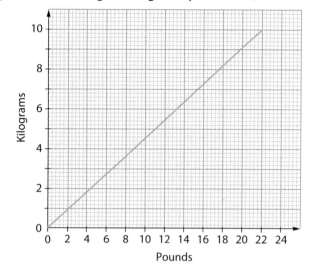

Investigation:

In some questions above there is a **direct proportion** between the variables in the graphs.

In these cases, there is a **constant of proportionality**, which can be used to quickly convert from e.g., kg to pounds or pounds to kg etc.

This constant allows us to say "to convert from kg to pounds .... by
.... "

By studying the graphs find the constants of proportionality for each of the following conversions:

  (i)   kg to pounds   (ii) pounds to kg
  (iii) litres to gallons   (iv) gallons to litres
  (v)   kilometres to miles   (vi) miles to kilometres.

Make a chart of your results.

6. The lines on the graph below show the lengths of two elastic strips when different weights are hung from them.

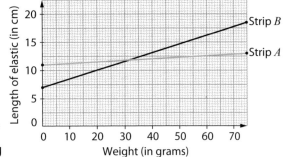

(i) What is the unstretched length of strip *A*?

(ii) What is the extended length of strip *B* when 65 grams are hung from it?

(iii) What weight produces the same length in both strips?

(iv) When 50 g is hung from both strips, what is the difference in their length?

(v) By what percentage is the length of strip *B* increased when a weight of 25 gram is hung from it?
Give your answer correct to the nearest whole number.

7. This is the conversion graph between °C and °F.

(i) Express 30°C in °F.

(ii) Express 50°F in °C.

(iii) Express 44°C in °F.

(iv) Express 90°F in °C.

(v) Use the information from the graph to convert 150°F to °C.
(It is very important to note that the graph does **not** start at 0°F)

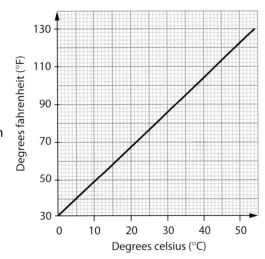

8. (i) Use the graph to convert
   (a) 4 pints to litres
   (b) 3.5 pints to litres
   (c) 1.7 pints to litres

(ii) Use the graph to convert
   (a) 3 litres to pints
   (b) 1.5 litres to pints
   (c) 0.9 litres to pints

Use the graph to help you convert 15 pints to litres.

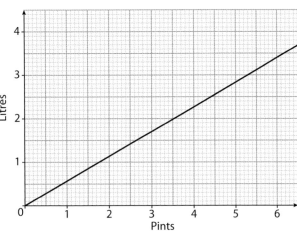

Investigation:

Obtain a sheet of paper in each of the sizes: A3, A4 and A5.

Investigate: (i) How the *areas* of the sheets are related. Give your answer as a ratio.

(ii) The ratio of the *length* to the *width* of each size. What do you find?

Section 11.5 Inverse proportion – Value for money _____

1. Inverse proportion ───────────────

If a car travels at a steady speed of 50 km/h, it will take 4 hours to travel 200 km.

As the chart shows on the right, as the speed increases the time for the journey decreases.

If the car travels at 100 km/h it will do the same journey in 2 hours.

This is an example of **inverse proportion** where an increase in one quantity causes a proportional **decrease** in another quantity or vice versa.

Speed	Distance	Time
50 km/h	200 km	$\frac{200}{50} = 4\,h$
60 km/h	200 km	$\frac{200}{60} = 3\frac{1}{3}\,h$
70 km/h	200 km	$\frac{200}{70} = 2\frac{6}{7}\,h$
80 km/h	200 km	$\frac{200}{80} = 2\frac{1}{2}\,h$
90 km/h	200 km	$\frac{200}{90} = 2\frac{2}{9}\,h$
100 km/h	200 km	$\frac{200}{100} = 2\,h$

Example 1

If 9 men can complete a job in 8 days, how long will it take 6 men to do the job if they work at the same rate?

(Here we are looking for time, so we keep time last.)

9 men can do the job in 8 days

1 man can do the job in 72 days   ... 9 times as long

6 men can do the job in $\frac{72}{6} = 12$ days   ... $\frac{1}{6}$ as long as 1 man

---

2. Best buys

When shopping we often have to make choices between products which are packed in various sizes and priced differently. If we want to buy the item which gives the **better value for money**, we must compare prices using the same units.

Example 2

Peanut butter is available in small or large jars, as shown.
Which size is the better value for money?

We compare the price per gram for each size.

Small: Price per gram $= \dfrac{€1.95}{250} = 0.78$ cent

Large: Price per gram $= \dfrac{€3.18}{454} = 0.7$ cent

The large size is cheaper per gram and so is better value.

Exercise 11.5

1. Here are two bags of potatoes at a supermarket.

  (i) Work out the cost of 1 kg in the Family Pack.

  (ii) Work out the cost of 1 kg in the Value Pack.

  (iii) Which pack gives you more for your money?

2. Which box gives the best value?

3. A standard bottle of mineral water contains 1.5 litres and costs €1.92.
A large bottle contains 2.5 litres and costs €3.

  (i) What is the cost of one litre of water in the standard bottle?

  (ii) What is the cost of one litre in the large bottle?

(iii) In which bottle does the water work out cheaper?

(iv) Why might you prefer to buy the standard bottle?

4. A whole foods store sells ground almonds in four sizes:

   S: 200 g for €1.80   *M:* 300 g for €2.30   *L:* 500 g for €4.10   *XL:* 800 g for €7.00

   Find the cost for 100 g in each size and decide which works out cheapest.

5. *Asco* bath lotion is sold in two sizes.

   The large size contains 400 ml and costs €3.

   The family size contains 1000 ml and costs €6.80.

   Which size is the best value for money?

   You must show your working.

6. Which of the two bottles of 'Active' drinks gives the better value for money?

7. Toothpaste is sold in small, medium and large sizes.

   The small size contains 75 ml and costs €2.40.

   The medium size contains 125 ml and costs €3.50.

   The large size contains 180 ml and costs €4.68.

   Which size is the best value for money?

8. Fill in the missing numbers in the following lines:

   4 men take 6 days to build a wall.

   1 man takes ☐ days

   3 men take ☐ days.

9. If 6 men build a wall in 3 days, how long would it take

   (i) 1 man   (ii) 3 men to build the wall?

10. Three women can complete a house-to-house survey in 15 days.

    How long would it take five women working at the same rate to complete the job?

11. When a dog eats 200 g of dogfood each day, a container lasts him 10 days.

    How long would a container last him if he eats

    (i) 100 g per day   (ii) 400 g per day   (iii) 250 g per day?

12. A shopkeeper has enough money to buy 60 books at €9 each.
    If the price of the books was increased to €12, how many of them could she buy for the same amount of money?

13. A motorist driving 80 km per day has enough petrol to last her 9 days. If she reduces her driving to 45 km per day, how long will the petrol last?

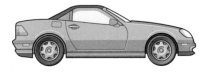

14. Five women can complete a computer assignment in 12 days.
    How long would it take
    (i) Ten women   (ii) Three women to complete the assignment?

15. Three painters can paint an office block in 12 days.
    (i) How long would it take four painters to paint the block?
    (ii) If the office block had to be painted in 3 days, how many painters would be needed?

16. It takes 5 lorries 18 days to remove the topsoil for an extension to a motorway.
    (i) How long would it take 15 lorries to remove the topsoil?
    (ii) How many lorries would be needed to remove the topsoil in 10 days?

17. A poultry farmer has enough corn to feed 30 hens for 9 days.
    (i) How long would the corn last 15 hens?
    (ii) How many hens could be fed with the corn for 6 days?

18. Tap *A* can fill a bath in 12 minutes.
    Tap *B* can fill it in 6 minutes.
    (i) What fraction of the bath does tap *A* fill in 1 minute?
    (ii) What fraction of the bath does tap *B* fill in 1 minute?
    (iii) If both taps are working together, what fraction of the bath will they fill in 1 minute?
    (iv) How long will it take both taps working together to fill the bath?

Test yourself 11

1. Express each of these ratios in its simplest form:
   (i) $5:30$ (ii) $6:9$ (iii) $20:30$ (iv) $21:28$ (v) $24:16$

2. Ava and Barry share €90 between them in the ratio $7:2$.
   (i) What fraction of the €90 does Ava get?
   (ii) What fraction of the €90 does Barry get?
   (iii) How much money does each of them get?

3. (i) What proportion of the given figure is shaded?
      Give your answer as a fraction.
   (ii) What is the ratio of the shaded area to the total
      area of the square?
   (iii) If the area of the shaded portion is 36 cm², find the area of the whole square.

4. Darina uses this recipe to make apple crumble.
   She wants to make it for 10 people.
   (i) How much flour does she need?
   (ii) How much butter does she need?
   (iii) How many apples does she need?

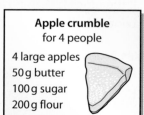

Apple crumble
for 4 people

4 large apples
50 g butter
100 g sugar
200 g flour

5. Mr Brown makes some compost.
   He mixes soil, manure and leaf mould in the ratio $3:1:1$.
   Mr Brown makes 75 litres of compost.
   How many litres of soil does he use?

6. The ratio of elephants to tigers in a safari park is $5:4$.
   If there are 300 elephants in the park, how many tigers are there?

7. A prize fund is divided between A and B in the ratio $5:2$.
   If A gets €330, find the total prize fund.

8. If 7 kg of meat cost €64.75, find the cost of 9 kg of the meat.

9. *Ecowash* washing liquid can be bought in four sizes.

Large 3 litre	Standard 1 litre	Economy 1.5 litre	Travel 0.5 litre
€6.48	€2.28	€3.39	€1.55

   (i) Find the cost of 1 litre for each size.
   (ii) Write the sizes in order of price per litre, the cheapest first.

10. €900 is divided between Sarah, Jack and Ciara in the ratio $1:2:3$.
    How much does each receive?

11. A tin of biscuits contains enough for 12 people if each person eats 6 biscuits. If the
    same number of biscuits was divided among 8 people, how many would each receive?

12. (i) What proportion of this figure is red?
Give your answer as a percentage.
(ii) Express the ratio red : green in its lowest terms.

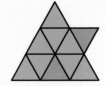

13. Write down the missing numbers for each of these ratios:

(i) $3 : 5 = 9 : \square$ (ii) $3 : \square = 9 : 21$ (iii) $\square : 4 = 3 : 12$

14.

Mortar is made by mixing 5 parts by weight of sand with 1 part by weight of cement.
(i) How many kg of sand is in 90 kg of mortar?
(ii) If there are 100 kg of sand in the mortar, how many kg of cement does it contain?

15. A car travels 110 km on 8 litres of diesel.
How far will it travel on 20 litres?

16. The three angles of this triangle are in the ratio 4 : 3 : 2.
Find the sizes of the three angles.

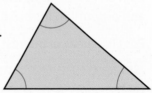

17. On a full tank of petrol of 40 litres, a van completed 420 kilometres.
(i) What distance would you expect the van to complete with 22 litres of petrol in the tank?
(ii) How many litres of petrol would you need to travel 630 kilometres?

18. A 500 g packet of *Healthy Flakes* costs €3.20.
A 750 g packet of *Healthy Flakes* costs €4.50.
Which size packet is the better buy?
Show all your calculations and explain your answer clearly.

19. This packet of sugar cubes costs €1.92.

How much would you expect to pay for this packet?

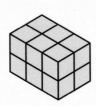

20. The graph shows the relationship
between the voltage, *V*, and the current,
I, in an electrical experiment.

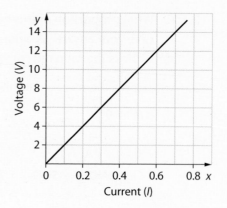

   (i)   Is there a direct proportion between
         Current and Voltage? Explain your answer.
   (ii) What is the current if the voltage is 10v?
   (iii) What would the current be if the voltage
         was 20 volts?

Learning Experience   Unit 11

Assignment 1

Collect 4 sets of data from your maths class and present your results in ratio
and proportion form. E.g. **Ratio**, girls to boys = 4 : 5. **Proportion** $\frac{4}{9}$ girls, $\frac{5}{9}$ boys.

Possible areas of interest are suggested in the table below.

Student homework	Students who do more than 1 hour homework.	Students who do less than 1 hour of homework.
Siblings in school	Siblings in school	No siblings in school.
Sport	Actively involved in sport.	Not actively involved in sport.
Social Media	Have a social media account.	Do not have a social media account.

The areas above are general suggestions only.

Assignment 2

Pick any *two* items of food prepared in the kitchen,
e.g. bread, buns, cake, etc., write the ingredients on a chart as a **ratio**.

	Ingredient 1 : Ingredient 2 : Ingredient 3 : Ingredient 4 : Ingredient 5
Food 1	? : ? : ? : ? : ?
Food 2	: : : :

Problem 1

Using *direct* and *inverse proportion*, find how long it takes 1 man to plough 1 field, given that it takes 5 men 5 days to plough 5 fields.

Present your answer by copying and completing the table format as follows:

Men	Days	Fields	Type of proportion
5 men	5 Days	5 fields	
1 man	?	5 fields	?
1 man	?	1 field	?

Problem 2

A car with five tyres (four road tyres and a spare) travelled 30 000 km. All five tyres were used equally.

Explain why each tyre received 24 000 km of wear.

Chapter 11 review 1

Using the terms from the chapter, copy and complete the following sentences:

1. Ratios compare _____ to _____ of the quantity.

2. Proportions compare _____ to _____ of any quantity.

3. Ratios can be simplified by dividing by a _____ _____.

4. The same _____ must be used when comparing two quantities using ratios.

5. When dividing any quantity in ratio, first find the total number of _____ needed.

6. It is easier to compare proportions when they are given as _____s.

7. To change from one quantity (10 kg) of a substance to a different quantity (3 kg) of a substance, we use the _____ _____, i.e. we find _____ kg first.

8. A direct proportion when plotted produces a _____-_____ graph through the _____.

9. We deal with two types of proportion, direct and _____ proportion.

Chapter 11 review 2

You should now be able to:

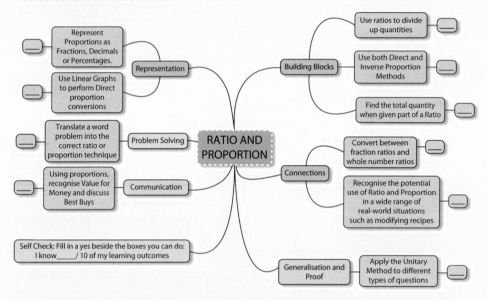

In this chapter, you will learn to:

- plan a **survey**,
- use a **pilot** survey
- collect **data**,
- identity **numerical data**,
- identity **categorical data**,

- understand **populations**,
- write **questionnaires**,
- get a simple **random sample**,
- understand **bias** in sampling,
- get **representative samples**.

Section 12.1 Collecting data – Surveys and Experiments

Television has become a large part of many people's lives.
Lots of questions could be asked about people's attitudes to TV.

- What programmes do thirteen year-olds like best?
- How much TV do children under six watch each day?
- What percentage of households watch TV during meal-time?

To answer these questions, you would need to do a **survey**.

A **survey** is a way of finding information from people for a particular purpose. It involves

- asking questions
- recording what people say
- presenting the information in a way that makes it easy to understand.

Companies will sometimes ask their customers to complete a questionnaire. They can then use the information to find ways in which they can improve the service that they offer.

Planning a survey

Before you begin a survey, you need to plan it carefully using these steps.

1. **What do you want to find out?**

   You must have a clear idea of the purpose of the survey and what you want to find out.

   Example How much pocket money do first-year pupils get each week?

2. **Decide what data you need to collect.**

   Example In relation to the pocket money from the question above, you need to give amounts of money that the pupils receive in the response boxes.

   > Data is information that you or somebody else collects.

   These could be the choices that are given:

   €1– €5 ☐   €5– €10 ☐   €10– €15 ☐   More than €15 ☐

   Always ask questions that will give answers that are suitable to work with.
   Keep the questions simple and clear.
   Avoid anything too personal.
   Do not ask too many questions.

3. **Decide where to collect the data from and how much to collect.**

   Example When dealing with the amount of pocket money first-year pupils get each week, you must decide on
   - the number of pupils you want to survey
   - where you will find these pupils so that you get a result that will adequately represent all first-year pupils.

Collecting data

When data is being collected for simple surveys, a **data collection sheet** or **tally chart** is generally used.

Here is a tally chart from a traffic survey.

Type of vehicle	Tally	How many
Bus	ЖЖ ЖЖ ІІ	12
Car	ЖЖ ЖЖ ЖЖ ЖЖ ІІ	22
Lorry	ЖЖ ІІ	7
Van	ЖЖ ЖЖ І	11
Motorcycle	ЖЖ ЖЖ ЖЖ	15

> ЖЖ represents 5.

Types of Data

1. **Numerical data**

   Data which can be counted or measured is called **numerical data** because the data collected is in number form.

   Examples of numerical data:

   (i) The number of goals scored by a team in each of their matches over a season.

   (ii) The number of rooms in a house.

   (iii) The number of students in a school / class.

   (iv) The temperature at the seaside over a number of hours.

   (v) The measured length of a football pitch.

   (vi) The speed of a car.

2. **Categorical data**

   Collecting data about the (i) colour (ii) makes of cars in a large carpark, we notice that the colours fall into groups or categories such as blue, red, silver, ... Data such as this is called **categorical data**.

   Examples of categorical data:

   (i) gender (male, female)

   (ii) favourite colour (red, blue, pink, ...)

   (iii) counties (Galway, Mayo, Wexford, ...)

Colour of car	Tally
Blue	卌 ‖
Red	卌 卌 ‖
Silver	卌 ‖‖

   Some categorical data is collected in ordered groups as

   (iv) first division, second division, third division, ...

   (v) lower income group, middle income group, higher income group.

   (vi) very often, often, sometimes, rarely, very rarely.

Example 1

State whether each of the following data are numerical or categorical.

(i) The numbers of desks in the classrooms of your school.

(ii) The temperatures of babies in a creche.

(iii) The types of animals on a farm.

(iv) The number of goals scored by a number of teams on a Saturday.

(v) The colour of cars passing a certain point outside your school.

(vi) The heights of trees in a public park.

    (i) Numerical   (ii) Numerical   (iii) Categorical

    (iv) Numerical   (v) Categorical   (vi) Numerical

Exercise 12.1

1. The tally chart shows the number of
   glass bottles put into a bottle bank one day.
   (i) How many green bottles were put into
       the bottle bank?
   (ii) How many brown bottles were put into
        the bottle bank?

Colour of glass	Tally
Clear	ЖІ ЖІ ЖІ ІІ
Brown	ЖІ ЖІ ЖІ ЖІ І
Green	ЖІ ЖІ ЖІ

2. The tally chart below shows the colours of cars in a car park.

Colour of car	Tally	Frequency
Black	ІІ	
Blue	ЖІ ЖІ ІІІ	
Green	ІІІІ	
Red	ЖІ ЖІ І	
Silver	ЖІ ІІ	
White	ЖІ ЖІ ІІІІ	
		Total =

   (i) How many blue cars are recorded?
   (ii) How many cars are recorded altogether?
   (iii) What is the most popular colour?

3. Denise carried out a survey to find how students travelled to school.
   Her frequency table looked like this:

Method of travel	Tally	Frequency
Walk	ЖІ ЖІ ЖІ ЖІ ЖІ ІІІ	A
Car	ЖІ ЖІ ІІ	B
Bus	ЖІ ЖІ ЖІ ЖІ ІІІ	C
Bicycle	ЖІ	D
Taxi	ІІ	E

   (i) Write down the values for A, B, C, D and E.
   (ii) What is the most common way of travelling to school?
   (iii) What fraction of the students cycled to school?
   (iv) Which two methods of travel were used by exactly one half of the students?

4. State whether each of the following is numerical data or categorical data:
   (i) The number of horses that ran in each of the six races at a meeting.
   (ii) The cost of posting each of seven parcels.
   (iii) The hair colours of the students in your class.
   (iv) The types of crop grown on a tillage farm.
   (v) The numbers of jigsaw pieces in a selection of jigsaw boxes.

5. Rory bought a new golf bag.
   He wrote down   (i) the colour of the bag
                   (ii) the number of pockets in the bag.
   State whether each of these data types is numerical or categorical.

6. Here are the colours of 40 cars in the forecourt of a car dealership.

red	red	blue	green	white	red
blue	red	red	blue	white	green
red	white	white	blue	red	white
blue	blue	green	black	white	blue
red	silver	silver	blue	red	red
silver	white	white	red	blue	green
red	blue	silver	white		

   (i) Copy and complete the tally chart below:

Colour of car	Tally	Frequency
Red		
Blue		
Green		
White		
Silver		
Black		

   (ii) How many white cars are in the forecourt?
   (iii) What is the most popular colour?
   (iv) Which colour represents 25% of the total?

7. The ages, in years, of 40 people are shown below.

43	24	33	26	35	15	27	34	19	20
42	49	34	56	37	19	21	50	39	29
54	57	30	28	26	18	20	34	3	33
9	10	1	27	12	47	11	7	25	37

Copy and complete the **grouped** tally chart for the data given.

Age (years)	Tally	Frequency
0–9		
10–19		
20–29		
30–39		
40–49		
50–59		

When data has a wide range of values, it can be sorted into groups or classes.

(i) What is the width of each class interval?
(ii) How many people are in the class interval 30–39?
(iii) How many people are less than 20 years old?
(iv) How many people are 40 years of age or older?

8. There are three pieces of data in this sentence:
' Niall bought a saloon car for €20 000 and drove home at a steady speed of 50 km / hr.
(i) What are three pieces of data?
(ii) State whether each is numerical or categorical.

9. Mr and Mrs Jones carried out a survey in their local sports club.
They asked the members of the club four questions.
(i) How many times did you visit the club last week?
(ii) How many children are there in your family?
(iii) What was their preferred activity?
(iv) How long did it take you to travel to the club?
What numerical data and categorical data was collected?

10. The numbers of birds in a garden are recorded at the same time each day over a
50-day period. These numbers are given below.

4	24	11	24	3	7	8	12	23	14
22	15	5	6	7	8	11	3	8	25
3	7	5	7	17	9	1	13	7	12
1	2	8	18	13	12	3	6	6	9
17	15	11	9	8	17	7	14	16	4

Construct a tally chart similar to Q7 above using groups of
1–5,   6–10,   11–15,   16–20,   21–25.

  (i)   On how many days were there 16 or more birds in the garden?
  (ii) Which group had the highest number of birds?
  (iii) On how many days were there between 11 and 20 (inclusive) birds in the garden?

Investigation:

Ask all the students in the class to write down the different countries they
have visited. Make a list of these countries. Use a tally to record the numbers of
students who visited each country:

  (i)   Which of the countries was visited most often?
  (ii) Which of the countries was the least visited?
  (iii) By extending the chart using one more column indicate whether the
        purpose each visit was (A) a holiday (B) to meet family living abroad
        (plus a holiday).
  (iv) Make a chart of the results.

Section 12.2 Sampling

If you are carrying out a survey in a mixed school and question the first two students on
each class register, you may end up asking all boys or all girls.

Ideally you should ask everyone in the school, but this may not be practical as the
numbers may be too big and it would take too long to complete the survey. Instead you
could ask a limited number of students the relevant questions and hope that the results
will be **representative** of the whole school.

In statistics, we call this limited group **a sample**.

You need to make sure that each student in the school has an equal chance of being
picked to be part of the survey. For example, five students from each class could be
selected by drawing their names from a hat. This is called a **simple random sample**.

When you question a random sample, you should get a result that is very similar to the
one you would get if you questioned all the members of the group. The size of a sample
is important. If it is too small, the results may not be reliable. If the sample is too large,
the data may take too long to collect and it may also be too costly.

A population

If you carry out a survey in a single school, then all the pupils in that school are referred to as the **population**. In statistics, a population is everybody or everything that could be included in a survey. For example, if you want to find out how people in a large company travel to work, then the population is all the people who work for that company.

If you are going to ask questions of some of the people in this picture, the **population** being considered is **all** the people in the football stadium.

Bias

The sample you select for your study is very important. If the sample is not random and does not fairly represent the whole population, the results may be **biased**. If bias exists, the results will not give you a clear picture of the whole population.

In a **random** sample, every member of the group has the same chance of being selected.

Example 1

Cian wants to do a survey to find out if people are in favour of a new pedestrian crossing near a school.
Which of these three groups should he ask?
Give a reason for your answer.
  (i) Car drivers using the road.
  (ii) Local residents.
  (iii) Mothers of children attending the school.

The most suitable group would be local residents as they are the most likely to give a balanced response that would represent the whole population.
Car drivers are more likely to say that they do not want a new pedestrian crossing.
The mothers are very likely to want the new crossing as they would be very concerned about the safety of their children.

Exercise 12.2

1. Niamh is doing a survey to find out how far the pupils in her school travel to get to school. One day she asked every pupil at the school bus stop.
Explain why the sample is likely to be biased.

2. James wanted to do a survey to find out if people thought *Coldplay* was a good pop group.
Which of the following groups is the most suitable for the survey?
Explain your answer.
   (i)   The students in his school.
   (ii) People attending a Coldplay concert.
   (iii) Residents in a nursing home.

3. David is doing a survey to find out which sports people most like to watch.
He stands outside a football stadium and questions people as they leave.
Explain why this survey may be biased.

4. Ciara wants to do a survey to find out how often people take exercise each week.
Which of the following groups is the most suitable for her survey?
Give the reasons for your selection.
   (i)   People walking in the park.   (ii) People in a town centre.
   (iii) Members of the local sports centre.

5. Hannah wanted to do a survey to find out if people were in favour of banning cars and lorries from the city centre.
She surveyed all car and lorry drivers near the city centre for one hour on a particular day.
Explain why this sample may be biased.

6. Rachel is doing a survey to find out what students thought of the meals in the school canteen.
She asks every fifth person going into the canteen for lunch.
Explain why this may not be a good sample.

7. A supermarket thinks that as many men as women shop at their store.
To investigate this, they set up a survey one Saturday morning between 9 a.m. and 10 a.m. where they count the number of men and women going into the store.
Do you think that a survey done on a Saturday morning would give a true picture of what happens over the course of a full week?
Give two reasons for your answer.

Section 12.3 Data-Handling-Cycle

In the sections so far, we have focused on surveys and data collection. It is important to keep in mind the data-handling-cycle that these belong to.

As stated already we first must;
- ask a question,
- collect responses(data) to the question from our target group,
- analyse the responses(data),
- draw conclusions from the analysis,
- finally, a new question may be needed to clarify some of the analysis.

In chart form the cycle is as follows:

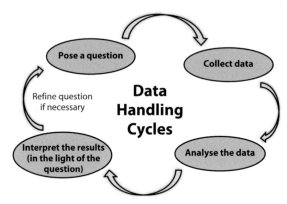

Questionnaires

A **questionnaire** is a set of questions designed to obtain information or data from individuals.

There are two main ways in which a questionnaire can be used.
- A person (or interviewer) asks the questions and fills in the responses himself/herself.
- People are given a questionnaire to complete in their own time and the completed questionnaire is either returned or collected.

When you are writing questions for a questionnaire, the following points should be kept in mind.

1. Questions should be clear, short and easily understood.

Example

> **Questionnaire**
>
> **1.** How do you generally travel to school? Tick one box
>
> Walk ☐   Bus ☐   Car ☐   Train ☐   Cycle ☐   Other ☐
>
> **2.** How long does it take you (in minutes)?
>
> 1–10 ☐   11–20 ☐   21–30 ☐   31–40 ☐   >40 ☐

2. **Start with simple questions to encourage the person who is completing the questionnaire.**

   Example

   > **Questionnaire**
   >
   > 1. Are you male or female?   Male ☐   Female ☐
   >
   > 2. Have you visited the new leisure centre?   Yes ☐   No ☐

3. **Avoid leading questions.**
   These are questions that suggest a particular response.

   Example

   > **Questionnaire**
   >
   > 1. Do you think that politicians are overpaid?
   >   Yes ☐   No ☐
   >
   > 2. Don't you agree that people drink too much alcohol?
   >   Yes ☐   No ☐

   > Avoid personal questions like 'How old are you?'.

4. **Avoid questions that may upset or embarrass people.**

   Example

   > **Questionnaire**
   >
   > 1. Have you ever stolen goods from your local store?
   >   Yes ☐   No ☐
   >
   > 2. Have you ever driven a car while over the drink-drive limit?
   >   Yes ☐   No ☐

Whenever you undertake a survey, it is advisable to first do a **pilot survey**. A pilot survey is one that is carried out on a very small scale to make sure the design and questions in the survey are likely to produce the information required. It should, in particular, identify problems with the wording of the questions and the likely responses.

Exercise 12.3

1. Give a reason why each of the following questions is unsuitable to put in a questionnaire.
   A: What age are you?
   B: Do you agree that RTE 1 provides the best news coverage?
   C: The new supermarket seems to be a great success.

Do you agree?

D: How many times did you have a shower or bath in the past week?

E: How much money do you earn each week?

F: Are you young, middle-aged or old?

G: Wouldn't you agree that the government is doing a good job?

2. This question appeared on a questionnaire:

Q: All sensible people like dogs. Do you like dogs?

This is an example of a **biased** question.

(i) Explain why it is biased.

(ii) Write two other questions that could well be considered biased.

3. Here are two questions from a survey about the amount of homework given to pupils in *St. Jude's High School*.

A: Do you agree that pupils in this school are given too much homework?

Yes ☐   No ☐

B: The amount of homework set to pupils in this school is: [Tick one box.]

Not enough ☐   About right ☐   Too much ☐   Don't know ☐

Which of these two questions is the more suitable for a questionnaire?

Explain your answer.

4. Here is a question and the response boxes given in a questionnaire.

Q: How many hours of TV do you watch?   1 ☐   2 ☐   3 ☐

Suggest how you would improve the question and responses for this survey.

5. A market research company intended to ask the following question in a questionnaire:

How old are you?

(i) Why is this question unacceptable?

(ii) Rewrite the question to make it more acceptable.

6. Jane is doing a survey about how often people have a meal out in a restaurant. Here are two questions she has written.

Q1. How often do you eat out?   ☐ A lot   ☐ Sometimes   ☐ Never

Q2. What food did you have the last time you ate out?

(i) Give a reason why each of these questions is unsuitable.

(ii) Write a better version of Q1 by being more specific in the responses.

7. Emma says, 'I go to the gym twice a week after school.'

She decides to do a survey to find out what exercise other pupils take outside school.

Write down **two** questions you think she should ask.

8. For each of these survey questions,
   - state why this may not be the best way to ask the question
   - write a better version.

   (i) What is your favourite sport: cricket, tennis or athletics?
   (ii) Do you do lots of exercise each week?
   (iii) Don't you think this government should encourage more people to recycle waste?

9. 'The older you get, the less sleep you need.'

   Write down three questions and the responses to each question to test the truth or otherwise of this statement. In addition, suggest a location in which it may be easy to get an unbiased sample of respondents.

10. Alan wants to find out what people think of the *Democratic Party*.
    He is trying to decide between these two questions for his questionnaire.

    A: Do you agree that the *Democratic Party* is the best party?
    Agree ☐   Disagree ☐

    B: Do you think the policies of the *Democratic Party* are
    Very good ☐   Good ☐   Fair ☐   Poor ☐   Very poor ☐ ?
    Which question should he use?
    Explain your answer.

11. Denise wants to find out what people think of their local bus service.
    Part of the questionnaire she has written is shown.

    > **Q1.** What is your address? ....
    >
    > **Q2.** Don't you agree that waiting times for the next bus are too long?
    > Yes ☐   No ☐
    >
    > **Q3.** How many times did you travel by bus last week?
    > Very often ☐   Occasionally ☐   Seldom ☐

    (i) Why should Q1 not be asked?
    (ii) Give a reason why Q2 is unsuitable.
    (iii) Explain why Q3 is unsuitable in its present form.
         Rewrite the question to make it suitable for a questionnaire.

12. A new variety of soup, 'Cheese and Onion', is to be launched by a leading manufacturer. They wish to know if it will be popular and sell well.
    People are asked to try a free sample and comment on their impression.
    Write three questions and suitable responses to test people's opinions.

Test yourself 12

1. State whether each of the following data is numerical or categorical:
   (i) the colours of the cars in a showroom
   (ii) the number of houses on your street
   (iii) the types of animals on a farm
   (iv) the blood groups of the students in your class
   (v) the number of countries in the EU
   (vi) the different nationalities of Premier League soccer players.

2. Ella wants to buy a new computer.
   She looks on the internet for information to answer the following questions.
   (i) How much is a computer monitor?
   (ii) In what colours are the monitors available?
   (iii) What are the sizes of the monitors?
   (iv) How big is the computer's hard drive?
   For each question, write down if the data required is numerical or categorical.

3. Louise spends her summer holiday working in a shop that hires out hats for weddings and other functions.
   Give one example of (i) numerical data (ii) categorical data that could associated with hats.

4. State whether each of the following results is numerical or categorical data.
   (i) Standing at a supermarket exit door and asking the customers what they thought of the service they had received.
   (ii) Checking Garda records to find the number of road-traffic accidents that occurred during the past month.
   (iii) Counting the number of cars that turn left at a particular junction.
   (iv) Checking the internet to find the most popular cars.
   (v) Asking all the students in your class to give the numbers of sisters and brothers they have.

5. Daniel wrote down the numbers of minutes his phone calls lasted.

   | 8 | 10 | 16 | 3 | 1 | 24 | 25 | 30 | 36 | 17 | 19 | 11 |
   | 16 | 18 | 4 | 3 | 7 | 2 | 1 | 4 | 17 | 19 | 23 | 26 |

   Make a copy of this data collection sheet.
   Fill it in.

   What percentage of calls lasted between 11 and 20 minutes inclusive?

Number of minutes	Tally	Frequency
1–10		
11–20		
21–30		
31–40		

6. Karen is doing a survey to find out how often people go to the cinema and how much they spend. She stands outside a cinema and asks people as they go in. Write a reason why this sample could be biased.

7. Here are some questions that are not suitable for a questionnaire.
   Why do you think that they are not suitable? Suggest a better question.

   Q1. Most people agree that it would be a good thing to lower the drink-drive limit.
   Do you?
   Yes ☐   No ☐   Don't know ☐

   Q2. Do you agree that we need a change of National Anthem?
   Yes ☐   No ☐   Don't know ☐

   Q3. Soccer is more exciting to watch than rugby.
   Do you agree?
   Yes ☐   No ☐   Don't know ☐

8. Jack wants to find out what percentage of adults have cars.
   He interviews 100 people in an out-of-town shopping centre to find out if they own a car.
   Explain why this sample may be biased.

9. Describe what is meant by **a simple random sample**.

10. A market research company is conducting a survey to find out whether, last year, most people had a holiday in Ireland, elsewhere in Europe or in the rest of the world. It also wants to know if they stayed in self-catering accommodation, hotels or went camping. Design **two** questions and responses that could be used in a questionnaire to find out all this information.

Learning Experience   *Unit 12*

Assignment 1

Collecting data:

We want to find what is the most commonly-used vowel in the English language.

Select about 80 words at random from any of your textbooks.

Make a tally chart similar to the one shown.

Count the number of times each vowel appears.

Letter	Tally	How many
a		
e		
i		
o		
u		

Compare results with other students.

Add together the results from all the students of the class and find in order, the three most popular vowels.

Assignment 2

Write a definition of the word random.

- Describe how to select a random sample of 5 students from your class.

- Describe how to select a random sample of 5 students from your school.

Question: How does the number of children in a family vary?

Select a *random sample* of 5 students in your class.

- Ask them to write down the number of children (including themselves) in their families.

- Make a chart of the number of families with 1 child, 2 children, 3 children, …

- Now find the percentage (correct to the nearest whole number) of the five families who had 1 child, 2 children, …

Repeat the exercise with all the students in your class.

	1 child	2 children	3 children	4 children	5 children
Number (sample 5)					
Percentage					
Number (class)					
Percentage					

- Compare the percentage results of the sample with those of the whole class.

- What conclusion could you make about the size of the sample?

- Suggest an advantage and disadvantage of using (i) a small sample (ii) a large sample.

Assignment 3

Making predictions:

In groups of 4/5, answer the following questions and make predictions about the answers you think would get from your whole class.

     (i)   Do you have a pet?
    (ii)   Are you female?
   (iii)   Were you born in Ireland?
   (iv)   What is your favourite sport?
    (v)   What colour eyes do you have?

(a) State how you can use your answers to make predictions for the whole class?

(b) Write down what issues arose with your group answers that made it difficult to predict the class answers?

(c) Discuss how best to select a representative sample group and write down your groups conclusions.

Assignment 4

Total number of students	Main method of travel	Number of males	Number of females
108,400	Bus	52,639	55,761
101,036	Car	48,418	52,618
74,346	Walked	36,416	37,930
7,377	Cycled	6,856	521
4,672	Train	2,673	1,999

Study the table of data above (data taken from Census@School).

Carry out a survey in your class to find out how everyone gets to school and lay out your results in a table as above.

Calculate the percentage of males and females in your class that travel by each mode of transport.

Calculate the percentages of males and females in the table that travel by each mode of transport.

By comparing the sets of data write down any conclusion you can draw about the 'method of travel' for your particular class.

Note:

Data you collect yourself by means of surveys / questionnaires is called Primary data.

Data that is sourced from books / internet is called Secondary data.

Chapter 12 review 1

Using the terms from the chapter, copy and complete the following sentences:

1. To answer statistical questions you need to do a _____.

2. _____ is information that you collect.

3. A tally sheet usually counts in groups of _____.

4. Data in the form of numbers is called _____ data.

5. Types of houses is an example of _____ data.

6. The duration of a basketball match is an example of _____ data.

7. Everybody who could be included in a survey is called the _____.

8. When sampling it is very important to avoid _____.

9. A _____ sample is one in which every member of the population has the same chance of being selected.

10. In questionnaires avoid _____ questions because they suggest a particular response.

11. In questionnaires avoid _____ questions because they may cause upset or embarrassment.

Chapter 12 review 2

You should now be able to:

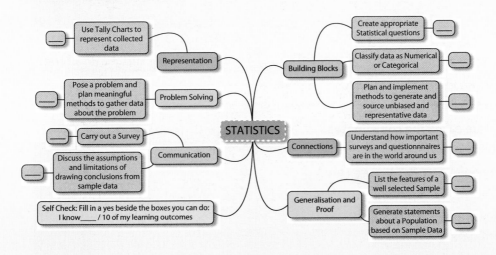

13 Coordinates

In this chapter, you will learn to:

- make a **grid,**
- use **coordinates,**
- draw **x** and **y axes,**
- label the **origin,**
- name the four **quadrants,**
- use a **coordinated plane,**

- identify a **Cartesian plane,**
- locate the **midpoint** of a line segment,
- find the **slope** of a line segment,
- draw a graph of a line segment.

Section 13.1 Grids

The sketch of the wall of a room is 13 cm across and 9 cm up.

To mark the position of a light switch S, we need two measurements.

If we start from the corner marked O, the light switch is 8 cm **across** and 4 cm **up.**

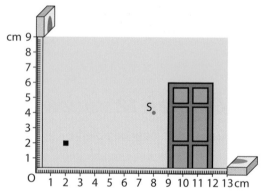

These measurements give us the location of a point on the flat surface (or **plane**).

The location 8 across and 4 up is written as (8, 4).

(8, 4) are called the **coordinates** of the point.

Every point on a flat surface can be found using a **grid.**

For example, the lock L has coordinates (9, 3).

The socket P has coordinates (2, 2).

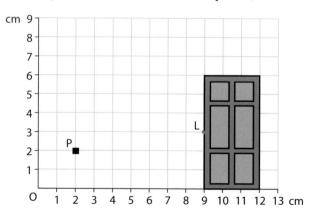

To make a grid, we draw two lines, a horizontal line and a vertical line. These are called **axes**.

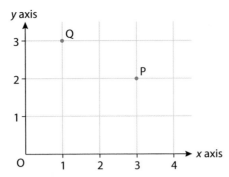

The horizontal line is called the **x-axis**. The vertical line is called the **y-axis**.
The point P has coordinates, $(x, y) = (3, 2)$.
The first number is the **x-coordinate**. The second number is the **y-coordinate**.
The point O is called the **origin**. The point Q has coordinates, $(x, y) = (1, 3)$.
Every point in the plane can be represented by the **couple**, (x, y).

Exercise 13.1

1. Write the coordinates of the points marked A, B, C and D in the given figure.

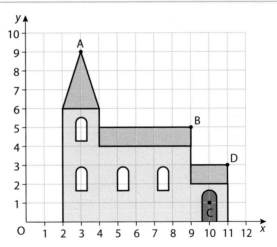

2. From the given grid, write down the coordinates of the points marked A, B, C, D, E, F and G.

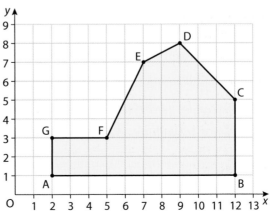

3. Write down the coordinates of the points marked A to L in the given figure.

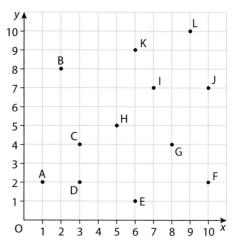

4. Draw a grid on squared paper from 0 to 10 across and from 0 to 8 up.
Mark these points on the grid and join them in the order given.

   (i) (1, 1), (1, 3), (3, 3), (3, 1), (1, 1)   (ii) (2, 4), (2, 7), (5, 7), (5, 4), (2, 4)

Describe the figure made in each case.

5. In the figure below, each letter represents a pair of coordinates.

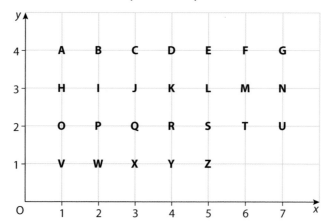

By writing the letter represented by the given coordinates, work out each of the following:

  (i) Write down the name of the animal given by each of these coordinates:

      (a) (4, 4)   (1, 2)   (7, 4)

      (b) (1, 3)   (1, 2)   (4, 2)   (5, 2)   (5, 4)

      (c) (6, 3)   (1, 2)   (7, 3)   (4, 3)   (5, 4)   (4, 1)

  (ii) Write down the name of the river given by each of these coordinates:

      (a) (5, 3)   (2, 3)   (6, 4)   (6, 4)   (5, 4)   (4, 1)

      (b) (2, 4)   (1, 2)   (4, 1)   (7, 3)   (5, 4)

      (c) (5, 2)   (5, 3)   (1, 4)   (7, 3)   (5, 4)   (4, 1)

6. (i) Write down the coordinates of these places on the given map:

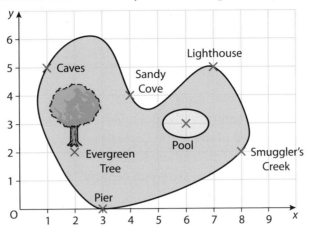

(a) Smuggler's Creek   (b) Lighthouse   (c) Sandy Cove

(ii) Write down the names of the places on the map with these coordinates:

(a) (1, 5)   (b) (6, 3)   (c) (3, 0)   (d) (2, 2)

7. On which axis do these points lie?

(4, 0)   (2, 0)   (3, 0)   (6, 0)

8. Name four points on the *y*-axis.

9. This grid shows the map of a village.

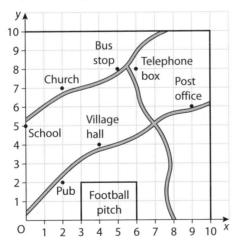

(i) Write down the coordinates of these:

(a) the church   (b) the post office   (c) the village hall   (d) the school

(ii) What is at the point (6, 8)?

(iii) Which two locations have the same *x*-coordinate?

(iv) Which two locations have the same *y*-coordinate?

(v) Write down the coordinates of the corners of the football pitch.

Section 13.2 The four quadrants

In the previous section, all the points that were plotted had positive numbers only.

If we extend the grid to include negative numbers, we can then describe the location of any point in the plane.

In the diagram opposite, we have a horizontal line and a vertical line meeting at the point O. It is called the **coordinated plane** or the **Cartesian Plane** in honour of the French mathematician, René Descartes, who lived in the sixteenth century.

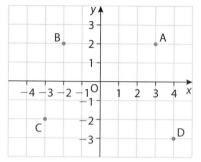

The coordinates of the **origin** O are (0, 0).

The coordinates of A are (3, 2).

The coordinates of B are (−2, 2).

The coordinates of C are (−3, −2).

The coordinates of D are (4, −3).

The diagram on the right shows that the *x*-axis and *y*-axis divide the plane into four quarters.

Each of these is called a **quadrant**.

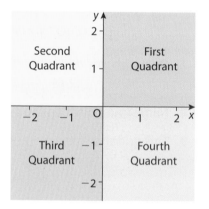

Exercise 13.2

1. Write down the coordinates of the points marked on the diagram below:

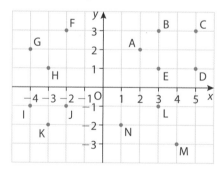

2. Draw a pair of axes, as in Question 1 above, and mark in the following points:

   A(2, 3),   B(3, 5),   C(−2, 1),   D(−3, 2)

   E(4, 0),   F(−4, −1),   G(2, −3),   H(−1, −3)

3. Write down the coordinates of the fourth vertex in each of the figures given below:

(i) ABCD is a square

(ii) PQRS is a rectangle.

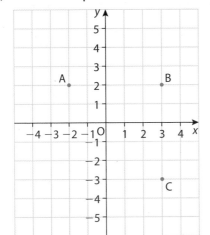 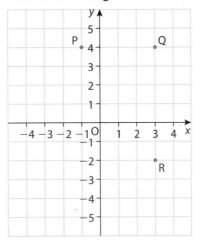

4. Using the given figure, write down the letters and coordinates of each of these:

(i) two points in the first quadrant

(ii) two points in the third quadrant

(iii) two points in the fourth quadrant

(iv) two points on the *x*-axis

(v) two points on the *y*-axis.

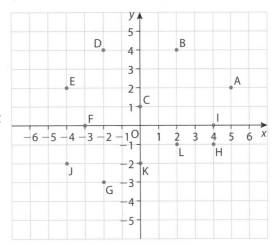

5. In which quadrant does each of the following points lie?

A(2, 3),   B(4, −1),   C(−3, −1),   D(−2, −4)

6. On which axis is each of the following points?

(i) (2, 0)   (ii) (0, 3)   (iii) (−3, 0)   (iv) (0, −2)   (v) (0, 0)

7. Draw *x* and *y* axes from 0 to 5.

(i) Plot the points (2, 1), (5, 1) and (5, 4). These are three corners of a square.

(ii) What are the coordinates of the fourth corner of the square?

8. Draw *x* and *y* axes from −2 to 4.

(i) Plot the points A(3, 2), B(3, −1) and C(−1, −1).

(ii) Points A, B and C are three corners of a rectangle.
     Point D is the fourth corner of the rectangle. Plot point D on your diagram.

(iii) What are the coordinates of point D?

9. Look for a pattern in these coordinates.
   Use the pattern to find the missing coordinates.
   (i)   (3, 5)   (5, 6)   (7, 7)   (9, 8)   (…, …)   (…, …)
   (ii) (3, 0)   (5, 2)   (7, 4)   (9, 6)   (…, …)   (…, …)
   (iii) (4, 6)   (5, 4)   (6, 2)   (7, 0)   (…, …)   (…, …)
   (iv) (0, 6)   (−2, 3)   (−4, 0)   (−6, −3)   (…, …)   (…, …)

10. Look at these coordinates: (2, 6)   (4, 4)   (5, 3)   (8, 0).
    (i) Describe a pattern in these.
    (ii) Use the pattern to fill in the missing numbers in these coordinates
         (7, …)   (0, …)   (−2, …)

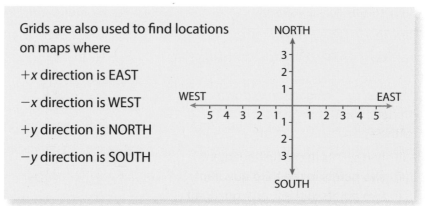

Grids are also used to find locations on maps where

+x direction is EAST

−x direction is WEST

+y direction is NORTH

−y direction is SOUTH

11. Draw a grid on squared paper as shown and mark the following points on it.

    A. (5 km East, 3 km South)
    B. (3 km West, 3 km South)
    C. (2 km West, 3 km North)
    D. 3 km East
    E. 2 km South

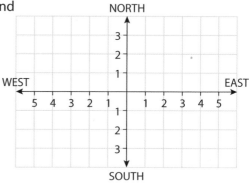

12. Draw a grid from −2 to 8 on the x-axis and from 8 to −4 on the y-axis.
    A girl starts at the origin and cycles to her friend A (3 km EAST, 2 km NORTH).
    From there, she cycles to her friend B (4 km EAST, 5 km SOUTH).
    Mark A and B on your grid.

13. Mark leaves his house at the origin and travels (3 km EAST, 4 km SOUTH).
    From there, he travels (5 km WEST, 2 km SOUTH).
    His brother Sean is back at the origin.
    What is Mark's location relative to Sean's location?

14. Here are some tiles in the shape of a parallelogram.

Each tile has a corner marked with an *.
The coordinates of the first corner are (3, 2).

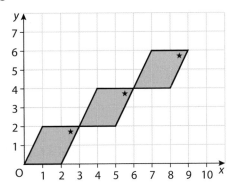

  (i) Write down the coordinates of the
second and third corners that you see.

 (ii) You cannot see the fourth corner which
has an *.
By following the pattern, write down
the coordinates of this fourth corner.

(iii) Can you now find the coordinates of the
fifth corner that has an *?

Assignment:

Copy this grid onto a large poster.

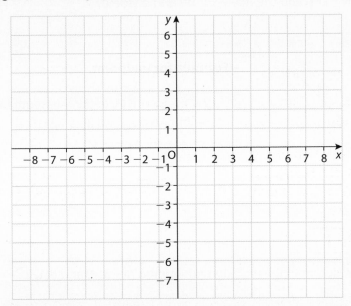

Plot these points and join them in order.

$(-7, 4), (-3, 6), (-1, 4), (-1, 0), (-2, -1), (7, -1), (2, -4), (4, -6), (-2, -6),$
$(-5, -4), (-5, 0), (-3, 2), (-3, 4), (-7, 4).$

Put a large dot at $(-3.5, 4.5)$. What picture did you get?

Section 13.3 Midpoint of a line segment

The given diagram shows the points A(2, 1) and B(6, 5).

If we join A to B, we get the line segment [AB].

M is the midpoint of [AB].

From the grid, we can see that the coordinates of M are (4, 3).

Notice that the x-coordinate 4 is halfway between the x-coordinates of A and B, i.e. 2 and 6.

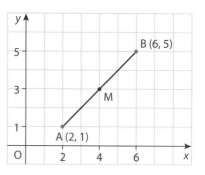

Similarly, the y-coordinate of M, 3, is halfway between 1 and 5.

Thus $M = \left(\dfrac{2 + 6}{2}, \dfrac{1 + 5}{2}\right) = (4, 3)$.

> To find the midpoint of a line segment, add the two x-values and divide by 2 and add the two y-values and divide by 2.

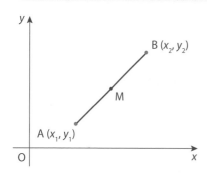

Formula for midpoint

The midpoint, M, of the line segment joining $A(x_1, y_1)$ and $B(x_2, y_2)$ is

$$M = \left(\frac{x_1 + x_2}{2}, \frac{y_1 + y_2}{2}\right).$$

Example 1

Find the midpoint of the line segment joining A(-3, 4) and B(1, 2).

$$\text{Midpoint} = \left(\frac{x_1 + x_2}{2}, \frac{y_1 + y_2}{2}\right)$$
$$= \left(\frac{-3 + 1}{2}, \frac{4 + 2}{2}\right)$$
$$= \left(\frac{-2}{2}, \frac{6}{2}\right) = (-1, 3)$$

Exercise 13.3

1. The given grid shows four
   points A, B, C and D.

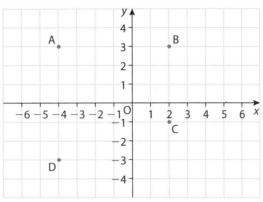

   (i) Write down the coordinates of each of these points.
   (ii) Use the grid to write down the coordinates of the midpoint of
       (a) [AB]   (b) [BC]   (c) [AD].

2. (i) Write down the coordinates of A, B and C in
       the given grid.

   (ii) Write down the coordinates of the
        midpoint of
        (a) [AB]   (b) [BC]

   (iii) If ABCD is a rectangle, find the coordinates
        of D.

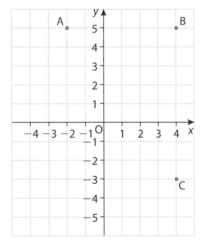

3. In the given grid, M is the midpoint of the line
   segment [AB].

   (i) Use the grid to write down the coordinates of M.

   (ii) Is there another way to find the coordinate of M?
        Use it to show that your answer in (i) above is
        correct.

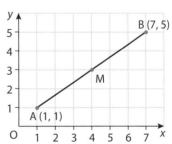

4. Find the coordinates of the midpoints of the line segments joining the following
   pairs of points:
   (i) (2, 1) and (4, 3)   (ii) (1, 1) and (5, 5)   (iii) (1, 3) and (3, 5)
   (iv) (4, 3) and (6, 1)   (v) (0, 4) and (6, 2)   (vi) (5, −2) and (1, 4)

5. A(1, 1), B(5, 1), C(5, 4) and D(1, 4) are four points in the plane.
   (i) Find the coordinates of M, the midpoint of [AC].
   (ii) Show that M is also the midpoint of [BD].

6. Use the formula $\left(\dfrac{x_1 + x_2}{2}, \dfrac{y_1 + y_2}{2}\right)$ to find the midpoints of the line segments
   joining these pairs of points:
   (i) (3, 5) and (1, 3)   (ii) (7, 4) and (1, 2)   (iii) (6, 2) and (−2, 0)
   (iv) (0, 7) and (4, 3)   (v) (1, −3) and (3, 5)   (vi) (4, −3) and (2, −3)

7. Find the midpoint of the line segment joining A(−3, 6) and B(5, −6).
   On which axis does the midpoint lie?

8. Work out the coordinates of the midpoint
   of each of these line segments:
   (i) [AB]
   (ii) [BC]
   (iii) [AD].

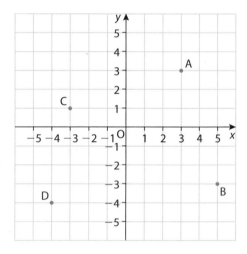

9. A, B, C and D are the vertices of a rectangle

   (i) Find the coordinates of the midpoint of [AC].

   (ii) Investigate if this is also the midpoint of [BD].

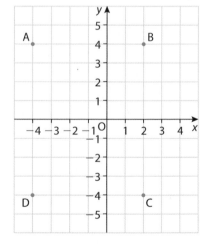

10. Show that the midpoint of the line segment joining P(5, −3) and Q(−5, 7) is on the *y*-axis.

11. The points C(8, 6) and D(2, 2) are the endpoints of the diameter of a circle k.
Find the coordinates of the centre, O, of the circle.

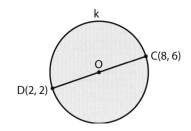

Section 13.4 The slope of a line

Consider the line segments [AB] and [EF].

It is clear that [AB] is steeper than [EF] and represents a greater challenge to a skateboarder.

Although both ramps have the same height, the horizontal lengths are different.

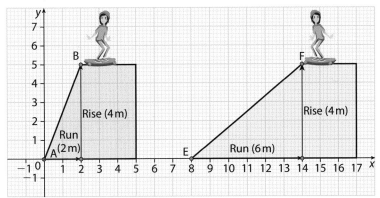

To measure how steep a line or a line segment is we use the idea of a mathematical **slope**.

The slope is calculated using the value of the ratio; $\dfrac{\textbf{vertical height}}{\textbf{horizontal length}} = \dfrac{\textbf{rise}}{\textbf{run}}$.

The slope of ramp [AB] $= \frac{4}{2} = \frac{2}{1} = 2$

The slope of [EF] $= \frac{4}{6} = \frac{2}{3}$

The slope of [AB] is greater than the slope of [EF] because $2 > \frac{2}{3}$.

In general, the slope, *m*, of the line passing through points $A(x_1, y_1)$ and $B(x_2, y_2)$ is given by:

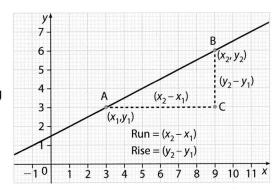

$$\text{Slope} = m = \frac{Rise}{Run} = \frac{y_2 - y_1}{x_2 - x_1}$$

Example 1

Find the slope of the given ramp using the grid, where each unit is 1 metre.

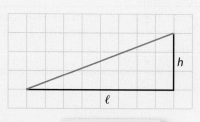

For this ramp: $h = 3$ ... Rise of 3

$\ell = 8$ ... Run of 8

$\text{Slope} = \dfrac{h}{\ell} = \dfrac{3}{8}$

1 unit = 1 m

Example 2

Find the slope of the line through the points A(1, 2) and B(3, 4).

$\text{Slope of AB} = \dfrac{y_2 - y_1}{x_2 - x_1} = \dfrac{4 - 2}{3 - 1}$

$= \dfrac{2}{2} = 1$

$\therefore$ Slope of AB $= 1$

$$\begin{array}{cc} (1, 2) & (3, 4) \\ \downarrow & \downarrow \\ (x_1, y_1) & (x_2, y_2) \end{array}$$

Negative slopes

As we observe a line from **left to right**, it either rises or falls.

Rising   Falling

Rising lines have **positive** slopes.

Falling lines have **negative** slopes.

+   −

Positive slope   Negative slope

Example 3

Find the slopes of the line segments [AB] and [BC].

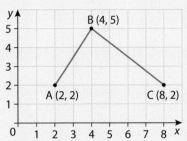

Slope of AB $= \dfrac{y_2 - y_1}{x_2 - x_1}$ (2, 2)   (4, 5)

   $\qquad\qquad\qquad\quad \downarrow \qquad \downarrow$

$= \dfrac{5 - 2}{4 - 2} = \dfrac{3}{2}$ $(x_1, y_1) \ (x_2, y_2)$

Slope of BC $= \dfrac{y_2 - y_1}{x_2 - x_1} = \dfrac{2 - 5}{8 - 4}$ (4, 5)   (8, 2)

   $\qquad\qquad\qquad\qquad\qquad\quad \downarrow \qquad \downarrow$

$= \dfrac{-3}{4} = -\dfrac{3}{4}$ $(x_1, y_1) \ (x_2, y_2)$

(Notice that the slope of BC is negative as the line falls from left to right.)

Exercise 13.4

1. State whether the slope of each of these lines is positive or negative:

(a)   (b)   (c)   (d)   (e)   (f)

2. The diagram shows four lines a, b, c and d.

 (i) Which lines have positive slopes?

 (ii) Which lines have negative slopes?

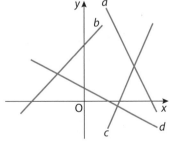

3. Use the grid and the value of $\dfrac{\text{rise}}{\text{run}}$ to find the slope of the red line segment in each of these diagrams:

(i)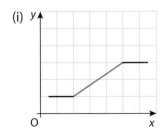

(ii)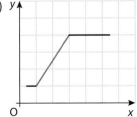

(iii)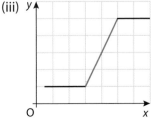

4. Work out the slope of each of the lines below:

(i)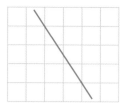

(ii)

(iii)

5. Why is the slope of the given line negative?
Use the grid to work out the slope of the line.

6. Find the slopes of the following lines:

(i)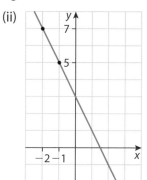

(ii)

(iii)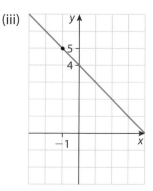

7. Using the coordinates given, calculate the slope of each of the following line segments:

(i)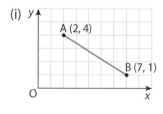

(ii)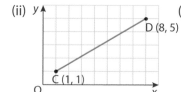

(iii)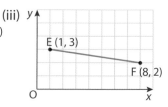

8. Find the slope of the line through each pair of points:

   (i) (1, 2) and (4, 5)   (ii) (2, 3) and (3, 7)   (iii) (1, −3) and (4, 2)

  (iv) (−2, 4) and (2, 6)   (v) (1, 5) and (3, −1)   (vi) (−3, 2) and (1, −4)

 (vii) (−2, −6) and (1, 2) (viii) (1, −4) and (−2, 3)   (ix) (2, −4) and (3, −1)

9. A(2, 4), B(6, 7), C(10, 5) and D(6, 2) are four points.
   Show that the slope of AB is the same as the slope of CD.

10. A cyclist rides up an incline that rises
    3 metres for every 60 metres it runs.

    (i) What is the slope of the incline?
    (ii) How much will the incline rise for
        a run of 120 metres?

11. A horizontal mine shaft is bored into the
    side of a mountain whose slope is 0.4
    (as shown).

    An air vent is to be installed 150 m along the shaft, directly up to the surface.
    (i) If y is the length of the air vent, write an equation for the slope of the
        mountain in terms of y.
    (ii) Using algebra, find the value of y.

Investigation:

Copy this grid onto a large sheet of paper.
Given the point A(4, 3), mark points on the grid so that:

(i) [AB] has a slope of 3
(ii) [AC] has a slope of 1
(iii) [AD] has a slope of $\frac{1}{2}$
(iv) [AE] has a slope of -2
(v) [AF] has a slope of $-\frac{3}{4}$.

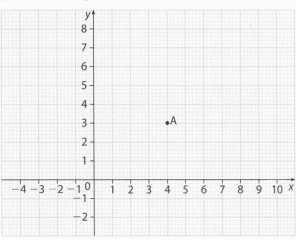

Test yourself 13

1. (i) Write down the coordinates of the points marked A to G in the given figure.
   (ii) Write down the coordinates of the four corners of the door.

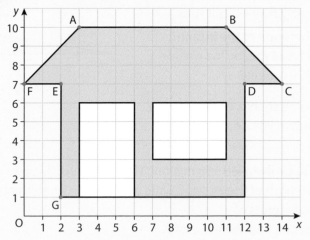

2. A number of places are shown on the given graph.
   (i) Write down the coordinates of
      (a) the playground
      (b) home
      (c) the post office
      (d) granny
   (ii) One day Paula left home and travelled to $(-3, -1)$; then onto $(1, 0)$ and then to $(3, -1)$.
      Write down the places she visited.

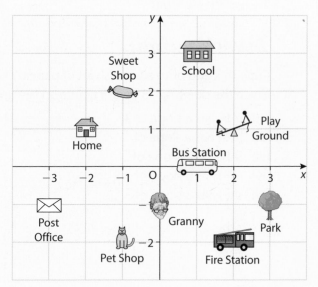

3. Make a copy of this grid.

   Plot the points A(1, 5), B(4, 7), C(7, 5).

   If D has coordinates (7, 1), what shape is ABCD?

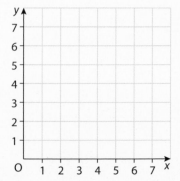

4. Write down the coordinates of each labelled point:

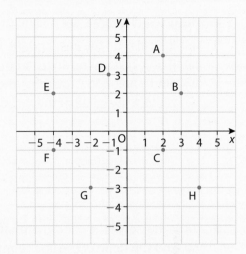

5. (i) Write down the coordinates of the given points A, B and C.

(ii) If ABCD is a rectangle, find the coordinates of D.

(iii) Find the coordinates of the midpoints of

(a) [AB] (b) [BC] (c) [AC].

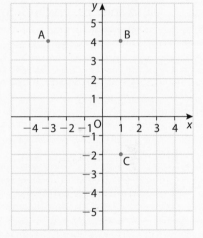

6. The given diagram shows three lines a, b, and c.

Match the lines with these slopes:

2, $\frac{1}{2}$, 1.

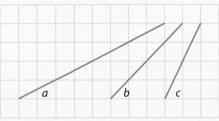

7. Work out (i) the coordinates of the midpoint (ii) slope of each of these line segments.

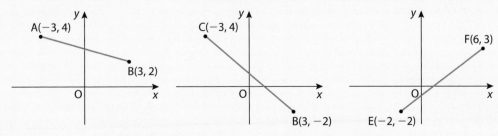

8. The given diagram shows a line ℓ.

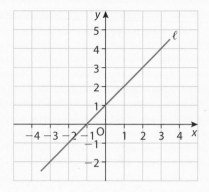

   (i) If $(2, a)$ is on the line, find the value of a.

  (ii) If $(-3, b)$ is on the line, find the value of b.

 (iii) Find a point on ℓ such that the y-coordinate is twice the value of the x-coordinate.

9. (i) Write down the coordinates of A and B.

  (ii) Find the slope of the line segment [AB].

 (iii) A line ℓ passes through the midpoint of [AB] and through the point C. Find the slope of ℓ.

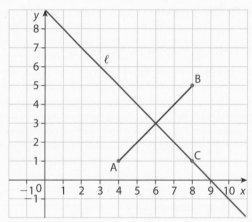

Learning Experience   Unit 13

Assignment 1

(a) Write down the coordinates of points A, B, C, D and E.

(b) Calculate the slope of each line segment.

(c) What conclusion can be made about the slope of the line segments as C is lowered down to B?

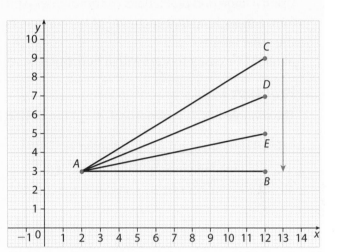

(d) What conclusion can you make about the slope of a horizontal line?

(e) Write down the coordinates of the points H, J, K, L, M, N and I.

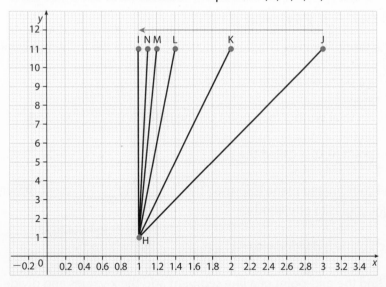

(f) Calculate the slope of each line segment as J is brought over to I?

(g) What conclusions would you make about the slope of a vertical line?

Assignment 2

Using a large grid plot 3 pairs of coordinates which form a triangle so that each side of the triangle has the same length.
(It might be easier to start with a horizontal base!)

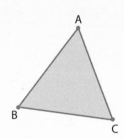

Problem 1

The triangle ABC is symmetrical about the dotted line.

Explain (justifying any assumptions you make) how to find the area of the triangle using the coordinates given.

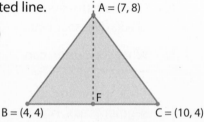

$A = (7, 8)$

$B = (4, 4)$ $C = (10, 4)$

Chapter 13 review 1

Using the terms from the chapter, copy and complete the following sentences:

1. To fix a point on a plane we need its _____.

2. The general symbol for a point on the plane is (_____, _____).

3. The point (0, 0) is called the _____.

4. The coordinated plane is formed by _____ and _____ axes, drawn at right angles to one another.

5. Each plane is divided into 4 _____ by the *x* and *y* _____.

6. To find the mid-point of a line segment add the *x*-values and divide by _____, add the y-values and divide by _____.

7. The slope of a line measures the _____ of the line.

8. The slope of the line is calculated by dividing the _____ by the _____.

9. The symbol for the slope of a line is _____.

10. A _____ line has a slope of 0.

Chapter 13 review 2

You should now be able to:

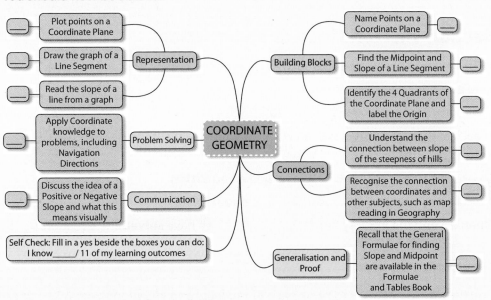

315

chapter

14 Solving Equations

In this chapter, you will learn to:

- **form equations,**
- use symbols for **unknowns,**
- solve equations using the **balancing method,**
- find **solutions,**

- solve equations with unknowns on both sides of the equation,
- solve equations with brackets,
- use algebra to solve problems.

Section 14.1 The idea of an equation

In Chapter 6, we used **symbols** such as $\square$, $\blacktriangle$ and $*$ to represent unknown numbers.

Here are some examples:

$$\square + 6 = 10 \qquad \blacktriangledown \times 4 = 20 \qquad * - 9 = 3$$

In each of these examples, we can write down the value of the mystery number without too much difficulty.

An example such as $\square + 6 = 10$ is called an **equation**.

It is called an equation because $\square + 6$ is **equal to** 10.

When we find the mystery number, we say that we have **solved** the equation.

Exercise 14.1

Find the missing number to make each of the following equations true:

1. $\square + 6 = 8$

2. $4 + \square = 11$

3. $\square + 8 = 19$

4. $\square - 3 = 9$

5. $14 - \square = 1$

6. $3 \times \square = 36$

7. $\square \times 5 = 60$

8. $4 \times \square + 3 = 27$

9. $\square \times 5 - 3 = 27$

10. $6 \times \square - 6 = 30$

11. $30 \div 3 - \square = 6$

12. $\square \div 5 = 7$

13. $72 \div \square = 9$

14. $\dfrac{\square}{4} = 6$

15. $4 + 4 + \dfrac{\square}{4} = 9$

The mass (in grams) of one shape is given in each of the following diagrams.
Find the mass of the other shape.

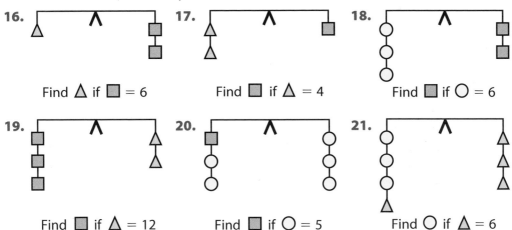

16. Find △ if ▢ = 6

17. Find ▢ if △ = 4

18. Find ▢ if ○ = 6

19. Find ▢ if △ = 12

20. Find ▢ if ○ = 5

21. Find ○ if △ = 6

22. This one is more difficult.

What is the mass of each chick in grams?

Section 14.2 Forming simple equations

Consider this problem:

> I think of a number and take 6 away from it.
> If the result is 12, find the number.

> Of course the mystery
> number is 18.

If we let x stand for the number, we could write the problem as follows:

$x - 6 = 12$

We have changed the word problem into an equation.

If we solve the equation, we find the mystery number.

Another word for
an equation is a
mathematical sentence.

The equation is: $x - 6 = 12$

Add 6 to both sides: $x - 6 + 6 = 12 + 6$

$\therefore \quad x = 18 \dots$ the required number.

Here are some examples of information changed to mathematical sentences:

> When 5 is added to a certain number,
> the result is 8.
>
> **Equation:** $x + 5 = 8$

> When 3 is taken from twice a certain
> number, the result is 10.
>
> **Equation:** $2x - 3 = 10$

317

Exercise 14.2

1. I think of a number and call it x. What number is
    (i) 2 bigger than x
    (ii) 4 bigger than x
    (iii) 3 less than x
    (iv) 10 less than x
    (v) 14 more than x
    (vi) twice x
    (vii) five times x
    (viii) 2 greater than twice x ?

2. Write an equation for each of the following. Use x as the unknown number.

    (i) I think of a number.
       I add 6.
       The result is 12.

    (ii) I think of a number.
       I subtract 7.
       The result is 10.

    (iii) I think of a number.
       I double it.
       The result is 14.

    (iv) I think of a number.
       I double it and then add 5.
       The result is 19.

    (v) I think of a number.
       I treble it and subtract 6.
       The result is 15.

    (vi) I think of a number.
       I add 2 to it.
       I multiply my answer by 4.
       The result is 28.

3. Write an equation for each of the following. Use n as the unknown number.

    (i) I think of a number.
       I multiply it by 3.
       I then add 7.
       The result is 19.

    (ii) I think of a number.
       I multiply it by 4.
       I then subtract 5.
       The result is 17.

    (iii) I think of a number.
       I add 3 to it.
       I multiply the result by 4.
       The result is 28.

    (iv) I think of a number.
       I subtract 2 from it.
       I multiply the result by 3.
       The result is 9.

4. Construct a series of short sentences which would result in the following equations. Start with 'I think of a number and call it x'.
    (i) $x + 4 = 9$
    (ii) $x - 8 = 4$
    (iii) $2x = 14$
    (iv) $3x = 27$
    (v) $2x + 3 = 13$
    (vi) $3x - 1 = 14$
    (vii) $5x + 1 = 31$
    (viii) $4x - 3 = 25$
    (ix) $2(x + 3) = 10$

Section 14.3 **Solving equations**

Equations are all about balancing the two sides of the equation.

In question 22 of section 14.1, we saw that 4 chicks 'balanced' with 1 chick and 24 grams.

The four diagrams below show that balancing can be used to solve the equation $x + 7 = 10$.

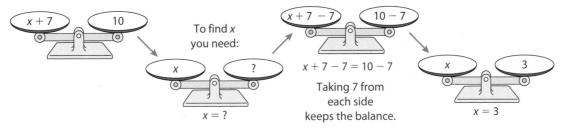

We say $x = 3$ is the **solution** to the equation.

The 'balancing' method for solving equations can be used in a more structured way as shown in the following two examples. These examples illustrate that whatever operation is performed on one side of an equation, the same operation must be performed on the other side.

Example 1

Solve the equation $x + 7 = 16$

$$x + 7 = 16$$

Take 7 from both sides: $x + 7 - 7 = 16 - 7$

$$\therefore \quad x = 9$$

Example 2

Solve the equation $3x - 5 = 16$

$$3x - 5 = 16$$

Add 5 to both sides: $3x - 5 + 5 = 16 + 5$

$$3x = 21$$

Divide both sides by 3: $x = 7$

Investigation:

Sophie is saving her money to help pay for a school trip. She has €25 to start with and plans on saving €15 each week. In groups, try to come up with as many ways as you can to represent her savings after a number of weeks.

(i)   How much money does she have after 6 weeks?
(ii) How much money does she have after 16 weeks?
(iii) How much money would she have if she saved for a whole year?
(iv) Which of your methods is easiest to use? Why?
(v)   If she needs to save €200 for her school trip, how many weeks does she need to save for?
(vi) If you haven't already done so, write an equation to solve part (v)
(vii) Make a poster of your work

Exercise 14.3

1. Write down the mass, in grams, of each object if the scales are balanced in each diagram:

(i)   (ii)

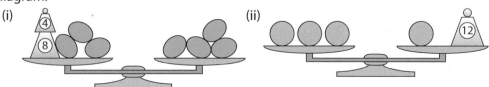

Solve each of the following equations:

2. $x + 4 = 10$	**3.** $x + 6 = 18$	**4.** $x + 7 = 12$	**5.** $x + 3 = 11$
6. $x - 4 = 7$	**7.** $x - 6 = 4$	**8.** $x - 7 = 1$	**9.** $x - 9 = 2$
10. $x + 6 = 14$	**11.** $2x = 8$	**12.** $3x = 15$	**13.** $4x = 12$
14. $5x = 25$	**15.** $6x = 30$	**16.** $7x = 28$	**17.** $9x = 18$
18. $x + 9 = 14$	**19.** $7x = 14$	**20.** $x + 7 = 11$	**21.** $x - 5 = 6$
22. $5x = 35$	**23.** $2x + 1 = 9$	**24.** $3x + 2 = 14$	**25.** $2x - 3 = 7$
26. $3x - 1 = 8$	**27.** $5x + 2 = 12$	**28.** $4x + 2 = 14$	**29.** $3x - 5 = 16$

30. $2x - 7 = 5$ **31.** $2x + 3 = 11$ **32.** $3x + 6 = 9$ **33.** $7x + 2 = 30$

34. $3x - 12 = 18$

Work out what x stands for in each of the following diagrams.

35. 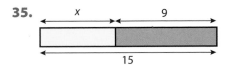   **36.**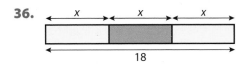

37. 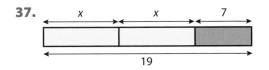   **38.**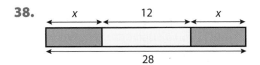

39. In the given diagram, the number in each box is found by adding the two numbers above it. Find the value of x.

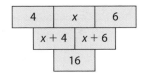

40. Write an equation in x and solve it in each of the following:

(i) 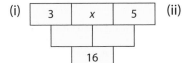   (ii) 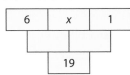   (iii)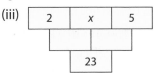

Section 14.4 Equations with letters on both sides

Consider the equation $5x + 1 = 2x + 10$.

This equation has letters on both sides.

Here we take $2x$ from each side to get rid of the xs on the right-hand side.

Again $5x + 1 = 2x + 10$

$5x + 1 - 2x = 2x - 2x + 10$ … take $2x$ from each side

$3x + 1 = 10$

$3x + 1 - 1 = 10 - 1$ … take 1 from each side

$3x = 9$

$x = 3$ ... divide both sides by 3

Example 1

Solve the equation $x - 15 = 9 - 2x$

In this equation, we will add $2x$ to both sides to get rid of the letter term on the right-hand side.

Add $2x$ to each side: $x - 15 + \mathbf{2x} = 9 - 2x + \mathbf{2x}$

$\therefore \qquad 3x - 15 = 9$

Add 15 to each side: $3x - 15 + \mathbf{15} = 9 + \mathbf{15}$

$3x = 24$

Divide both sides by 3: $x = 8$

Exercise 14.4

1. The scales on the right are balanced.
If x is the weight of 1 cake in grams, use the
diagram to write down an equation in x.
Now solve the equation to find the value of x.

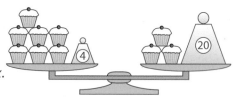

Solve the following equations:

2. $3x + 3 = 2x + 7$ **3.** $8x + 5 = 7x + 10$ **4.** $5x + 2 = 4x + 8$

5. $7x + 3 = 5x + 9$ **6.** $5x + 1 = 3x + 11$ **7.** $6x + 2 = 3x + 5$

8. $6x - 2 = 4x + 10$ **9.** $7x - 9 = 3x + 11$ **10.** $9x - 15 = 3x + 3$

11. $x + 7 = 2x - 1$ **12.** $2x + 6 = 4x - 6$ **13.** $3x + 1 = 5x - 13$

14. $5x - 2 = 40 - x$ **15.** $3x + 7 = 32 - 2x$ **16.** $6 + 2x = 33 - x$

17. Work out the value of x in each of these diagrams:

(i)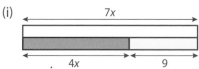

(ii)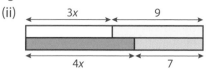

18. The perimeter of the given triangle is 36 cm.
Find the value of x.

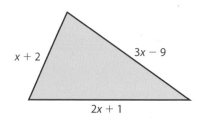

19. What is the sum of the three angles of a triangle?

Now write an equation and solve it to find the value for x in each of these triangles:

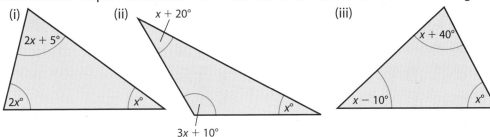

(i) $2x + 5°$ $2x°$ $x°$

(ii) $x + 20°$ $x°$ $3x + 10°$

(iii) $x + 40°$ $x - 10°$ $x°$

20. The solution to each equation below stands for a letter.
Use the table on the right to find the letters.
Rearrange them into the name of an animal.

$3x + 6 = 12$ $16 - 2x = 6$

$21 - 3x = 2x + 11$ $4x + 4 = 16$

$6x - 2 = 4$ $6x - 9 = 5x$

1	T
2	B
3	A
4	F
5	R
6	G
7	E
8	S
9	I

Section 14.5 **Equations with brackets**

In chapter 8, you learned how to remove the brackets in an expression.

For example, $3(2x - 1) = 6x - 3$.

When solving equations involving brackets, we first remove the brackets as shown in the following example.

Example 1

Solve the equation: $4(2x - 3) = 2(3x - 5)$.

In this type of equation, we first remove the brackets:

$$4(2x - 3) = 2(3x - 5)$$

Remove the brackets: $8x - 12 = 6x - 10$

Add 12 to both sides: $8x - 12 + \mathbf{12} = 6x - 10 + \mathbf{12}$

$\therefore \quad 8x = 6x + 2$

Take $6x$ from both sides: $8x - \mathbf{6x} = 6x + 2 - \mathbf{6x}$

$2x = 2$

Divide both sides by 2: $x = 1$

Exercise 14.5

Solve the following equations:

1. $2(x + 3) = 12$

2. $2(x - 1) = 6$

3. $3(x + 4) = 18$

4. $5(x - 1) = 10$

5. $3(2x + 1) = 33$

6. $4(2x - 3) = 36$

7. $3(2x + 1) = 2x + 11$

8. $5x + 5 = 2(2x + 5)$

9. $3(2x - 10) = 2x + 10$

10. $5(2x - 1) = 8x + 7$

11. $4(2x - 3) = 2(3x - 5)$

12. $3(2x - 6) = 2(2x + 1)$

13. $3(5x - 2) = 4(3x + 6)$

14. $5(3x - 2) = 7(2x - 1)$

15. $5(x + 4) - 3(x - 2) = 32$

16. $5(2x - 4) = 3(2x - 1) - 1$

17. $6(1 + 2x) = 5(3x - 1) - 4$

18. $2(x + 2) - 3(x - 3) = x + 7$

19. Use the given diagram to write down an equation in x.
    Now solve the equation to find the value of x.

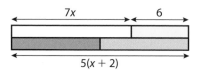

20. By forming an equation, find the value of x in the given diagram.

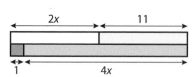

Section 14.6 Writing and solving equations

In section 14.2, we learned how to change statements into equations.

In this section, we will continue with this process and then solve the equation.

Example 1

When 3 is taken from five times a certain number, the result is the same as adding 6 to twice the number. Find this number.

Equation: $\qquad 5x - 3 = 2x + 6$

Add 3 to each side: $\qquad 5x - 3 + 3 = 2x + 6 + 3$

$\qquad \therefore \qquad 5x = 2x + 9$

Take $2x$ from each side: $\qquad 5x - 2x = 2x + 9 - 2x$

$\qquad\qquad 3x = 9$

$\qquad \therefore \qquad x = 3$

The required number is 3.

Example 2

One number exceeds another number by 6. When 4 is added to three times the smaller number, the result is the same as twice the larger number. Find the numbers.

Let x and $(x + 6)$ be the numbers ...... [$(x + 6)$ is the larger]

Equation:
$$3x + 4 = 2(x + 6)$$
$$3x + 4 = 2x + 12$$

Take 4 from both sides: $\quad 3x + 4 - 4 = 2x + 12 - 4$
$$3x = 2x + 8$$

Take $2x$ from both sides: $\quad 3x - 2x = 2x + 8 - 2x$
$$\therefore \quad\quad x = 8$$

The first number, x, is 8.
The second number, $(x + 6)$, is $8 + 6 = 14$
$\quad \therefore \quad$ the numbers are 8 and 14.

Exercise 14.6

Write each of the following statements as equations and then solve the equation.

1. I think of a number, add 8 to it and the result is 14. Find the number.

2. I think of a number, double it and then add 5.
   If the result is 19, find the number.

3. I think of a number, treble it and take 6 from my answer.
   If the result is 18, find the number.

4. To four times a certain number I add 16 and the result is 28. Find this number.

5. If I multiply a number by 3 and then subtract 4, the result is the same as twice the number. Find this number.

6. When 3 is taken from five times a certain number, the result is the same as adding 6 to twice the number. Find this number.

7. One number is 5 greater than another number.
   If the sum of the two numbers is 59, find the numbers.

8. When 3 is taken from twice a certain number, the result is the same as adding 3 to the number. Find this number.

9. One number is 5 greater than another number. If twice the smaller number is added to the larger one, the result is 26. Find the two numbers.

10. Write an equation for each of these shapes.
Solve it to find the value of a.

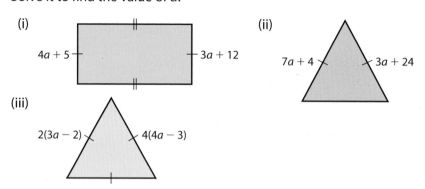

(i) $4a + 5$ $3a + 12$

(ii) $7a + 4$ $3a + 24$

(iii) $2(3a - 2)$ $4(4a - 3)$

11. Write an equation and solve it to find the value of x in the given figure.

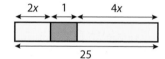

$2x$ 1 $4x$

25

12. When a number is increased by 4 and the result is doubled, the answer is 22. Find the number.

13. One number exceeds another number by 6.
Write these two numbers in terms of x.
When twice the larger number is added to three times the smaller number, the result is 32.
Find the two numbers.

14. Ann is 5 years older than Mary.
If the sum of their ages is 51, find the age of each.

15. Write and solve an equation to find the value of n.
Use this to find the missing numbers.
Part (i) has been started for you.

The number in each box is the sum of the two numbers above it.

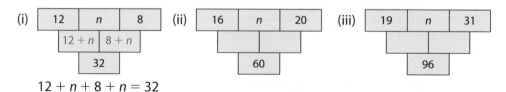

(i)
12	n	8

$12 + n$	$8 + n$

32

(ii)
16	n	20

60

(iii)
19	n	31

96

$12 + n + 8 + n = 32$

16. In each of these problems, use angle facts to form an equation.
Solve it to find the unknown. The angles are measured in degrees.

(i)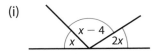

(ii)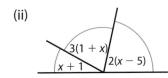

17. Alan is x years of age and his father is three times as old.
If the sum of their ages is 64 years, find Alan's age.

18. This is an isosceles triangle where equal sides are marked.
If the perimeter of the triangle is 76 cm,

(i) write down an equation in a
(ii) solve the equation to find the value of a
(iii) find the length of the equal sides.

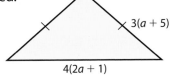

19. Jack is seven years older than Conor.

(i) If Jack's age is x years, what is Conor's age?
(ii) Write down an expression for the sum of their ages.
(iii) If twice the sum of their ages is 66 years, find Conor's age.

Investigation:

When forming equations from written sentences, we need to translate from
English into Maths symbols.

Construct a table of these words as below. Try to think of as many words as
you can that mean the same as each column heading:

+	−	×	÷	=

Compile a class list and display in the classroom.

Test yourself 14

1. Solve each of these equations:

   (i) $2x + 5 = 9$

   (ii) $3x + 2 = x + 4$

   (iii) $6x - 2 = x + 8$

2. The given scales are balanced.
   If x units is the weight of each cat,
   write an equation in x and solve it to
   find the value of x.

3. Write an equation and solve it to find the value of x in each of the figures below:

   (i)

   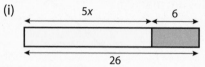

   (ii)

   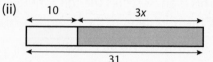

4. Solve each of these equations:

   (i) $7x = 21$

   (ii) $5x + 3 = x + 27$

   (iii) $2(x - 3) = 4(x - 4)$

5. When 4 is taken from three times a certain number, the result is the same as adding 5 to twice the number. Find the number.

6. The perimeter of the given rectangle is 22 cm.

   Form an equation and solve it to find the value of x.

   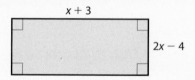

7. Solve these equations:

   (i) $3x - 12 = 6$

   (ii) $5(x - 3) = 3x - 3$

   (iii) $3(2x - 1) = 15$

8. The lengths of the sides of the given triangle are in centimetres.
   If the perimeter is 26 cm, find the value of x.

   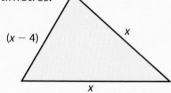

9. Use the given figure to write an equation in x.
   Now solve it to find the value of x.

   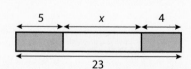

10. Solve each of these equations:

    (i) $2x - 9 = x - 5$

    (ii) $4(x - 2) + 2 = 3(x - 2)$

11. I think of a number.

When I add 2 to the number and multiply my answer by 4, the result is 20.

What is the number?

12. The given rectangle measures $(3x - 7)$ cm by $(x + 5)$ cm.

Find the value of x if the rectangle is a square.

$(3x - 7)$ cm

$(x + 5)$ cm

13. The number in each box is the sum of the numbers in the two boxes above it.

For each diagram, form an equation in n and solve it to find its value.

(i)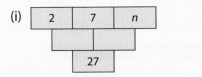

(ii)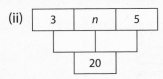

14. Write down two expressions for the length of the given figure.

By equating the lengths, solve the equation to find the value of x.

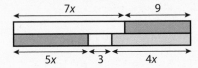

Learning Experience   Unit 14

Assignment 1

If you are given 6 identical coins, one of which is a little lighter than the other 5, describe how you could find the light coin in just *two* weighings (using the scales shown)?

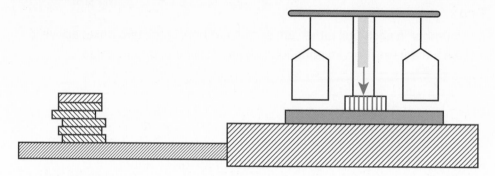

Assignment 2

If #A = 8, #B = 7 and # (A ∪ B) = 10, show how to find # (A ∩ B) using algebra. i.e.

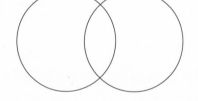

A(8)   B(7)

(i)   let x = the unknown
(ii) fill in the Venn diagram using x
(iii) form an equation using x
(iv) solve the equation for x
(v)   verify your result.

Problem 1

This panel is on the front of a safe.

The letters P, Q, R and S stand for whole, positive numbers.

To open the safe all numbers must be revealed.

The numbers at the side and the bottom show the sum of each row and column.

Describe how to find what numbers the letters P, Q, R, and S stand for.

4	R	Q	P	15
4	Q	S	P	14
R	P	Q	4	15
Q	P	S	R	16
16	14	14	16	

Problem 2

My niece Michelle is 6 years old and I am 40.
In how many years will I be three times as old as her.

Let x = the number of years, make a large poster of the
equation needed to find the value of x, labelling each
part of the equation.
Find x.

Chapter 14 review 1

Using the terms from the chapter, copy and complete the following sentences:

1. In algebra we use $x, y, a, b, etc.$ to represent an _____ quantity.

2. Information in problems is changed into _____ using algebra.

3. Central to every equation is the _____ sign.

4. If we find a value for $x, y, a, etc.$, we have _____ the equation.

5. When solving an equation, we use the "_____" method.

Chapter 14 review 2

You should now be able to:

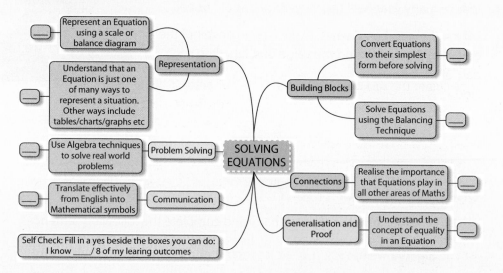

Geometry 2

In this chapter, you will learn to:

- name a triangle,
- calculate the size of an unknown angle,
- identify an **exterior angle**,
- recognise an **equilateral** triangle,
- recognise an **isosceles** triangle,
- recognise a **right-angled** triangle,
- recognise a **scalene** triangle,
- construct the **bisector** of a given angle using only compass and straightedge,

- **construct** the perpendicular bisector of a line segment,
- construct a line **perpendicular** to a given line *l*, passing through a given point,
- draw a line **parallel** to a given line *l*, passing through a given point,
- divide a line segment into three equal parts,
- draw a line segment of a given length on a given ray.

Section 15.1 Angles of a triangle

A triangle has three sides and three angles.

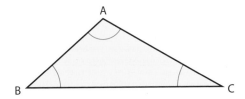

Each corner of the triangle is called a **vertex** (plural **vertices**).

The triangle above is called the triangle ABC or $\triangle$ABC.

It could also be named as $\triangle$BAC or $\triangle$CBA.

The angle at the vertex B can be written as $\angle$B or $\angle$ABC.

The size or measure of $\angle$ABC is written as $|\angle$ABC$|$.

The triangle is enclosed by the three line segments [AB], [AC] and [BC].

Investigation:

Cut a triangle from a piece of
paper and mark each angle (a, b, c).
Then tear off the corners.
Place the corners together and
investigate the result.
Turn some pieces keeping the
corners together.
What results from the reassembly each time.
Compare your results with other students
Based on this investigation what **conclusion** can be drawn about **all** triangles.

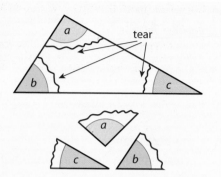

Example 1

Find the sizes of the angles marked with
letters in the given diagram.

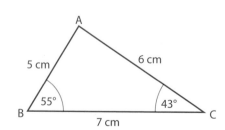

Angles in a straight line add
up to 180°.

$$|\angle E| + 55° = 180°$$
$$|\angle E| = 180° - 55°$$
$$|\angle E| = 125°$$

Angles in a triangle add up to 180°.

$$|\angle A| + 55° + 84° = 180°$$
$$|\angle A| + 139° = 180°$$
$$|\angle A| = 180° - 139°$$
$$|\angle A| = 41°$$

Exercise 15.1

1. For the given triangle, write down

    (i) $|\angle ABC|$ (ii) $|\angle ACB|$

  (iii) $|\angle BAC|$ (iv) $|AB|$

   (v) $|AC|$ (vi) $|BC|$

2. Copy the given triangle and mark these measurements
on your sketch.

$$|XY| = 3, |XZ| = 4.2, |YZ| = 5$$
$$|\angle XYZ| = 68° \text{ and } |\angle YXZ| = 80°$$

Find $|\angle XZY|$.

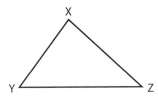

3. Draw any triangle and use your protractor to verify that the three angles of a
triangle add up to 180°.

4. If the symbol ⌐ denotes a right angle (90°), find the size of the angle marked with a
letter in each of these triangles:

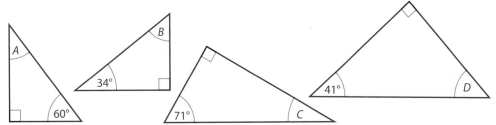

5. Find the size of the angle marked with a letter in each of the following triangles:

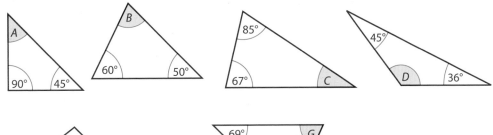

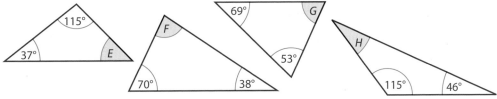

6. Remembering that a straight angle is 180°, find the size of the angle marked with a letter in each of the following triangles:

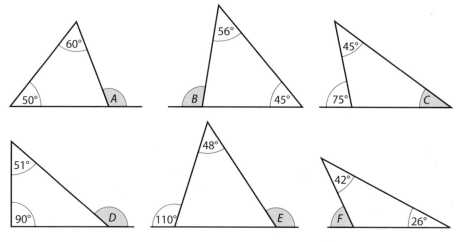

7. Find the values of *a* and *b* in each of these diagrams:

(i)   (ii)   (iii)

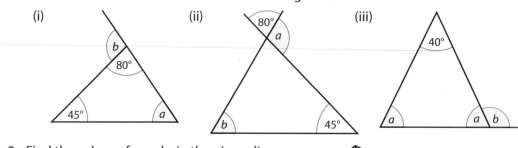

8. Find the values of *x* and *y* in the given diagram.

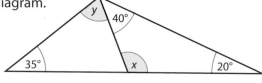

9. Find the angles marked with letters in this diagram.
   Explain your answers by using one of the explanations on the right below.

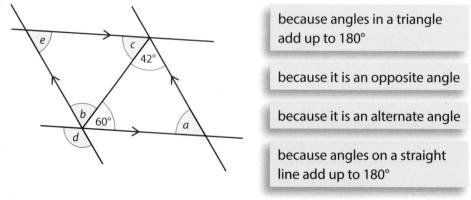

because angles in a triangle add up to 180°

because it is an opposite angle

because it is an alternate angle

because angles on a straight line add up to 180°

10. Explain why a triangle can never have a reflex angle within it.

Section 15.2 **Exterior angle of a triangle**

In the given diagram, one side of the triangle is
extended or produced.

The shaded angle is called an **exterior angle**
because it is outside the triangle.

The angles marked 1 and 2 are called
interior remote angles relative to the shaded angle.

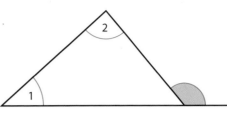

> The shaded exterior angle is equal in size to the sum of the interior remote angles.

Here's why!

The given triangle contains the angles
A, B and C and an exterior angle D.

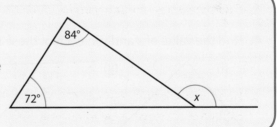

$$|\angle D| + |\angle C| = 180° \text{ ... straight angle}$$
$$\text{Also} \quad |\angle A| + |\angle B| + |\angle C| = 180° \text{ ... angles in a triangle}$$
$$\therefore \quad |\angle D| + |\angle C| = |\angle A| + |\angle B| + |\angle C|$$
$$|\angle D| = |\angle A| + |\angle B| \text{ ... take } \angle C \text{ from both sides}$$

Example 1

Find the value of the angle marked x
in the given triangle.

$$|\angle x| = 84° + 72° \text{ ... exterior angle}$$

$$\therefore \quad |\angle x| = 156°$$

Exercise 15.2

1. Name the two exterior angles in the given triangle.

(i) Name the angle that is equal to $1 + 3$.
(ii) Name the angle that is equal to $1 + 2$.
(iii) How many degrees in $1 + 2 + 3$?

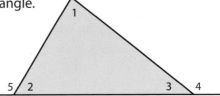

2. Find the value of the angle marked with a letter in each of the following triangles:

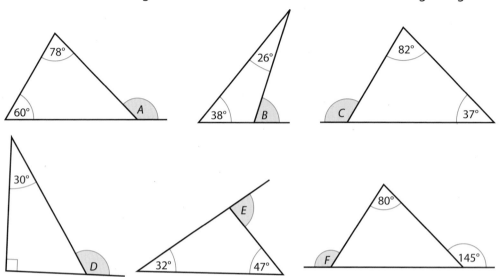

3. Find the value of *x* in each of these triangles:

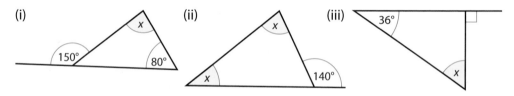

4. Find the value of *x* and *y* in each of these figures:

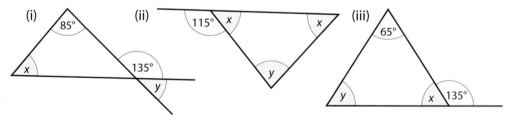

5. Show that angle *a* = angle *b*.

Write down all your working and reasons.

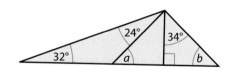

6. Find the value of *x* and the value of *y* in the given figure.

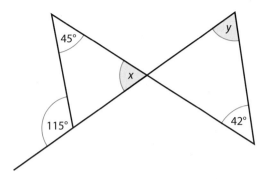

Section 15.3 Special triangles

1. Equilateral triangle

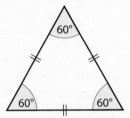

> All three sides are the same length.
> All three angles are the same size. All are equal to 60°.

2. Isosceles triangle

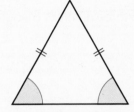

> Two sides equal in length.
> The angles opposite the equal sides are equal.

Similar symbols on lines show that sides are equal in length.

3. Right-angled triangle

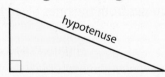

> One angle is a right angle (90°).
> The side opposite the right angle is called the **hypotenuse**.

4. Scalene triangle

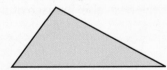

> Three unequal sides.
> Three unequal angles.

Example 1

Find the size of the angle marked *a* in the given triangle.

Since the triangle is isosceles, the unmarked angle is also *a*.

$$\text{Sum of angles} = 180°$$
$$\therefore \quad |\angle a| + |\angle a| + 48° = 180°$$
$$2a + 48° = 180°$$
$$2a = 180° - 48°$$
$$2a = 132°$$
$$a = 66°$$

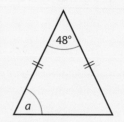

Exercise 15.3

1. Name three different triangles in this diagram.

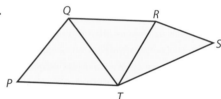

2. In the given diagram,
$$|AE| = |BE| = |BD| = |DE|$$
and CDE is a straight line.
   (i)   What special name is given to the
        triangle ABE?
  (ii)   What special name is given to the triangle BDE?
 (iii)   The triangle BDC is scalene.
        Name another scalene triangle in the diagram.

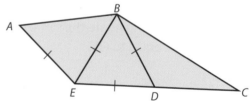

3. Pick the best label for each of the following triangles from the ones given below.

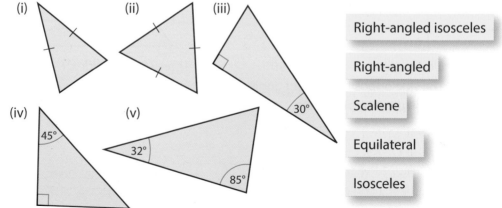

Right-angled isosceles

Right-angled

Scalene

Equilateral

Isosceles

4. Name the equal angles in each of the following isosceles triangles:

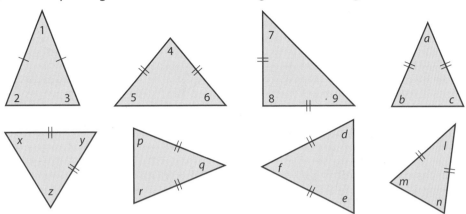

5. Calculate the measure of the angle marked with a letter in each of the following triangles:

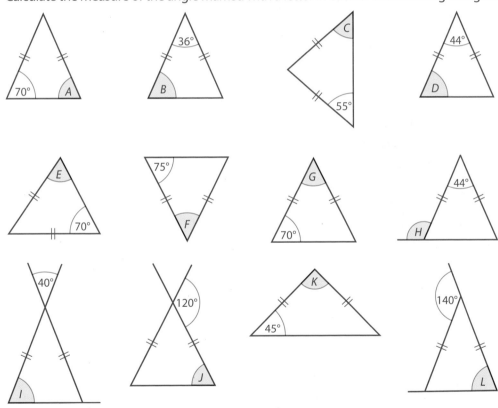

6. In the diagram, $|AD| = |DB| = |BC| = |CD|$.

    (i) What type of triangle is *BCD*?

    (ii) What is the size of angle *BDC*?

    (iii) Work out the size of angle *ABC*.

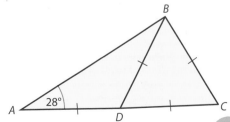

7. Find the value of *x* in each of the following diagrams:

(i)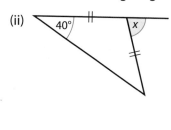

(ii)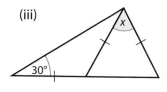

(iii)

8. In the diagram, $|AB| = |BD| = |DA|$ and $|BC| = |CD|$.
CD is extended to E.

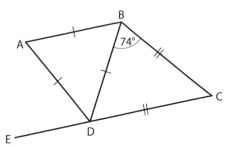

   (i) What type of triangle is *BCD*?
  (ii) What is the size of angle *BDC*?
 (iii) What is the size of angle *DAB*?
 (iv) Work out the size of angle *ADE*.

9. In each of the following diagrams, the arrows indicate that the lines are parallel.
Find the value of *x* in each diagram.

(i)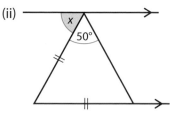

(ii)

(iii)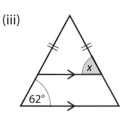

10. In the given diagram, equal sides are marked.
Find the sizes of the angles marked *c* and *d*.

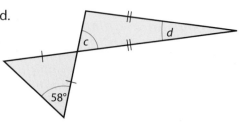

Investigation:

By cutting out strips of paper/cardboard can you make triangles with the following sets of sides?

Side 1	Side 2	Side 3	Yes/No
5 cm	7 cm	10 cm	
4 cm	5 cm	11 cm	
5 cm	4 cm	3 cm	
12 cm	5 cm	5 cm	
6 cm	6 cm	6 cm	

Can you write a statement explaining why it is **not always** possible to make a triangle with 3 lengths.

Section 15.4 **Constructions** —————————

1. **Bisector of a given angle using only compass and straightedge** ——

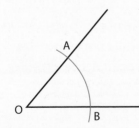 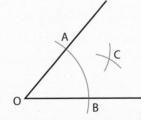 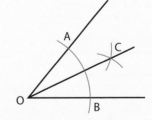

To bisect the given angle, place the point of the compass at O and draw an arc to cut both arms of the angle at A and B.

With the point of the compass at A, and keeping the same radius, draw an arc between the arms of the angle. Repeat at B, cutting the first arc at C.

Using the straightedge, join the point O to C.
OC is the bisector of the angle AOB.

2. How to construct the perpendicular bisector of a line segment

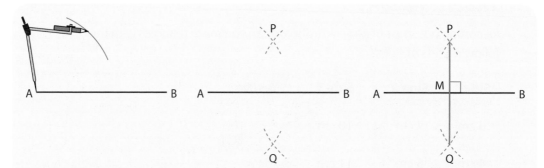

Set your compass to over half the length of [AB]. With A as centre, draw an arc above and below the line.

Keep your compass with the same radius. With B as centre, draw two more arcs. These arcs intersect the first two arcs at P and Q.

Join P and Q.
PQ is the perpendicular bisector of [AB].
M is the midpoint of [AB].

3. Line perpendicular to a given line ℓ, passing through a given point on ℓ

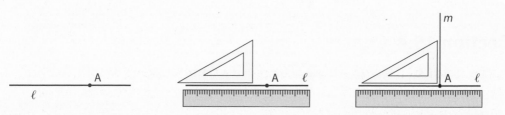

Given a line ℓ and the point A on ℓ.

Place the ruler along the line ℓ and place the set square on the ruler.

Move the set square along the ruler until it reaches the point A. Draw the line m through A.
m is perpendicular to ℓ.

4. How to draw a line parallel to a given line, through a given point

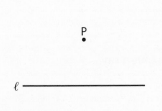
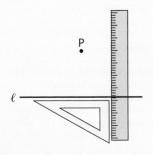
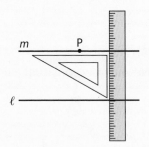

Given a line ℓ and a point P.	Place one side of the set square along the line ℓ. Place the ruler along the other side and hold firmly.	Slide the set square along the ruler up to the point P. Draw a line m through P. The line m is parallel to ℓ.

5. Division of a line segment into three equal parts

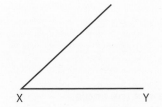
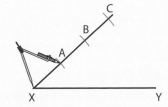
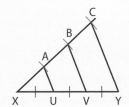

Draw a line segment [XY]. Draw a line through X making an acute angle with [XY].	Use a compass with X as centre and draw an arc crossing the line at A. With A as centre and with the same radius, draw another arc crossing the line. Mark this point B. Repeat the process at point B and mark the new point C.	Join C to Y. Using a set square and ruler, draw lines through A and B parallel to CY. These lines meet [XY] at the points U and V, respectively. U and V divide [XY] into three equal parts.

6. How to draw a line segment of a given length on a given ray

A ————————— B

[AB is a given ray.
We will now construct a line segment 6 cm in length on the given ray.

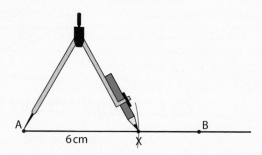

Use your ruler and compass to find a length of 6 cm.

Place the point of the compass on the point A and draw an arc intersecting the ray at the point X. The required line segment is [AX].

Exercise 15.4

1. Use your protractor to draw an angle of 70°.
   Now use your compass and ruler to construct the bisector of the angle.

2. Use your set square to draw a right angle.
   Now use your compass and ruler to divide the angle into two equal parts.
   Use your protractor to verify that each part is 45°.

3. Draw a line segment 6 cm in length.
   Use your compass to construct the perpendicular bisector of this line segment.
   Verify that each half is 3 cm in length.

4. Draw a line segment 7 cm in length.
   Bisect the line and verify that both halves are equal in length.

5. The diagram shows a line segment [AB] and a
   line AY in which |AX| = |XY|.
   Use your set square and ruler to draw XM parallel to YB.
   Verify that M is the midpoint of [AB].

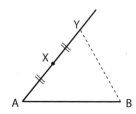

6. Draw a line segment 9 cm in length.
Now use your compass, ruler and set square to divide the line into 3 equal parts.
Use your ruler to verify that each part is 3 cm in length.

7. Draw a triangle ABC having the same measurements as those shown on the right.
Use your compass to bisect the three sides of the triangle.
If your drawing is accurate, the three lines should intersect at the same point.
Now use this point as the centre to draw a circle through A, B and C.
This circle is called the **circumcircle** of the triangle.

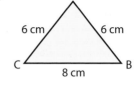

8. Draw a triangle with base 7 cm and other sides of length 5 cm and 6 cm.
Bisect the three angles using a compass and ruler.
The three bisectors should meet at the one point.
Using this point as centre, draw a circle which touches the three sides of the triangle.
This circle is called the **incircle** of the triangle.

Test yourself 15

1. Find the missing angles in these triangles.

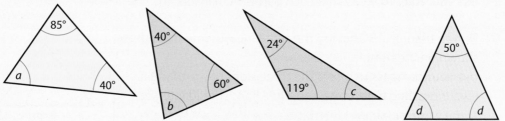

2. Find the size of the angle marked with a letter in each of these triangles:

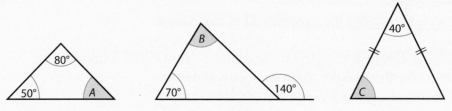

3. Calculate the size of each angle marked with a letter.
Give reasons for your answers.

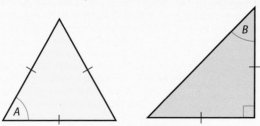

4. Find the sizes of the angles marked
A and B in the given triangle.

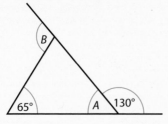

5. Find the size of angle C.
Triangle ABC is equilateral.
Explain why.

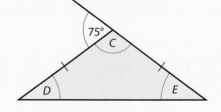

6. Say whether each of these statements is true or false:
   (i)   A triangle can have two right angles.
   (ii) A triangle can have a right angle and two acute angles.
   (iii) A triangle can have an acute angle and two obtuse angles.
   (iv) A triangle can contain a right angle and an obtuse angle.
   (v)   An equilateral triangle could contain a right angle.

Learning Experience   *Unit 15*

Assignment 1

The diagram below shows "regular" geometric shapes, i.e., all the sides have the same length. By studying the shapes (the blue dotted lines break the square and the pentagon into triangles) copy and complete the chart below.

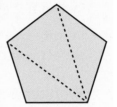

Remember that "the sum of all the angles in a triangle is 180°".

	Triangle	Square	Pentagon
Number of sides			
Number of angles			
Sum of all the angles			
The size of each angle			

Assignment 2

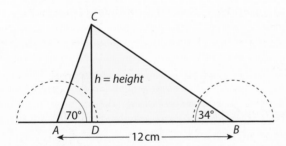

On a large sheet of paper draw a line segment [AB], 12 cm long.
At the point A, using a protractor, create ∠70°.
At the point B, using a protractor, create ∠34°.
Continue the line segments until they meet at C.
Using a ruler and set square draw a line perpendicular to [AB] through C.
Measure |CD| accurately, correct to the nearest mm.
Given that $h = 6.5$ cm. Find the error in your answer.
Using the fraction $\frac{error}{6.5} \times \frac{100}{1}$ express your error as a percentage.
Find the area of the triangle.

Problem 1

The diagram shows a triangle with the base extended.
Two external angles are
formed 165° and 75°.

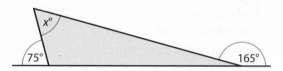

Describe how to show that the
size of the interior angle $x°$ is 60°.

Problem 2

Explain why

$$a + b + c + d + e + f = 720°$$

(Hint! Name each of the interior angles and
check section 15.2)

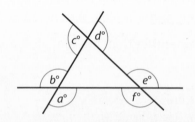

Chapter 15 review 1

Using the terms from the chapter, copy and complete the following sentences:

1. Each corner of a triangle is called a _____.

2. The _____ _____ of a triangle add up to 180°.

3. When any side of a triangle is extended an _____ angle if
   formed.

4. The _____ angle of a triangle is equal in size to the sum of the
   interior remote angles.

5. All the angles of an _____ triangle measure 60°.

6. In an isosceles triangle only _____ of the sides have the same length.

7. A triangle with all three sides the same length is called an _____ triangle.

8. A scalene triangle has three _____ sides and three unequal _____.

9. In a right-angled triangle the side opposite the right angle is the _____.

10. In a right-angled triangle the longest side is the _____.

11. To construct a bisector of an angle a _____ and _____ are needed.

12. To construct a line parallel to a given line a _____ and _____ are needed.

Chapter 15 review 2

You should now be able to:

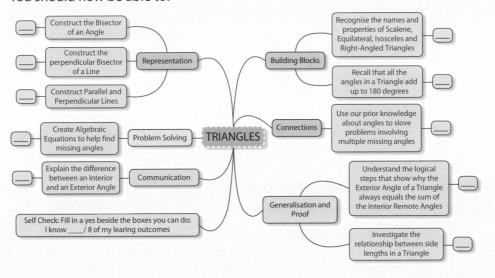

16 Presenting Data

In this chapter, you will learn to:

- make and interpret **line plots**,
- make and interpret **bar charts**,
- make and interpret **stem and leaf plots**,
- understand the **key** of a stem and leaf plot,
- understand how bar charts measure **frequency**.

Section 16.1 Line plots

Twenty five pupils in a class were asked to write down the numbers of children in their families.

The results are given in the table below:

Number of children per family	1	2	3	4	5	6
Number of families	4	6	7	5	2	1

We will now show this information on a **line plot**.

On the horizontal line, we write the number of children per family.

Each child is represented by a dot (•) as shown below.

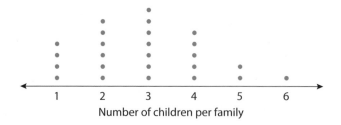

From the line plot, it is easy to see that there are seven families that have three children.

A line plot is very suitable for categorical data.

Exercise 16.1

1. The line plot below shows the number of goals scored per match on a Saturday afternoon in a football league.

Number of goals scored

   (i)   What does each dot represent?
   (ii) How many matches were played on that Saturday?
   (iii) In how many matches were 3 goals scored?
   (iv) In how many matches was an even number of goals scored?
   (v)   How many matches ended in a 0-0 draw?
   (vi) What is the greatest number of matches that could have ended 2-2?

2. The table below gives the different ways in which the pupils in a first-year class travel to school.

Way of travel	Walk	Bicycle	Bus	Car	Train
Number of pupils	7	3	8	4	3

   (i)   Draw a line plot to illustrate this data.
   (ii) How many pupils are there in the class?
   (iii) What was the most frequently-used method of travelling to school?
   (iv) What percentage of pupils travelled by bus?

3. The colours of cars in a car-park are listed below:

   white   red   blue   green   blue   red   silver
   blue   silver   white   silver   blue   red   green
   silver   blue   red   blue   silver   green   white

   Represent this data on a line plot.

4. The frequency table below shows the numbers of text messages received by a group of students on a particular day:

No. of messages	1	2	3	4	5	6	7
Frequency	2	4	4	7	5	4	2

   (i)   Represent this data using a line plot.
   (ii) How many students were in the group?
   (iii) How many students received 5 text messages or more?
   (iv) What percentage of the group received 4 text messages?

Section 16.2 Bar charts

Bar charts are a simple but effective way of displaying data.

A bar chart consists of a series of bars of the same width, drawn either vertically or horizontally.

The bars are generally (but not always) separated by narrow gaps of equal width, which make the chart easier to read.

Both axes must be clearly labelled.

The height of each bar gives the frequency.

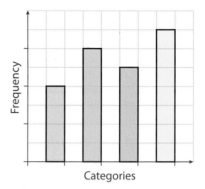

The bar chart below shows how 60 first-year students generally travel to school.

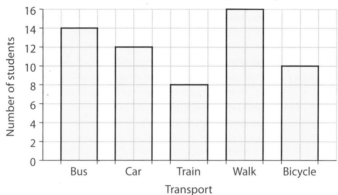

It can be seen from the bar chart that 14 travel by bus, 12 by car, 8 by train, 16 walk and 10 cycle.

Notice that the numbers of students who travel by the different methods are shown on the vertical line (or axis).

Bar charts are particularly suitable for making comparisons. It is instantly clear from the given bar chart that the most common way of travelling to school is by walking, while the least common way is by train.

Example 1

The table below gives the make of 120 cars in a car park.

Make of car	Ford	VW	Toyota	Fiat	Nissan	Opel	Others
Number of cars	32	16	24	8	12	20	8

(i) Draw a vertical bar chart to show this information.

(ii) What percentage of the cars are Nissan?

(i)

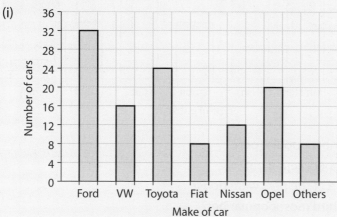

(ii) Percentage of cars that are Nissan is

$$\frac{12}{120} \times \frac{100}{1}\% = \frac{1200}{120} = 10\%$$

Exercise 16.2

1. The bar chart below shows the colours of cars in a car park.

   (i) How many red cars were in the car park?

   (ii) What was the most popular colour of car in the car park?

   (iii) Find the total number of cars in the car park.

   (iv) What fraction of the cars were red?

   (v) What percentage of the cars were black?

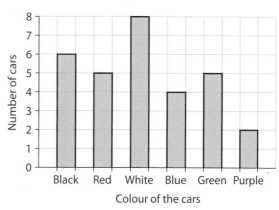

2. The bar chart below shows the type of pet kept by members of a youth club. No member kept more than one type of pet.

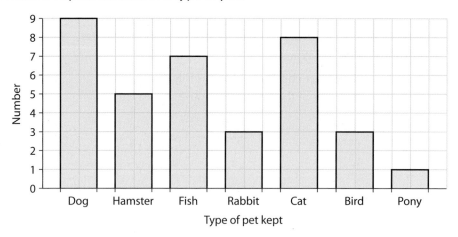

(i) Which was the most popular pet?
(ii) How many members kept a pet?
(iii) What percentage of the pets were dogs?
(iv) Which was the third most popular pet?
(v) What fraction of the pets were rabbits?

3. The students of first-year carried out a traffic survey by standing outside the school gates for half an hour one morning. Their results are illustrated by the bar chart opposite. (Note; in this chart the bars are side by side)
(i) How many lorries passed during the survey?
(ii) Find the total number of vehicles which passed.
(iii) What fraction of the vehicles were buses?
(iv) What percentage of the vehicles were vans?
(v) How many more lorries than jeeps passed?

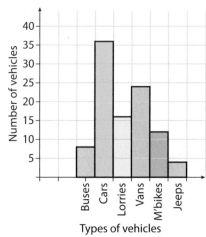

4. This bar chart gives the number of students in each of the first four year-groups of a school.

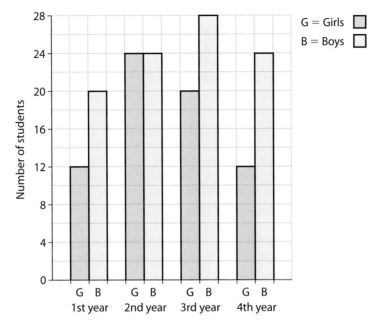

   (i)   Find the number of students in each of the four years.
  (ii)   In which year is the number of boys the same as the number of girls?
 (iii)   In which year is the number of boys twice the number of girls?
 (iv)   In which years are there 8 more boys than girls?
  (v)   Which year has the least number of students?
 (vi)   What fraction of first-year students are girls?

5. The bar chart below gives the favourite subject chosen by each pupil in a class of 30.

   (i)   How many students chose Maths?
  (ii)   What subject was chosen by four students as their favourite subject?
 (iii)   How many subjects were more popular than English?
 (iv)   What percentage of students chose PE?
  (v)   One subject was $2\frac{1}{2}$ times more popular than another subject. Name these two subjects.

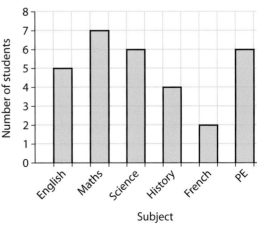

6. The following table gives the shoe sizes for a class of 30 first-year students:

Size of shoe	4	5	6	7	8
Number of students	4	8	10	6	2

Draw a vertical bar chart to represent this information.
Mark the shoe size on the horizontal axis and the number of students on the vertical axis.

7. The table below gives the number of children per household on a certain street.

Number of children per household	0	1	2	3	4	5	6
Number of households	12	6	10	14	8	6	4

Draw a bar chart to illustrate this information.

   (i) How many households were on the street?
  (ii) How many households had four children or more?
 (iii) What fraction of the households had no children?
 (iv) What percentage of the households had 2 or 3 children?
  (v) What was the third most common number of children per household?

8. The following bar chart represents the marks scored by a class of 30 pupils in a test:

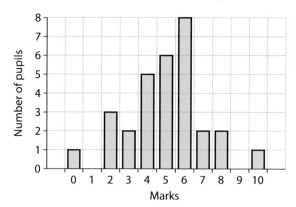

   (i) How many pupils scored 7 marks or more?
  (ii) Which mark was scored most frequently?
 (iii) What percentage of the pupils got less than 4 marks?
 (iv) Which mark was scored by exactly 3 students?

9. For her survey on fitness, Doreen asked a sample of people, as they left a sports centre, which activity they had taken part in. She then drew a bar chart to show her data.

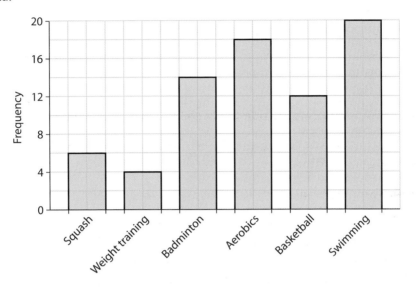

  (i) Which was the most popular activity?

 (ii) How many people took part in Doreen's survey?

(iii) Give a probable reason why fewer people took part in weight training.

(iv) Is a sports centre a good place in which to do a survey on fitness? Explain why.

10. The bar chart on the right shows the amount of money raised for new computers by the five year-groups in a school.

Does year 1 have fewer pupils than year 3?

Select one of these answers.

     1. Yes   2. No   3. Can't tell

Explain your selection.

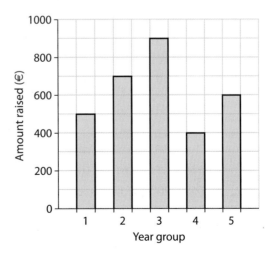

11. These graphs show the temperatures for three weeks of the year. Match these sentences to the bar charts.

(i) It was very warm at first, then suddenly it got much colder.

(ii) Every day was colder than the day before.

(iii) Every day was hotter than the day before.

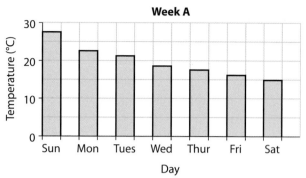

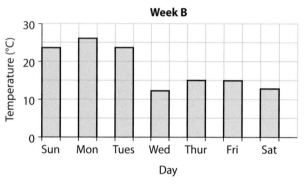

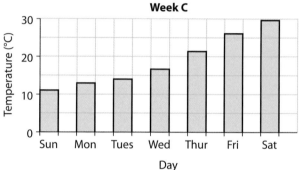

Investigation:

Using a suitable Computer Software Program, create a Bar chart to display a set of data you have available.

This could be from a survey you carried out in Chapter 12, or think of a new question to ask the students in your class.

Use the different options in the program to present the data as clearly as possible.

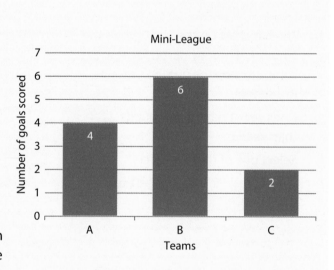

Section 16.3 Stem and leaf plots

A **stem and leaf plot** is a very useful way of presenting **numerical** data.

It is useful because it shows all the original data and gives you an overall picture that shows the shape of the data.

It is similar to a horizontal bar chart, with the numbers themselves forming the bars. Stem and leaf plots are suitable only for small amounts of data.

A stem and leaf plot is made by splitting the number into two parts.

If the numbers consist of two digits, e.g. 34, 46, 57, ..., the stem will represent the tens and the leaf will represent the units.

Here is a typical stem and leaf plot:

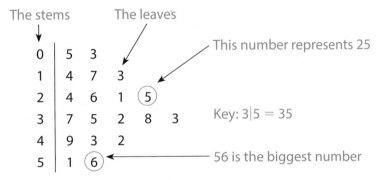

The stems   The leaves

This number represents 25

0	5	3
1	4	7	3
2	4	6	1	(5)
3	7	5	2	8	3
4	9	3	2
5	1	(6)

Key: 3|5 = 35

56 is the biggest number

You must always add a **key** to show how the stem and leaf combine.

The data or numbers represented above are:

5, 3, 14, 17, 13, 24, 26, 21, 25, 37, 35, 32, 38, 33, 49, 43, 42, 51, 56

We will now redraw the stem and leaf plot above, putting the numbers in **order of size**.

This is shown on the right.

0	3	5
1	3	4	7
2	1	4	5	6
3	2	3	5	7	8
4	2	3	9
5	1	6

Key: 2|1 = 21

Example 1

The times, in seconds, taken by 20 students to complete a puzzle are shown below.

$$17, \quad 9, \ 23, \ 28, \ 14, \ 12, \ 26, \ 32, \ 23, \ 19,$$
$$34, \ 13, \quad 8, \ 28, \ 42, \ 36, \ 23, \ 33, \ 11, \ 44$$

Construct a stem and leaf plot to represent this information.

The smallest number is 8 and the largest is 44.
The stem of the diagram will be in tens starting with 0 and finishing with 4.

Now work through the numbers and put the second digit in the appropriate row.

```
0 | 9  8
1 | 7  4  2  9  3  1
2 | 3  8  6  3  8  3
3 | 2  4  6  3
4 | 2  4
```

We now rewrite the diagram with all the leaves in order, with the smallest nearest to the stem.

```
0 | 8  9
1 | 1  2  3  4  7  9
2 | 3  3  3  6  8  8
3 | 2  3  4  6
4 | 2  4            Key: 2|6 = 26
```

Exercise 16.3

1. The stem and leaf plot below shows the marks obtained by students in a maths test.

```
4 | 1  5  7
5 | 0  3  5  9
6 | 2  3  4  7  8
7 | 1  4  7  8
8 | 2  5  8
9 | 3                Key: 6|2 = 62
```

(i) How many students took the test?

(ii) What was the highest mark achieved?

(iii) How many students got between 60 and 70 marks?

(iv) How many students got 80 marks or more?

(v) If an A-grade is 85 marks or more, how many students got an A-grade?

2. The stem and leaf plot below shows the ages of the first 25 customers to enter a shop one morning.

```
0 | 7  9
1 | 5  7  8  9
2 | 0  2  3  5  6  8  9
3 | 2  4  7  8  9
4 | 1  3  6  8
5 | 2  4  5          Key: 1|8 = 18
```

(i) What age was the youngest customer?

(ii) How many customers were aged between 20 and 30 years inclusive?

(iii) What fraction of customers were aged between 30 and 40 years?

(iv) How many customers were in their teens?

(v) How many were younger than the oldest customer?

3. The stem and leaf plot below shows the times, in seconds, taken by a group of first-year pupils to complete a 200-metre race.

```
2 | 6  8  9
3 | 1  5  6  8  9
4 | 0  2  5  5  8  9
5 | 1  3  6  7
6 | 2  5  7  8
7 | 0  1            Key: 4|0 = 40 seconds
```

(i) What was the fastest time recorded?

(ii) How many pupils ran the race in less than 40 seconds?

(iii) How many pupils took part in the race?

(iv) What was the time of the 8th fastest pupil?

(v) What was the time of the 3rd slowest pupil?

(vi) What was the difference between the times of the fastest and slowest pupils?

(vii) If a time of 40 seconds or less qualifies a pupil for a further race, how many pupils qualified?

4. Twenty pupils were asked how many DVDs they had in their collection.
   The results are shown below:

   6, 14, 8, 11, 15, 24, 17, 25, 23, 6, 9, 15, 19, 21, 28, 32, 10, 34, 12, 23

   (i)   Draw a stem and leaf plot to show this information.
         (The stems are done for you.)
   (ii) How many students had more than 20 DVDs?
   (iii) How many students had 15 or less DVDs?
   (iv) What was the difference between the highest and
         lowest numbers of DVDs in the collections?

   ```
   0 |
   1 |
   2 |
   3 |
   ```

5. The numbers of points gained by the teams in a football league at the end of the
   season are as follows:

   ```
   38   62   33   46   24   53   47   66   41   62
   38   80   46   45   51   54   39   52   62   34
   ```

   (i)   Draw a stem and leaf plot to represent this data.
   (ii) How many teams got 60 or more points?
   (iii) What was the difference between the highest and lowest number of points?
   (iv) What percentage of the teams scored between 40 and 50 points?

6. Here are the marks, out of 50, scored by pupils in a Science test:

   32, 36, 41, 14, 23, 27, 34, 11, 21, 28, 9, 32, 46, 24, 31, 43, 36, 27, 34, 36

   (i)   Draw a stem and leaf plot to represent this data.
   (ii) How many pupils scored more than 30 marks?
   (iii) What was the difference between the highest and lowest mark?
   (iv) Marks between 30 and 39 inclusive got grade B.
         How many pupils achieved grade B?
   (v)   What was the mark that was scored most frequently?

7. The stem and leaf plot below shows the lengths of time it takes members of a class
   to complete one length of a swimming pool.

   ```
   17 | 3  5  8
   18 | 2  6  7  8  9
   19 | 0  1  6  7  7  7  9
   20 | 2  5  6  9  9
   21 | 1  3  7
   22 | 2  5
   ```
   Key 20|2 = 20.2 seconds

    (i) What was the time of the slowest swimmer?

    (ii) How many members had a time of 20 seconds or more?

    (iii) How many members had times of less than 19 seconds?

    (iv) What was the difference in times between the fastest and slowest swimmers?

    (v) What percentage of the members took 21 seconds or more?

8. One Saturday, Conor recorded the ages of the first 30 customers at a supermarket. The ages are shown below.

    24   32   18   45   34   27   16   41   36   8   21   39   19   22   31

    35   28   17   24   35   15   26   34   34   24   48   27   34   43   14

    (i) Construct a stem and leaf plot to represent this data.

    (ii) What was the age of the third youngest person?

    (iii) How many customers were aged between 20 and 30 years?

    (iv) What was the most frequently recorded age?

9. The stem and leaf diagram opposite shows the ages, in years, of 26 people who wished to enter a 10-km walking race.

    (i) How many people were less than 20 years old?

    (ii) Write down the most frequently recorded age.

    (iii) Exactly half the people entering the walk are more than a certain age. What is that age?

    (iv) Shauna says that two people will not be allowed to enter.

        Using the information in the stem and leaf diagram, suggest a possible reason for this.

stem	leaf
0	8 9
1	4 4 6 9
2	1 3 6 6 6 8
3	3 5 5 7 9
4	0 2 3 3 7 7
5	1 2 4

Key: 1|4 = 14 years old

10. The weights, in grams, of 20 cherry tomatoes are shown.

    5.4   4.6   6.7   3.9   4.2   5.0   6.3   5.4   4.8   3.5

    4.6   5.6   5.8   6.0   2.8   4.4   4.7   5.6   5.1   4.6

    (i) Draw a stem and leaf diagram to represent this information.

    (ii) What is the difference between the highest and lowest weight?

    (iii) How many tomatoes weighed 5 grams or more?

    (iv) What was the most frequently recorded weight?

11. These are the numbers of visits to the library by women members in one year.

12	43	24	0	37	32	8	15	14	21	36	14
23	33	15	0	34	13	13	3	16	3	38	29
22	16	44	12	41	18	26	8	12	15		

(i) Record this data in a stem and leaf diagram like this one. Put the leaves in order.

(ii) Use your stem and leaf diagram to find

    (a) the difference between the highest and lowest number of visits

    (b) the number of members who made 30 or more visits to the library.

Library visits by women

0	
1	
2	
3	
4	

12. These are the numbers of library visits made by the men in one year.

(i) Write down the lowest and highest numbers of visits made by these men.

(ii) Make two statements about the differences between the numbers of visits made to the library by men and women (in Q11 above).

Library visits by men

0	0	0	2	4	5	5	5	7	8	8	9
1	2	2	4	4	6	6	7	7	8		
2	0	1	2	5	7	8					
3	1	5									

Key: $2|1 = 21$ visits

Test yourself 16

1. The bar chart below shows information about the sales of fresh and frozen poultry at a butcher's shop on a particular Saturday.

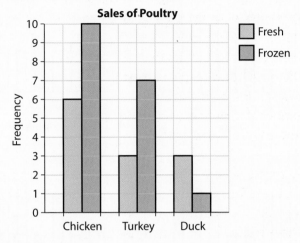

(i)   How many frozen chickens were sold?

(ii) How many fresh turkeys were sold?

(iii) How many ducks were sold altogether?

(iv) What fraction of the turkeys sold were frozen?

(v)   What percentage of the ducks sold were fresh?

2. The result of throwing a dice 30 times is shown.

```
1   2   3   3   5   2   1   6   5   4
2   4   5   3   2   3   1   4   2   6
6   3   6   5   3   1   3   4   6   5
```

(i) Copy and complete the frequency table for these scores.

(ii) Draw a bar chart to show the data. Which score occurs most often?

Score	Tally	Frequency
1		
2		
3		
4		
5		
6		

3. The table below gives the shoe sizes of third-year pupils in a school.

Shoe size	3	4	5	6	7	8	9
Number of pupils	2	6	9	7	6	4	1

(i)   Which is the most common shoe size?

(ii) How many pupils took part in the survey?

(iii) What fraction of the pupils wore size 7 or size 8?

(iv) Draw a line plot to show this data.

(v)   Name another diagram that could be used to represent this data.

4. These bar charts show the numbers of hours of TV watched by four boys one week.

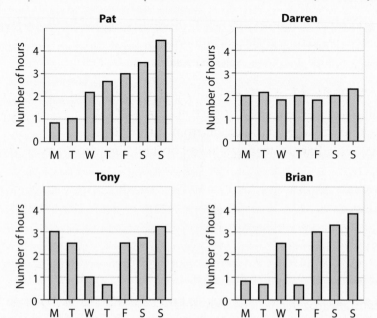

Whose graph matches these comments?

(i) I watched most TV at the beginning and end of the week.

(ii) I watched about the same amount of TV each day.

(iii) I watched quite a lot of TV on four days and not much on the other three days.

(iv) Each day I watched more TV than on the day before.

5. Here are the marks of 20 students in a science test displayed in a stem and leaf diagram.

(i) What is the lowest mark?

(ii) What is the difference between the lowest and highest marks?

(iii) If marks between 40 and 60 inclusive achieve grade C, how many got this grade?

(iv) What percentage of the students got a mark between 50 and 60?

stem	leaf
2	6 8
3	3 7 9
4	0 5 7 8
5	3 5 7 9
6	1 2 4 8
7	1 3 5

Key: 5|3 = 53

Learning Experience   Unit 16

Assignment 1

Collect data on the number of children per family from your class. Draw a large (i) line plot (ii) bar chart to represent the data from your class. If possible compare your results with the results from another class.

- From your diagrams state any relevant observation you can make about the data.
- From your diagrams state if either plot has an advantage over the other in regards to clarity.
- Would a stem and leaf diagram be a good way to represent this data? Explain your answer.

Assignment 2

Having completed the exercises in this chapter, compare the statistical presentations of (i) line plots (ii) bar charts (iii) stem and leaf plots by drawing a table as shown below.

Take into account (i) time taken to create the chart (ii) suitability (iii) clarity and other aspects that promote the use of one chart over the other.

	Line plots	Bar charts	Stem and Leaf plots
1.			
2.			
3.			
4.			

Problem 1

Three stem and leaf plots are given below. Match the letters in the plots with the correct values below to find out "What the computer did on Owenahincha beach"?

A	B	C
10 12 23 25 26 32 41 45 48 56	100 106 110 115 120 135 154 180 196 199	500 507 512 518 522 535 536 538 540
1 0 E 2 3 F 6 D 2 4 R 5 8 5 6	10 0 I 11 0 5 U 0 13 5 14 15 4 16 17 18 0 19 6 N	50 0 H 51 2 8 52 2 53 5 6 T 5S 0

‾‾   ‾‾   ‾‾   ‾‾   ‾‾   ‾‾   ‾‾   ‾‾   ‾‾   ‾‾   ‾‾   ‾‾   ‾‾   ‾‾

 6   8   4   12   1   5   2   3   8   7   2   9   2   8

Chapter 16 review 1

Using the terms from the chapter, copy and complete the following sentences:

1. A line plot represents each element of the _____ by means of a _____ or other suitable symbol.

2. The bars in a bar chart can be drawn _____ or _____.

3. The height (or length) of each bar is a measure of the _____.

4. A _____ is essential to understand the connection between the stem and the leaf in a stem and leaf plot.

5. A stem and leaf plot is used to represent _____ data.

6. A _____ _____ can be used to represent categorical data.

Chapter 16 review 2

You should now be able to:

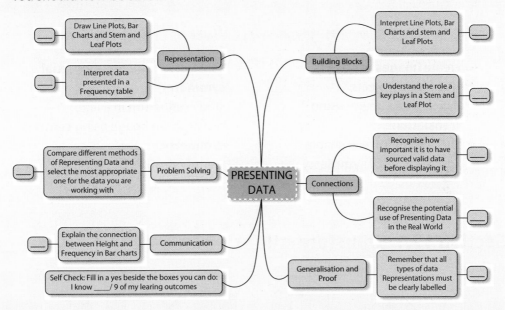

Representation
- Draw Line Plots, Bar Charts and Stem and Leaf Plots
- Interpret data presented in a Frequency table

Building Blocks
- Interpret Line Plots, Bar Charts and stem and Leaf Plots
- Understand the role a key plays in a Stem and Leaf Plot

Problem Solving
- Compare different methods of Representing Data and select the most appropriate one for the data you are working with

Connections
- Recognise how important it is to have sourced valid data before displaying it
- Recognise the potential use of Presenting Data in the Real World

PRESENTING DATA

Communication
- Explain the connection between Height and Frequency in Bar charts

Generalisation and Proof
- Remember that all types of data Representations must be clearly labelled

Self Check: Fill in a yes beside the boxes you can do:
I know _____/ 9 of my learing outcomes

Transformation Geometry

In this chapter, you will learn to:

- create **images** of objects,
- **transform** objects,
- construct an image using **translations**,
- study **symmetrical** shapes,
- identify **axes of symmetry**,
- construct an image using **axial symmetry**,
- study **reflection** in a line,
- construct an image using **central symmetry**,
- identify **centres of symmetry**.

Section 17.1 Transformations

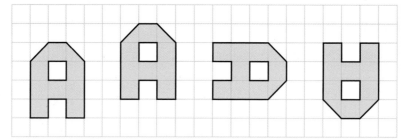

The letter A on the left above has been moved to three other positions in the plane.
The three As on the right are called **images** of the first A.

The shapes and sizes of these images do not change but two of them look different because one is on its side and the other is upside down.

These are examples of what we call **transformations**.

The original figure is called the **object**.

The new position of the figure is called the **image**.

In this chapter, we will consider three transformations.

These are
1. **Translations**
2. **Axial symmetry**
3. **Central symmetry**

Translations

The illustrations below show the movement of a man on an escalator. He is standing upright in both illustrations but has moved or 'glided' from one position to another.

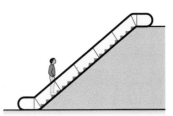 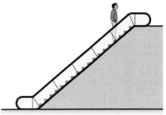

In Mathematics, movement in a straight line is called a **translation**.

When a shape is moved in a straight line,
   (i) the shape and size of the object do not change
  (ii) the object does not turn or rotate.

We use a line segment with an arrow like that shown on the right to illustrate the direction and distance in which an object is moved.

The translation AB is written as $\overrightarrow{AB}$.

In this diagram, shape A is mapped to shape B by a **translation**.
The red arrow shows the distance and direction of the movement.

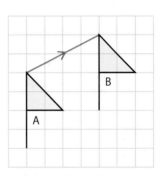

The translation may be described as a movement of 4 places to the right and 2 places up.

Shape B is the image of shape A, under this translation.

Note:

$\overrightarrow{BA}$ is a map in the opposite direction to $\overrightarrow{AB}$.

With $\overrightarrow{AB}$ the point D is the image of C

With $\overrightarrow{BA}$, the point E is the image of C

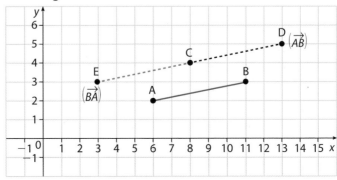

Constructing the image of a figure under a translation

On the right we have a translation $\overrightarrow{AB}$ and a point X. To find the image of X under the translation $\overrightarrow{AB}$, we move X along a line parallel to AB so that $|XX'| = |AB|$.

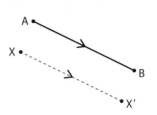

We use a set square and ruler to do this.

X′ is the image of X under $\overrightarrow{AB}$.

The diagram below shows $\triangle ABC$ and the translation $\overrightarrow{DE}$.

Place the set-square along the translation $\overrightarrow{DE}$.

Place the ruler along the set-square at right angles to the translation.

Move the set-square along the ruler until the point B is at the edge of the set-square.

Draw a line through B parallel to DE.

Continue along the ruler drawing parallel lines through C and A.

Measure $|DE|$. Mark a point F so that $|DE| = |BF|$

Repeat with points A and C. Then $|AG| = |CH| = |BF| = |DE|$

Join the points F, G and H.

$\triangle FGH$ is the **image of** $\triangle ABC$ under the **translation** $\overrightarrow{DE}$.

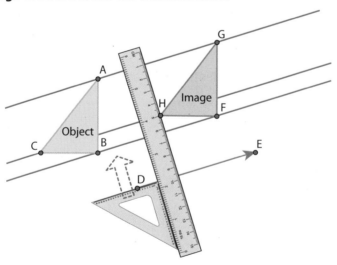

Exercise 17.1

1. Copy the diagrams below and then find the image of the point X under the translation $\overrightarrow{AB}$ in each of them:

2. Find the image of the line segment [XY] under the translation $\overrightarrow{AB}$ in each of the following two diagrams:

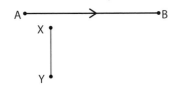
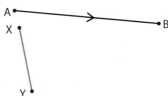

3. Draw a sketch of the image of each of the letters shown below under the given translation:

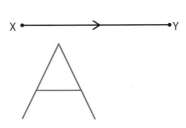
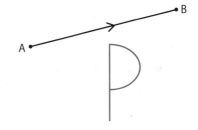

4. Draw the triangle ABC twice and then construct its image under

    (i) $\overrightarrow{BC}$ (ii) $\overrightarrow{AB}$.

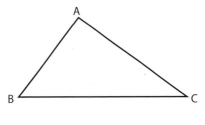

5. Copy the rectangle ABCD, as shown. Now construct the image of ABCD under the translation $\overrightarrow{AB}$.

6. Draw a rectangle similar to that shown in Question 5 and then construct its image under the translation $\overrightarrow{DB}$.

7. ABCD is a parallelogram with the diagonals intersecting at the point O.
    (i) What is the image of D under $\overrightarrow{DC}$?
    (ii) What is the image of A under $\overrightarrow{DC}$?
    (iii) What is the image of B under $\overrightarrow{AD}$?
    (iv) What is the image of the line segment [AD] under $\overrightarrow{AB}$?

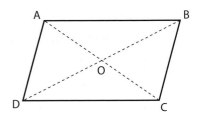

8. In the given diagram, the figure PQRS is mapped to the figure P'Q'R'S'.

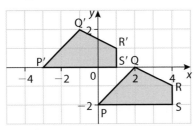

   Copy and complete this sentence:
       'The image figure P'Q'R'S' is found by moving the original figure PQRS ... squares to the left and then up ... squares.'
   Now describe how you could move P'Q'R'S' back to PQRS.

9. Which shape is reached after these translations?
    (i) Shape 3 by 6 right and 1 up
    (ii) Shape 1 by 4 left and 2 up
    (iii) Shape 2 by 7 left and 6 down.

10. Describe the translations which take
    (i) shape 1 to shape 2
    (ii) shape 3 to shape 1
    (iii) shape 1 to shape 4.

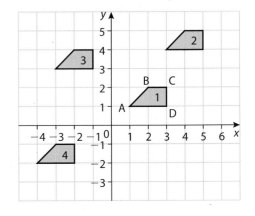

11. ABCD and ABEC are parallelograms.

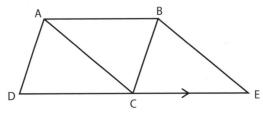

   Under the translation $\overrightarrow{CE}$, write down the image of
   (i) the point A   (ii) [AD]   (iii) △ADC   (iv) [AC].

12. In the given diagram, the square GFEB is the image
    of the square ABCD under the translation $\overrightarrow{DB}$.

    (i)   What is the image of B under $\overrightarrow{DB}$?
    (ii) What is the image of [AD] under $\overrightarrow{DB}$?
    (iii) What is the image of △BDC under $\overrightarrow{DB}$?
    (iv) What is the image of [AB] under $\overrightarrow{FE}$?
    (v)   What is the image of [GF] under $\overrightarrow{AD}$?

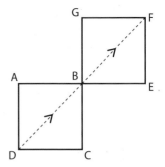

Section 17.2 Symmetrical shapes – Axial symmetry

When each of the shapes shown below is folded along the broken line, one half of the
figure fits exactly over the other half. These shapes are said to be **symmetrical**.

The fold line is called the **axis of symmetry**.

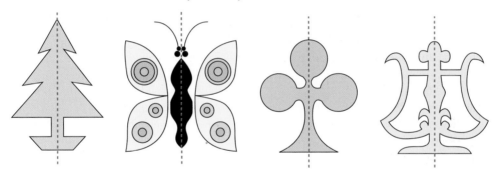

Each of the figures above has only one axis of symmetry.

Some figures have two or more axes of symmetry.

Examples of such figures are shown below.

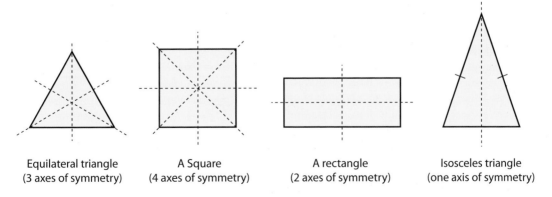

Equilateral triangle	A Square	A rectangle	Isosceles triangle
(3 axes of symmetry)	(4 axes of symmetry)	(2 axes of symmetry)	(one axis of symmetry)

Note: The diagonals of a rectangle with unequal sides are not axes of symmetry.

Axial symmetry

The diagram on the right shows a blue paper shape and the line *m*.

If we fold the paper along the line *m*, we get the green shape.

Notice that the image is 'flipped over' or 'back-to-front' relative to the given shape.

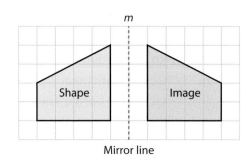

The process of finding the image of a figure (or point) by folding along a line is known as **reflection in a line** or **axial symmetry**.

The reflection line is also known as the **mirror line**.

In the diagrams below, the blue figures are the images of the green figures under axial symmetry in the given line, *m*.

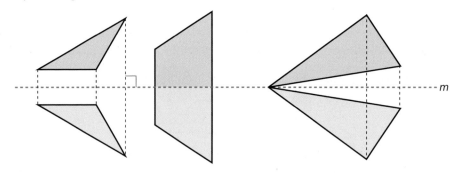

Note: If a point is on the mirror line, its image is the point itself.

Example 1

The diagram on the right shows the square EFGH, the image of the square ABCD under axial symmetry in the line *m*.
Find the image of each of the following under S*m*, axial symmetry in the line *m*.

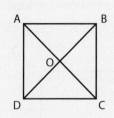
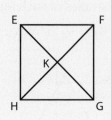

(i) [AD]   (ii) [AB]   (iii) [AC]   (iv) △BOC   (v) △AOB.

(i) The image of [AD] is [FG].   (ii) The image of [AB] is [FE].
(iii) The image of [AC] is [FH].   (iv) The image of △BOC is △EKH.
(v) The image of △AOB is △FKE.

Finding images under axial symmetry

On the right is a line ℓ and a point X.

To find the image of X under reflection in the line ℓ, we use a set square, as shown, and draw a broken line perpendicular to ℓ, through X.

We produce this line to X′ such that M is the midpoint of [XX′].

X′ is the image of X under S_ℓ, where S_ℓ is reflection in ℓ.

Note: A set square is essential to make sure that all construction lines are at **right angles** to the axis of symmetry.

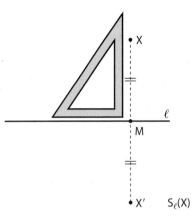

Investigation:

Symmetrical shapes appear all around us in nature, architecture, art etc. Make a poster with images of the most interesting symmetrical shapes you can find.

Draw the axis of symmetry in each case (where possible).

Exercise 17.2

1. Which of the following figures have an axis of symmetry?

(i) 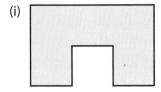　(ii) 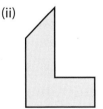　(iii) 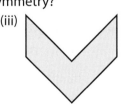　(iv)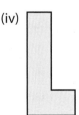

2. How many axes of symmetry has each of the following figures?

(i) 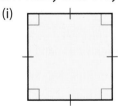　(ii) 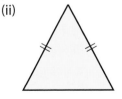　(iii)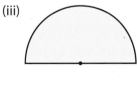

(iv) 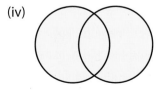　(v) 　(vi)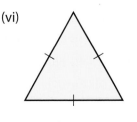

3. How many axes of symmetry (if any) has each of the letters shown below?

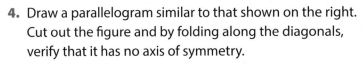

4. Draw a parallelogram similar to that shown on the right. Cut out the figure and by folding along the diagonals, verify that it has no axis of symmetry.

5. Make a copy of the rectangle shown and then draw in the axes of symmetry.

6. How many axes of symmetry has this figure?

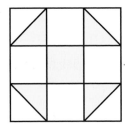

7. Use a set square and ruler to construct the image of X by S_ℓ, axial symmetry in the line ℓ, in each of the following diagrams:

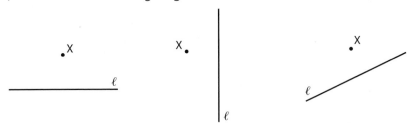

8. Draw a freehand sketch of the image of each of the following line segments under S_ℓ, axial symmetry in the line ℓ.

9. Some letters look the same after reflection in a vertical mirror line.
   (i) What do these three letters have in common?
   (ii) Can you draw any other capital letters that look the same when reflected in a vertical mirror line? (Exclude O.)

   M ⋮ M
   A ⋮ A
   H ⋮ H

10. These letters look the same when reflected in a horizontal mirror line.
    (i) What do these letters have in common?
    (ii) Can you draw any other capital letters that look the same when reflected in a horizontal mirror line? (Exclude O.)
    (iii) Can you draw a capital letter that looks the same when reflected in both a horizontal and vertical mirror line? (Exclude O.)

    E B C

    E B C

11. Use a set square or ruler to draw a rough sketch of the image of each of these shaded triangles under reflection in the mirror line *m*.

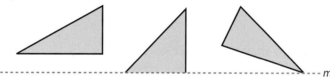

12. Construct the image of the given square ABCD under axial symmetry in the line BC.

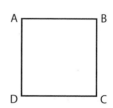

13. The diagram on the right shows the image of ABCD under an axial symmetry in the line ℓ.
    Write down the image of each of the following under $S_ℓ$, axial symmetry in the line ℓ:

    (i) the point A   (ii) the point C
    (iii) [DC]   (iv) [DA]
    (v) [BD].

14. In the given diagram, BEFC is the image of ABCD under axial symmetry in the line *m*.
    Write down the image of each of the following under axial symmetry in the line *m*:

    (i) D   (ii) [AD]
    (iii) [DC]   (iv) [BD]
    (v) [AC].

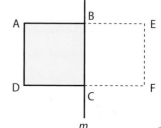

381

15. ABCD is a rectangle with the diagonals intersecting at the point O.

The line ℓ is perpendicular to DC.

Find the image of each of the following under reflection in the mirror line ℓ:

    (i) D   (ii) [AD]   (iii) [AO]

    (iv) [OC]   (v) △AOE   (vi) △AOD

    (vii) △COF   (viii) the figure EBCO.

16. On the right is the reflection of a clock in a mirror.

What time does the clock actually show?

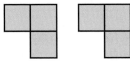

17. Rachel put these two shapes together, edge to edge.

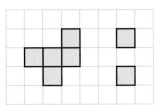

Her new shape had just 1 line of symmetry.

Show two ways Rachel might have done this.

18. Show how you can put these shapes together to make a single shape with a mirror line.

19. In the diagram on the right, we have the word THE and a mirror line.

Which of the following is the image of THE under a reflection in this mirror line?

       A   B   C   D   E

Section 17.3 **Central symmetry**

The diagram on the right shows two points A and X.

We join A to X and continue the line to A′ such that $|XA'| = |AX|$.

The point A′ is called the image of A under a reflection in the point X.

Another name for reflection in a point is **central symmetry**. Instead of using A′ we will use the notation $S_X(A)$ to denote the image of A under a central symmetry in the point X.

This notation is used in the given diagram to represent the images of A, B and C under S_X, reflection in the point X.

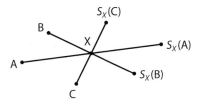

Finding the image of any figure under a central symmetry

The following diagrams illustrate how to find the images of

(i) a line segment [AB]　　　　(ii) the capital letter *T*

under S_X, central symmetry in the point X.

In each case, the red figure is the image of the blue figure.

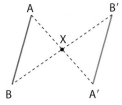 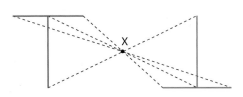

The diagram on the right shows the letter F and its image under S_X. Notice that the red image appears upside down and back-to-front in relation to the given blue figure.

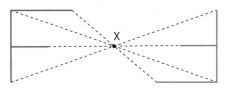

Centre of symmetry

All the figures shown below are mapped onto themselves under central symmetry in the point X.

  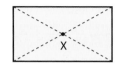 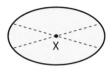

In each figure, X is the **centre of symmetry**.

Every point in each figure is mapped onto another point in the figure under reflection in the point X.

Not every figure has a centre of symmetry.

For example, no triangle has a centre of symmetry.

Exercise 17.3

1. The given diagram shows three points.
Describe in words the meaning of $S_X(A)$.

2. Copy the given three points and construct the image of A and B under S_X, central symmetry in the point X.

3. Construct the image of the given line segment under central symmetry in the point X in each of the following:

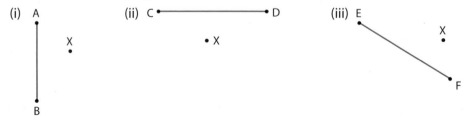

If you have done the constructions correctly, you will notice that each line segment is mapped onto a parallel line segment.

4. Sketch the image of the triangle ABC under S_C, central symmetry in the point C in each of the following:

(i)

(ii)

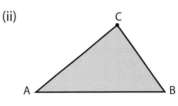

5. Draw a rough sketch of the image of each of the following letters under central symmetry in the point X:

Describe how each image appears in relation to the given figure.

6. Which of the following figures have O as the centre of symmetry?

(i)

(ii)

(iii)

(iv)

(v)

(vi)

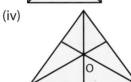 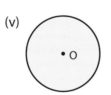 

7. Draw the image of ABCD under S_D, central symmetry in the point D.

8. ABCD is a square with the diagonals intersecting at the point O. Write down the image of each of the following under central symmetry in the point O.

(i) A
(ii) D
(iii) [AB]
(iv) [BC]
(v) [AO]
(vi) △AOD
(vii) △AOB
(viii) △ABD.

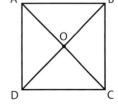

9. Examine the diagram on the right and now name the transformation that maps

   (i) F_1 onto F_2
   (ii) F_2 onto F_3
   (iii) F_3 onto F_4
   (iv) F_1 onto F_3.

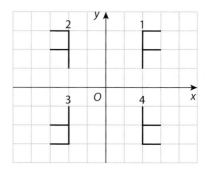

10. The diagonals of the given parallelogram intersect at the point M.

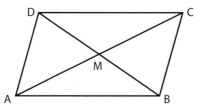

   Write down the answer to each of the following:
   (i) $S_M(D)$ (ii) $S_M[AD]$ (iii) $S_M[AB]$
   (iv) $S_M(\triangle DCM)$ (v) $S_M(\triangle AMB)$ (vi) $S_M(\triangle CAB)$.

11. Examine the two words shown on the right. You should eventually be able to see the words *upside-down*.

    Turn the page upside down.

    What do you see now?

    Does the figure have
    (i)   an axis of symmetry
    (ii) a centre of symmetry?

12. Name the transformation that will map

    (i)   A to D   (ii) D to C
    (iii) A to B   (iv) A to C
    (v)   D to E   (vi) C to B.

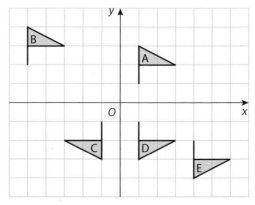

Test yourself 17

1. (i) Name the transformation that maps

   (a) F_1 onto F_2
   (b) F_2 onto F_3
   (c) F_1 onto F_3.

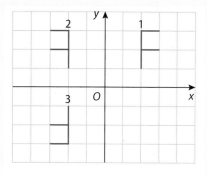

   (ii) Make two drawings of the rectangle ABCD.
   Now construct the image of ABCD under
   (a) the translation $\overrightarrow{DC}$
   (b) central symmetry in the point D.

2. (i) Say if each of the following figures could be its own image under a central symmetry:

 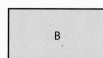 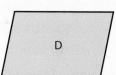

   (ii) The diagram shows a triangle ABC.
   A'B'C' is the image of the triangle ABC
   under an axial symmetry in the y-axis.
   (a) Write down the coordinates of A, B and C.
   (b) Write down the coordinates of A', B' and C'.

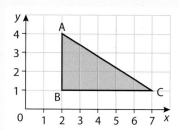

3. (i) How many axes of symmetry has each of the following figures?

   (a)    (b) 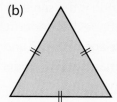   (c)

(ii) ABCD is a rectangle.

The diagonals intersect at the point O.

(a) What is the image of D under the translation $\overrightarrow{AB}$?

(b) What is the image of △DOC under central symmetry in the point O?

(c) What is the image of [AB] under the translation $\overrightarrow{BC}$?

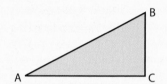

4. (i) Draw a sketch of the given triangle ABC.

Now draw the image of the △ABC under a central symmetry in the point C.

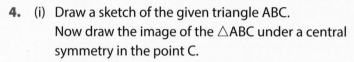

(ii) Which of the transformations A, B or C below will map

(a) K to L

(b) L to M

(c) L to N, where

A – Translation

B – Reflection in a line

C – Central symmetry ?

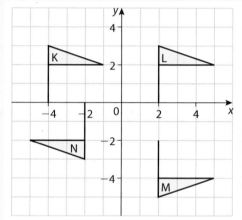

5. (i) How many axes of symmetry does this figure have?

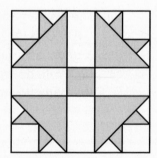

(ii) The parallelogram ZPQT is the image of the parallelogram XYZR under the translation $\overrightarrow{XZ}$.

(a) What translation is the same as $\overrightarrow{XR}$?

(b) What is the image of X under $\overrightarrow{TQ}$?

(c) What is the image of △XRZ under $\overrightarrow{XZ}$?

(d) What is the image of [TQ] under central symmetry in Z?

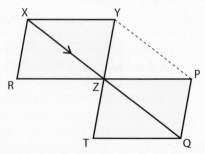

Learning Experience
Unit 17

Assignment 1

On squared paper draw a full-sized diagram of the patchwork design called "Palm Leaf".

Shade it as shown.

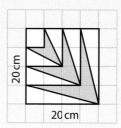

(i) Mark a line of symmetry on this design.

(ii) Using symmetry, calculate the area of the white section of the design.

(iii) What fraction of this design is white?

(iv) What percentage of this design is pink?

(v) What is the ratio of the white to pink section?

Assignment 2

On a large sheet of squared paper draw the design below.

The coordinates of the △ABC are given.

State what transformations are used to create each of the △CED, △DEF, △HIG.

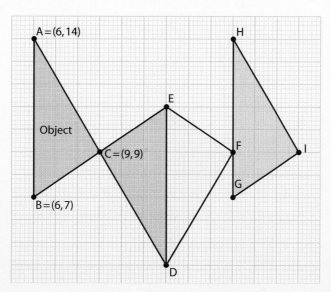

Write down the coordinates of D, E, F, G, H, I in your diagram.

Problem 1

An octagon is a plane figure with 8 sides.

An octagon is cut from a 6 cm × 6 cm card
as shown.

Describe, using symmetry, how to show

that the area of this octagon is 28 cm²

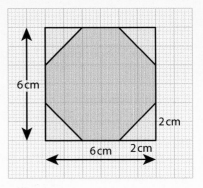

Problem 2

Reflect an **object** in the *y*-axis, then reflect the **image** in the *x*-axis.

In your diagram write in the coordinates of the vertices of the images.

State whether the **final image** could be obtained using any other
transformation of the object?

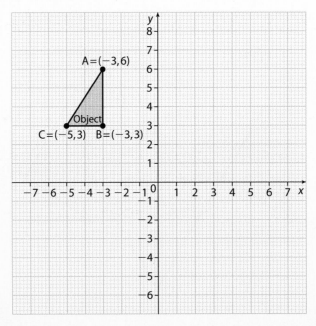

Chapter 17 review 1

Using the terms from the chapter, copy and complete the following sentences:

1. In transformations _____ of objects are formed.

2. A _____ creates an image by moving the object a fixed distance in a particular direction.

3. Axial symmetry _____ an object in a _____.

4. A _____ symmetry reflects an object in a _____.

5. To construct an image by translation you need a _____ _____ and a straight edge.

6. To construct an image by central symmetry you need a _____ _____.

7. If one half of a figure folds exactly over the other half, the figure is said to be _____.

8. The folding line in a figure is called an _____ of symmetry.

9. Reflection through a point is called _____ symmetry.

10. When an object is reflected in a point the image is _____ _____ and _____ - _____ - _____.

11. No _____ has a centre of symmetry.

Chapter 17 review 2

You should now be able to:

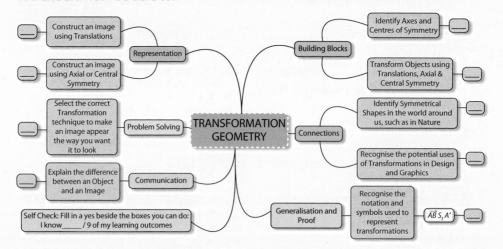

Answers

Chapter 1: Natural Numbers

Exercise 1.1

1. (i) T   (ii) F   (iii) F   (iv) T   (v) F
2. (i) 8, 10, 12, 14   (ii) 1, 3, 5, 7, 9, 11
    (iii) 1, 2, 3, 4   (iv) 7, 8, 9, 10
    (v) 5, 7, 9, 11, 13
3. (i) the first five natural numbers
    (ii) the first five odd natural numbers
    (iii) the first three even natural numbers
    (iv) four consecutive even natural numbers
        beginning with 6
    (v) consecutive odd natural numbers
        beginning with 9
    (vi) consecutive natural numbers beginning
        with 101
4. (i) 4   (ii) 400   (iii) 200
    (iv) 4000   (v) 40
5. 822, 3759, 61 208
7. (i) 7431   (ii) 1347
8. 3960
9. 30 303
10. 7173
11. (i) 709   (ii) 2309   (iii) 6004
    (iv) 20 402   (v) 90 090   (vi) 302 045
    (vii) 1 030 000
12. 931, 2988, 3079, 3098, 3190, 3297
13. (i) 10 D 800   (ii) 11 KE 1020
    (iii) 12 KY 8000
14. (i) 863 221   (ii) 122 368
15. (i) 0, 46, 64, 406, 604
    (ii) 26, 79, 85, 151, 210, 219, 401
16. 9421, 9412, 9241, 9214, 9142
17. 1121, 1122, 1211, 1212, 2112, 2211

Exercise 1.2

1. (ii) F   (iii) T; $9 \times 2 = 18$
    (iv) T; $5 \times 7 = 35$ (v) F
    (vi) T; $12 \times 5 = 60$ (vii) F
    (viii) T; $16 \times 3 = 48$
2. (i) $18 \times 1, 9 \times 2, 6 \times 3$
    (ii) $30 \times 1, 15 \times 2, 10 \times 3, 6 \times 5$
    (iii) $36 \times 1, 18 \times 2, 12 \times 3, 9 \times 4, 6 \times 6$
    (iv) $40 \times 1, 20 \times 2, 10 \times 4, 8 \times 5$
3. 5

4. (i) 1, 2, 3, 6   (ii) 1, 2, 4, 8
    (iii) 1, 3, 5, 15   (iv) 1, 2, 3, 4, 6, 8, 12, 24
    (v) 1, 2, 4, 7, 14, 28   (vi) 1, 5, 7, 35
    (vii) 1, 2, 3, 4, 6, 7, 12, 14, 21, 28, 42, 84
    (viii) 1, 2, 3, 4, 6, 9, 12, 18, 27, 36, 54, 108
5. $1 + 2 + 4 + 7 + 14 = 28$
6. (i) Y   (ii) N   (iii) Y   (iv) Y
7. (i) Y   (ii) Y   (iii) N   (iv) Y
8. (i) 1, 2, 3, 6, 9, 18   (ii) 1, 2, 3, 4, 6, 8, 12, 24
    (iii) 1, 2, 3, 6   (iv) 6
9. (i) 5   (ii) 7   (iii) 14
    (iv) 14   (v) 9   (vi) 9
10. (i) 9   (ii) 14   (iii) 13
11. 6 teams, (2 boys, 3 girls)
12. $19 + 7; 23 + 3; 13 + 13$
13. (i), (ii), (iv)
14. … 18, 24, 30, 36, 42, 48;
    … 11, 13, 17, 19, 23, 25, 29, 31, 35, 37, 41, 43,
    47, 49; 25, 35, 49
15. 3 friends (plus himself)
16. (i) F; 2 is a prime number
    (ii) T
    (iii) F, 9 is not a prime number
    (iv) F, there are four
17. 1, 2, 3, 4, 6, 8, 12, 16, 24, 48; two of them are
    prime numbers
18. 8 games, (7 points, 6 points)
19. (i) $2 \times 2 \times 3$ (ii) $2 \times 3 \times 5$
    (iii) $3 \times 3 \times 5$ (iv) $2 \times 2 \times 3 \times 7$
    (v) $2 \times 2 \times 3 \times 3 \times 3$
20. (i) $5 + 7$ (ii) $5 + 11$
    (iii) $5 + 19$ (iv) $3 + 29$
21. 5 and 7, 11 and 13, 17 and 19
22. Always a prime number
23. 8 bracelets, (2 white, 5 green, 3 orange)
24. (i) 3, 5   (ii) 3, 5, 10, 15, 30
    (iii) 12, 18, 30   (iv) four

Exercise 1.3

1. (i) 3   (ii) 21, 24   (iii) 27   (iv) 300
2. (i) 7, 14, 21, 28, 35, 42
    (ii) Yes   (iii) 147, 154
3. 9, 18, 27, 36, 45, 54, 63, 72
4. (i) 4, 8, 12, 16, 20, 24   (ii) 6, 12, 18, 24, 30, 36
    (iii) 12 and 24   (iv) 12

5. (i) 10   (ii) 24   (iii) 28
    (iv) 60   (v) 56

6. (i) 8   (ii) 12
    (iii) 30   (iv) 24

7. (i) 144   (ii) 168

8. Saturday

9. 24

10. (i)

12	24	36	48	60	72	→	60
15	30	45	60	75	90		

    (ii) 3, 4   (iii) 6, 7

11. (i) T   (ii) F   (iii) F   (iv) T

12. (ii) Line 3: multiples of 4;
       Line 4: multiples of 14
    (iii) Multiples of 10

13. 150 seconds

14. 8 bottles, 5 packets

15. 20 days

Exercise 1.4

1. (i) 16   (ii) 36   (iii) 144
    (iv) 196   (v) 25   (vi) 53
    (vii) 106   (viii) 36

2. (i) 16   (ii) 72   (iii) 400
    (iv) 98   (v) 32   (vi) 9
    (vii) 27   (viii) 92

3. (i) 36   (ii) 41   (iii) 15   (iv) 34

4. 36, 49, 64, 81

5. (i) 16   (ii) 36   (iii) 81   (iv) 121

6. (i) All square numbers
    (ii) Same

7. (i) 2^3 (ii) 3^3 (iii) 6^4 (iv) 2^5

8. (i) T   (ii) T   (iii) F

9. (i) 4^2 or 2^4 (ii) 2^3 (iii) 3^3
    (iv) 10^3 (v) 5^3 (vi) 11^2

10. (i) 3   (ii) 5   (iii) 8   (iv) 12   (v) 20

11. (i) 7   (ii) 81   (iii) 144
    (iv) 81   (v) 64   (vi) 1

12. (i) 100   (ii) 18   (iii) 2   (iv) 3

13. (ii)

14. (ii)

15. (i) 5 + 11   (ii) 7 + 29
    (iii) 2 + 47   (iv) 3 + 97

16. (i) 2, 3   (ii) 5, 6   (iii) 6, 7

17. (i) 13   (ii) 15   (iii) 21
    (iv) 26   (v) 31

18. (i) 2   (ii) 3   (iii) 2   (iv) 4

19. $$10 \times 10 \times 10 = 10^3$$
$$10 \times 10 \times 10 \times 10 = 10^4$$
$$10 \times 10 \times 10 \times 10 \times 10 = 10^5$$
$$10^6$$
    (i) Multiples of 10   (ii) They increase by 1

Exercise 1.5

1. 17   **2.** 17   **3.** 28

4. 2   **5.** 13   **6.** 39

7. 29   **8.** 21   **9.** 26

10. 27   **11.** 46   **12.** 18

13. 26   **14.** 45   **15.** 32

16. (i) +   (ii) ÷   (iii) ÷
    (iv) +   (v) ×   (vi) ÷, ×

17. (i) 44   (ii) 28   (iii) 54
    (iv) 22   (v) 12   (vi) 30
    (vii) 17   (viii) 3   (ix) 38

18. (i) 34   (ii) 31   (iii) 17
    (iv) 32   (v) 10   (vi) 50

19. (i) 5   (ii) 2   (iii) 10
    (iv) 4   (v) 21   (vi) 6

20. (i) 29   (ii) 64   (iii) 22
    (iv) 26   (v) 50   (vi) 5

21. (i) 7   (ii) 24   (iii) 48
    (iv) 38   (v) 92   (vi) 33

22. (i) 8   (ii) 1   (iii) 2

23. (i) 5   (ii) 31

24. (i) $5 \times (4 + 3) = 35$
    (ii) $20 - (3 + 8) = 9$
    (iii) $(8 + 10) \div 2 = 9$
    (iv) $48 \div (16 - 4) = 4$
    (v) $(11 - 6) \times 2 = 10$
    (vi) $(5 + 3) \times 4 - 2 = 30$

25. D; 36   **26.** E   **27.** (i)

Exercise 1.6

1. (i) 622   (ii) 1399   (iii) 8423   (iv) 3428

2. (i) 604   (ii) 486   (iii) 384
    (iv) 216   (v) 524

3. (i) 178   (ii) 919   (iii) 1065
    (iv) 6056   (v) 249   (vi) 1023

4. (i) 50   (ii) 50   (iii) 90
    (iv) 130   (v) 80   (vi) 160

5. (i) 120   (ii) 450   (iii) 1500
    (iv) 2400   (v) 400   (vi) 800
    (vii) 2000   (viii) 2400   (ix) 4800
    (x) 8100

6. (i) 6   (ii) 60   (iii) 40
    (iv) 70   (v) 70

7. (i) 423   (ii) 4686   (iii) 2581
    (iv) 8400   (v) 5208   (vi) 13 770
    (vii) 8742   (viii) 9796

8. €640

9. (i) 576   (ii) 458

10. (i) 561   (ii) 23   (iii) 6   (iv) 1683

11. (i)   5   (ii)   7
     55   20   35   63
   11   44   4   5   45   9

(iii)   6
54   48
9   72   8

12. 2 AD, 11 AD, 20 AD, 101 AD, 110 AD, 200 AD, 1001 AD, 1010 AD, 1100 AD

13. (i) 90   (ii) 19 each

14. (i) T   (ii) F   (iii) F   (iv) F
   (v) F   (vi) T

15. (i) C   (ii) B   (iii) D   (iv) A

16. (i)

	30	7
20	600	140

740

(ii)

	50	2
30	1500	60

1560

(iii)

	80
20	1600
7	560

2160

(iv)

	40
50	2000
6	240

2240

17. (i)

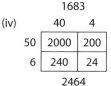

	30	7
20	600	140
1	30	7

777

(ii)

	50	1
30	1500	30
3	150	3

1683

(iii)

	80	2
20	1600	40
7	560	14

2214

(iv)

	40	4
50	2000	200
6	240	24

2464

18. (i) T   (ii) F   (iii) T   (iv) F

19. (i) D   (ii) A   (iii) B   (iv) A

20. 55

Exercise 1.7

1. (i) 630   (ii) 620   (iii) 640
   (iv) 600   (v) 600   (vi) 650
   (vii) 610   (viii) 650

2. 605, 615, 625, 635, 645

3. (i) 140   (ii) 80   (iii) 680
   (iv) 1760   (v) 3790

4. (i) 800   (ii) 300   (iii) 2200
   (iv) 3100   (v) 3700

5. (i) 3000   (ii) 6000   (iii) 8000
   (iv) 10 000   (v) 11 000

6. (i) 82 400   (ii) 82 000

7. (i) 28 500   (ii) 28 000   (iii) 30 000

8. (i) 849   (ii) 750

9. (i) 38 499   (ii) 37 500

10. (i) nearest 1000   (ii) nearest 10 000

11. (i) 2000   (ii) 1500
   (iii) 2100   (iv) 2900

12. (i) 60   (ii) 355   (iii) 225

13. (i) 23 650   (ii) 23 749

14.

	Greece	Italy	Netherlands
(i)	132 000 km²	301 000 km²	33 800 km²
(ii)	11 000 000	57 000 000	16 000 000

	Germany	Ireland
(i)	357 000 km²	70 300 km²
(ii)	83 000 000	3 900 000

   (iii) Italy (Netherlands)

Test yourself 1

1. (i) 492   (ii) 7

2. (i) 8   (ii) 18

3. (i) 2, 5, 11, 19
   (ii) 1, 2, 4, 7, 14, 28; $2 \times 2 \times 7$

4. A – 28, B – 43, C – 280, D – 460

5. (i) 11   (ii) 5   (iii) 30
   (iv) 24   (v) 32   (vi) 18

6. 376

7. (i) 1459   (ii) 9541
   (iii) [5] + [9] = [1] [4]

8. (i) 3, 13, 23   (ii) 28
   (iii) 3, 4, 15   (iv) 4, 9, 25, 64

9. (i) 120   (ii) 400   (iii) 800

10. (i) 44   (ii) 4

11. 264   **12.** 4, 6, 7, 8, 9, 12

13. (i) B – 31 000, L – 3000, S – 505 000,
     P – 92 000, F – 547 000
   (ii) Luxembourg
   (iii) Portugal and France
   (iv) Belgium and Portugal

14. (i)

	60	1
30	1800	30

1830

(ii)

	20	4
50	1000	200

1200

(iii)

	60	1
40	2400	40
2	120	2

2562

(iv)

	70	3
30	2100	90
6	420	18

2628

15. (i) 38   (ii) 57

16. (i) T
   (ii) F (8 is not a factor of 4)
   (iii) F (4 = 1, 2, 4)
   (iv) F (7 ≠ 5)
   (v) F (there are four)

17. 6 laps, 4 laps, 3 laps

Chapter 2: Integers

Exercise 2.1

1. (i) 0, −2, −4   (ii) −1, −3, −5
   (iii) −4, −8, −12   (iv) 3, 5, 7
   (v) 2, 4, 6   (vi) 2, −1, −7

2. (i) 10°C   (ii) 5°C   (iii) 0°C
   (iv) −5°C   (v) −6°C   (vi) −8°C
3. (i) 10°C   (ii) 3°C   (iii) −3°C
   (iv) −7°C   (v) −6°C   (vi) 0°C
4. (i) −4, −3, 0, 1, 3, 6
   (ii) −8, −5, −2, 0, 4, 6
   (iii) −8, −5, −2, 1, 3, 9
   (iv) −7, −4, −3, −1, 0, 3, 5
5. (i) 11°C   (ii) 18°C   (iii) 11°C
6. 32°C
7. (i) 3, 4, 5, 6
   (ii) −2, −3, −4, −5
   (iii) −6, −5, −4, −3
8. (i) T   (ii) T   (iii) F   (iv) F
   (v) T   (vi) F   (vii) F   (viii) T
9. 23°C
10. (i) Moscow   (ii) Moscow   (iii) Rome
11. (i) <   (ii) >   (iii) <   (iv) >
   (v) <   (vi) >   (vii) <   (viii) <

Exercise 2.2

1. (i) −2   (ii) −4   (iii) −3   (iv) −3
   (v) 3   (vi) 5   (vii) −4   (viii) −6
2. (i) −2 + 4   (ii) 2 − 4
   (iii) −6 + 5   (iv) 4 − 5
3. (i) 10   (ii) 2   (iii) 7   (iv) −2
   (v) −7   (vi) −6   (vii) −5   (viii) −4
4. (i) −3   (ii) −6   (iii) −6   (iv) −7
   (v) −11   (vi) 10   (vii) −15   (viii) −50
5. 8   **6.** 8   **7.** 9   **8.** 8
9. 7   **10.** 5   **11.** −5   **12.** 3
13. 9   **14.** 4   **15.** 9   **16.** 2
17. (i) 3   (ii) 11   (iii) −9
   (iv) 3   (v) −20   (vi) −9
19. (i) 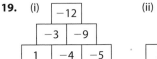 (ii)

20. (i)  (ii)

  (iii)

21. −8°C   **22.** €200
23. level 1   **24.** level −1

Exercise 2.3

1. (i) 24   (ii) −20   (iii) −56
   (iv) −45   (v) −54   (vi) 36
   (vii) 48   (viii) −70   (ix) −72
   (x) 66   (xi) −80   (xii) −54
2. (i) −6   (ii) −9   (iii) −4
   (iv) 3   (v) 3   (vi) −3
3. (i) 8   (ii) −2   (iii) −9
   (iv) −5   (v) 6   (vi) −5
   (vii) −9   (viii) 6   (ix) −9
   (x) −5
4. (i) −8   (ii) −6   (iii) 8
   (iv) 5   (v) −4   (vi) 21
5. −50
7. (i) −36   (ii) 24   (iii) 90
   (iv) 60   (v) 96   (vi) −42
8. (i) −2   (ii) −5   (iii) −6
   (iv) −6   (v) 27   (vi) −12
9. (i) 21, −7   (ii) −7, −2   (iii) −2, 3
   (iv) 10, −2   (v) −10, −2   (vi) 21, −3
10. (i) 9   (ii) 36   (iii) 49
   (iv) −8
11. (i) −21   (ii) −6   (iii) −14
   (iv) −45   (v) 14   (vi) 38
12. (i) −5, −2   (ii) −10, −3   (iii) −3, −2
   (iv) 6, −1   (v) −6, −2   (vi) −5, 3
13. (i) 50   (ii) 29
   (iii) 9 correct, 1 wrong

Test yourself 2

1. (i) 2   (ii) −2   (iii) −10   (iv) −7
   (v) −15   (vi) 18   (vii) −3   (viii) 2
2. (i) −12, −3, −1, 0, 4, 6, 9
   (ii) −9, −4, −3, 2, 7, 14
3. (i) −6°C (ii) −2°C (iii) 5°C (iv) 23°C
4. (i) >   (ii) <   (iii) >   (iv) >
5. (i) −8, 2   (ii) −5, 3
   (iii) −8, −5   (iv) −8, −5
6. −54
7. (i) −7   (ii) 13   (iii) 60
9. (i) −9°C   (ii) −7°C
   (iii) −12°C   (iv) −25°C
10. (i) −15   (ii) M
   (iii) (a) FIND   (b) PLAN   (c) MILK
12. −4°C   **13.** AUCKLAND   **14.** 7

Chapter 3: Fractions
Exercise 3.1

1. (i) $\frac{1}{2}$ (ii) $\frac{1}{4}$ (iii) $\frac{1}{3}$ (iv) $\frac{3}{5}$
   (v) $\frac{1}{8}$ (vi) $\frac{5}{6}$ (vii) $\frac{2}{3}$ (viii) $\frac{5}{8}$

2. (i) $\frac{1}{2}$ (ii) $\frac{3}{4}$ (iii) $\frac{2}{3}$ (iv) $\frac{2}{5}$
(v) $\frac{7}{8}$ (vi) $\frac{1}{6}$ (vii) $\frac{1}{3}$ (viii) $\frac{3}{8}$

3. $\frac{4}{6}, \frac{2}{3}$; equivalent fractions

4. (i) $\frac{1}{7}$ (ii) $\frac{1}{4}$ (iii) $\frac{3}{4}$ (iv) $\frac{1}{3}$

5. (i) 8 (ii) 4

6. (i) $\frac{1}{2}$ (ii) $\frac{3}{4}$ (iii) $\frac{2}{3}$ (iv) $\frac{2}{3}$
(v) $\frac{3}{4}$ (vi) $\frac{3}{5}$ (vii) $\frac{2}{3}$ (viii) $\frac{14}{21}$

7. (i) $\frac{1}{2}$ (ii) $\frac{1}{3}$ (iii) $\frac{1}{3}$ (iv) $\frac{1}{3}$
(v) $\frac{1}{6}$ (vi) $\frac{1}{3}$ (vii) $\frac{2}{3}$ (viii) $\frac{3}{5}$
(ix) $\frac{1}{3}$ (x) $\frac{1}{5}$

8. $\frac{3}{4}$

9. (i) $\frac{1}{4}$ (ii) $\frac{1}{2}$ (iii) $\frac{1}{5}$ (iv) $\frac{1}{4}$
(v) $\frac{1}{3}$ (vi) $\frac{3}{10}$ (vii) $\frac{1}{5}$ (viii) $\frac{4}{9}$

10. (i) $\frac{12}{24}$ (ii) $\frac{18}{24}$ (iii) $\frac{16}{24}$
(iv) $\frac{15}{24}$ (v) $\frac{22}{24}$;
(a) $\frac{2}{3}$ (b) $\frac{3}{4}$ (c) $\frac{11}{12}$

11. $a = \frac{4}{5}$, $b = \frac{2}{5}$, $c = \frac{2}{5}$, $d = \frac{9}{10}$, $e = 3\frac{7}{10}$, $f = 1\frac{1}{3}$

12. (i) < (ii) > (iii) < (iv) < (v) < (vi) >

Exercise 3.2

1. (i) P (ii) I (iii) P
(iv) I (v) I

2. (i) $1\frac{1}{5}$ (ii) $2\frac{2}{3}$ (iii) $5\frac{1}{2}$ (iv) $2\frac{3}{4}$
(v) $5\frac{1}{3}$ (vi) $4\frac{1}{6}$ (vii) $9\frac{2}{3}$ (viii) $4\frac{3}{11}$
(ix) $6\frac{3}{10}$ (x) $5\frac{3}{8}$

3. (i) $\frac{5}{3}$ (ii) $\frac{12}{5}$ (iii) $\frac{19}{8}$ (iv) $\frac{15}{4}$
(v) $\frac{19}{5}$ (vi) $\frac{14}{3}$ (vii) $\frac{20}{3}$ (viii) $\frac{47}{9}$
(ix) $\frac{37}{10}$ (x) $\frac{49}{9}$

4. (i) $\frac{2}{3}$ (ii) $\frac{3}{4}$ (iii) $\frac{3}{7}$ (iv) $\frac{3}{4}$
(v) $\frac{3}{5}$ (vi) $\frac{4}{5}$ (vii) $\frac{2}{9}$ (viii) $\frac{3}{4}$

5. (i) 6 (ii) 27 (iii) 26
(iv) 24 (v) 28 (vi) 280

6. (i) 30 km (ii) €72 (iii) 63 litres
(iv) 115 cm (v) €75 (vi) 138 m

7. (i) 24 (ii) 8 (iii) 4
(iv) 3 (v) 3 (vi) 3

8. (i) $\frac{3}{4}$ of 8 = 6 (ii) $\frac{2}{3}$ of 9 = 6
(iii) $\frac{3}{5}$ of 25 = 15 $\left[\text{or } \frac{3}{2} \text{ of 6} = 9 \text{ etc.} \right]$

9. 69

10. Ham = 140, Salad = 224, Tuna = 70,
Cheese = 126

11. (i) CAVE (ii) POLITICS

12. (i) (ii) 12

Exercise 3.3

1. (i) $\frac{3}{5} + \frac{1}{5} = \frac{4}{5}$ (ii) $\frac{1}{7} + \frac{4}{7} = \frac{5}{7}$
(iii) $\frac{3}{8} + \frac{3}{8} = \frac{6}{8} = \frac{3}{4}$ (iv) $\frac{5}{12} + \frac{4}{12} = \frac{9}{12} = \frac{3}{4}$

2. (i) $\frac{3}{5}$ (ii) $\frac{5}{7}$ (iii) $\frac{7}{9}$
(iv) $\frac{7}{11}$ (v) $\frac{2}{3}$ (vi) $\frac{1}{2}$
(vii) $\frac{3}{7}$ (viii) $\frac{11}{13}$ (ix) $\frac{9}{8}$

3. (i) $\frac{5}{8}$ (ii) $\frac{7}{10}$ (iii) $1\frac{1}{2}$
(iv) $\frac{1}{2}$ (v) $1\frac{1}{6}$ (vi) $\frac{1}{3}$
(vii) $\frac{5}{12}$ (viii) $\frac{1}{2}$ (ix) $\frac{7}{20}$

4. (i) $\frac{4}{5}$ (ii) $1\frac{5}{24}$ (iii) $1\frac{1}{2}$
(iv) $\frac{13}{18}$ (v) $\frac{11}{12}$ (vi) $\frac{13}{24}$

5. (i) $3\frac{1}{2}$ (ii) $3\frac{7}{12}$ (iii) $6\frac{1}{10}$
(iv) $5\frac{1}{10}$ (v) $4\frac{1}{6}$ (vi) $5\frac{8}{15}$
(vii) $4\frac{3}{10}$ (viii) $5\frac{13}{15}$ (ix) $1\frac{1}{6}$

6. A = R, B = P, C = S, D = Q, E = U, F = T

7. (i) $1\frac{5}{8}$ (ii) $1\frac{5}{12}$ (iii) $\frac{1}{3}$
(iv) $2\frac{1}{4}$ (v) $1\frac{1}{8}$ (vi) $2\frac{5}{12}$

8. (i) $3\frac{5}{12}$ (ii) $1\frac{9}{10}$ (iii) $8\frac{5}{9}$
(iv) $8\frac{5}{8}$ (v) $1\frac{4}{5}$ (vi) $2\frac{5}{24}$

9.

$5\frac{1}{3}$	2	$2\frac{2}{3}$
$\frac{2}{3}$	$3\frac{1}{3}$	6
4	$4\frac{2}{3}$	$1\frac{1}{3}$

Exercise 3.4

1. $\frac{3}{8}$ **2.** $\frac{3}{20}$ **3.** $\frac{9}{20}$

4. $\frac{8}{15}$ **5.** $\frac{8}{21}$ **6.** $\frac{2}{3}$

7. $\frac{3}{5}$ **8.** $\frac{4}{15}$ **9.** $\frac{1}{14}$

10. $\frac{1}{9}$ **11.** $\frac{3}{10}$ **12.** $\frac{1}{6}$

13. $\frac{3}{7}$ **14.** 1 **15.** $\frac{1}{4}$

16. $3\frac{1}{3}$ **17.** 3 **18.** $4\frac{1}{5}$

19. $5\frac{1}{4}$ **20.** 3 **21.** $4\frac{1}{2}$

22. 23 **23.** 15 **24.** 14

25. 52 **26.** 68 **27.** $3\frac{1}{3}$

28. (i) DESK   (ii) STOOL   (iii) BENCH

29. (i) $\frac{5}{14}$ (ii) $\frac{3}{10}$ (iii) 12

(iv) $\frac{3}{4}$ (v) 9   (vi) 14

Exercise 3.5

1. $\frac{2}{5}$

2. (i) $\frac{3}{7}$ (ii) $\frac{9}{4}$ (iii) $\frac{1}{6}$ (iv) 5   (v) $\frac{11}{3}$

3. (i) $\frac{3}{7}$ (ii) $\frac{9}{11}$ (iii) $\frac{1}{10}$ (iv) $\frac{5}{19}$ (v) $\frac{4}{5}$

4. (i) $1\frac{1}{2}$ (ii) $1\frac{1}{4}$ (iii) $\frac{4}{9}$ (iv) $\frac{7}{2}$

(v) 8   (vi) 27   (vii) 18   (viii) 36

5. (i) 10   (ii) $3\frac{1}{2}$ (iii) $3\frac{1}{2}$ (iv) 6

(v) $\frac{1}{2}$ (vi) 6   (vii) $\frac{9}{10}$ (viii) $\frac{5}{6}$

6. C

7. (i) $3\frac{4}{5}$ (ii) $3\frac{1}{3}$ (iii) $2\frac{8}{11}$ (iv) $\frac{2}{3}$

8. A = M, B = L, C = Q, D = P

9. (i) 2   (ii) $\frac{4}{5}$ (iii) 6

10. $\frac{1}{9}$

11. $C + D\left(\frac{5}{12}\right)$, $B + E\left(\frac{5}{18}\right)$, $F + G\left(\frac{5}{24}\right)$, $A + H\left(\frac{1}{12}\right)$

12. (i) $1\frac{2}{5}$ (ii) $\frac{2}{3}$ (iii) $\frac{5}{18}$

13. (i) ROME   (ii) PARIS   (iii) MADRID

14. 14 shelves

15. $\frac{2}{3} \times \frac{4}{3} = \frac{8}{9}$, $\frac{8}{9}$ of $\frac{3}{4}$ is $\frac{2}{3}$

Exercise 3.6

1. (i) $\frac{2}{3}$ (ii) $\frac{3}{7}$ (iii) $\frac{1}{5}$

(iv) $\frac{1}{5}$ (v) $\frac{2}{5}$ (vi) $\frac{1}{9}$

2. $\frac{2}{15}$

3. (i) TRICKS   (ii) PRECIOUS

(iii) DISAPPEAR

4. $4\frac{3}{20}$ km   **5.** €216

6. 26   **7.** 5 mins

8. (i) 9   (ii) 36

9. €117   **10.** 32   **11.** 48

12. 29 300   **13.** 18   **14.** 16

15. d

16. (i) $\frac{3}{10}$ (ii) 12

Test yourself 3

1. (i) $\frac{1}{3}$ (ii) $\frac{3}{4}$ (iii) $\frac{2}{3}$

(iv) $\frac{3}{5}$ (v) $\frac{3}{4}$

2. (i) $\frac{3}{2}$ (ii) $\frac{9}{4}$ (iii) $\frac{11}{3}$

(iv) $\frac{19}{4}$ (v) $\frac{14}{5}$

3. (i) $\frac{2}{12}$ (ii) $\frac{6}{15}$ (iii) $\frac{12}{21}$

4. (i) $\frac{5}{6}$ (ii) $1\frac{3}{8}$ (iii) $1\frac{1}{2}$ (iv) $\frac{13}{14}$

(v) $\frac{1}{6}$ (vi) $\frac{1}{12}$ (vii) $\frac{1}{12}$ (viii) $\frac{1}{3}$

5. $a = \frac{3}{4}$, $b = \frac{5}{6}$, $c = 1\frac{3}{8}$, $d = \frac{2}{5}$, $e = \frac{4}{5}$, $f = \frac{2}{5}$

6. (i) $\frac{3}{4}\left(\frac{9}{12}\right)$ (ii) $\frac{2}{5}\left(\frac{6}{15}\right)$

(iii) $\frac{2}{3}\left(\frac{8}{12}\right)$ (iv) $\frac{7}{11}\left(\frac{21}{33}\right)$

7. (i) $\frac{3}{10}$ (ii) 2   (iii) $1\frac{5}{8}$ (iv) 3

(v) $1\frac{1}{2}$ (vi) $\frac{5}{6}$ (vii) $\frac{2}{3}$ (viii) 4

8. (i) FISH   (ii) BREAD   (iii) PASTA

9. (i) $1\frac{5}{9}$ (ii) $1\frac{3}{10}$ (iii) 6   (iv) 4

10. $3\frac{5}{8}$ km   **11.** €14   **12.** 42

13. (i) $\frac{5}{12}$ (ii) 4

14. 60 cows

15. (i) $\frac{4}{9}$ (ii) 23   (iii) $2\frac{2}{3}$

16. (i) $\frac{3}{5}$ (ii) B = 150, C = 300

Chapter 4: Probability

Exercise 4.1

1. (i) 6   (ii) H1, H2, H3, T1, T2, T3

2. 8   **3.** HH, HT, TH, TT

4. (i) 10

(ii) H1, H2, H3, H4, H5, T1, T2, T3, T4, T5

5. 30   **6.** 20

7. (i) 12

(ii) G3, G4, G5, G6, B3, B4, B5, B6, R3, R4, R5, R6

8. 12   **9.** 25

10. 45   **11.** 24

12. HHH, HHT, HTT, HTH, THH, TTH, TTT, THT; 8

13. 24   **14.** 9

15.

	1	2	3	4	5	6
G	1G	2G	3G	4G	5G	6G
P	1P	2P	3P	4P	5P	6P
O	1O	2O	3O	4O	5O	6O

, 18 outcomes

16.

	1	3	5
2	2	6	10
4	4	12	20
6	6	18	30

, 9 outcomes

17. (i) Addition   (ii) 9

18.

	B_1	B_2	B_3
A_1	A_1B_1	A_1B_2	A_1B_3
A_2	A_2B_1	A_2B_2	A_2B_3
A_3	A_3B_1	A_3B_2	A_3B_3
A_4	A_4B_1	A_4B_2	A_4B_3

19. (i) 9 numbers, 2, 3, 4, 12, 13, 14, 22, 23, 24

(ii) 12 numbers, 135, 138, 145, 148, 235, 238, 245, 248, 335, 338, 345, 348

Exercise 4.2

1. a = Very Unlikely, b = Unlikely, c = Likely, d = Very Likely

2. (i) E   (ii) B   (iii) C

(iv) A   (v) D

3. (i) Certain   (ii) Even Chance

(iii) Impossible   (iv) Likely

(v) Likely   (vi) Even Chance

(vii) Unlikely   (viii) Certain

(ix) Even Chance   (x) Unlikely

(xi) Impossible

4. (i) E   (ii) C   (iii) A

(iv) B   (v) D

6. (i) D   (ii) A

(iii) B   (iv) D

7. A = Impossible, B = Very Unlikely, C $= \frac{1}{3}$, D = 0.5, E = Likely, F $= \frac{5}{6}$, G = Certain

9. (i) 0   (ii) $\frac{1}{2}$ (iii) $\frac{1}{2}$

(iv) $\frac{1}{4}$ (v) $\frac{3}{4}$ (vi) 1

10. (i) Lower   (ii) Higher

(iii) Equally Likely

Exercise 4.3

1. 1, 2, 3, 4, 5, 6;

(i) 2, 3, 4, 5   (ii) 2, 4, 6   (iii) 1, 6

(iv) 4, 5, 6   (v) 3, 5   (vi) 6

2. (i) 4   (ii) 3   (iii) 4

(iv) 1   (v) 3

3. (i) 3   (ii) 5   (iii) 2

(iv) 4   (v) 3   (vi) 3

4. Greater than 6

5. (i) Equally Likely   (ii) No

(iii) Equally Likely   (iv) No

6. (i) B   (ii) C   (iii) B   (iv) 3

7. (i) B   (ii) C   (iii) C

(iv) A   (v) B   (vi) C

8. (i) 6   (ii) 4   (iii) 2

(iv) 4   (v) 4

Exercise 4.4

1. (i) $\frac{3}{7}$ (ii) $\frac{2}{7}$ (iii) $\frac{4}{7}$ (iv) $\frac{5}{7}$

2. (i) $\frac{3}{8}$ (ii) $\frac{1}{4}$ (iii) $\frac{1}{4}$

(iv) $\frac{3}{8}$ (v) $\frac{5}{8}$ (vi) $\frac{5}{8}$

3. (i) $\frac{1}{6}$ (ii) $\frac{1}{2}$ (iii) $\frac{1}{3}$

4. (i) $\frac{1}{5}$ (ii) $\frac{2}{5}$ (iii) $\frac{2}{5}$

5. (i) $\frac{1}{2}$ (ii) $\frac{1}{2}$ (iii) $\frac{1}{3}$

6. (i) Blue   (ii) $\frac{1}{3}$ (iii) $\frac{5}{9}$

(iv) 1 yellow and 2 blue

(v) 1 yellow

7. (i) $\frac{1}{10}$ (ii) $\frac{3}{10}$ (iii) $\frac{1}{2}$ (iv) $\frac{2}{5}$

(v) $\frac{4}{5}$ (vi) $\frac{1}{5}$ (vii) $\frac{4}{5}$ (viii) $\frac{1}{10}$

8. (i) $\frac{1}{4}$ (ii) $\frac{1}{3}$ (iii) $\frac{2}{3}$ (iv) $\frac{1}{2}$

(v) $\frac{1}{4}$ (vi) $\frac{1}{4}$ (vii) $\frac{5}{12}$ (viii) $\frac{1}{4}$

9. (i) $\frac{1}{4}$ (ii) $\frac{3}{8}$ (iii) $\frac{1}{4}$ (iv) $\frac{5}{8}$

10.

2	4	6	, 0

1	3	5	7
3	5	7	9
5	7	9	11

11. (i) $\frac{1}{2}$ (ii) $\frac{1}{4}$ (iii) $\frac{1}{13}$ (iv) $\frac{1}{26}$

12. (i) $\frac{1}{2}$ (ii) $\frac{3}{10}$ (iii) $\frac{1}{2}$ (iv) $\frac{7}{10}$

13. (i) $\frac{1}{6}$ (ii) $\frac{1}{2}$ (iii) $\frac{1}{3}$ (iv) $\frac{2}{3}$

14. (i) $\frac{1}{9}$ (ii) $\frac{1}{3}$ (iii) $\frac{2}{9}$ (iv) $\frac{4}{9}$

15. (i) $\frac{1}{7}$ (ii) $\frac{3}{7}$ (iii) $\frac{4}{7}$

16. (i) 4   (ii) 5   (iii) $\frac{2}{5}$

17.

	1	2	3	4	5	6
H	1H	2H	3H	4H	5H	6H
T	1T	2T	3T	4T	5T	6T

P(Head, odd) $= \frac{3}{12} = \frac{1}{4}$

18. (i) $\frac{7}{15}$ (ii) $\frac{2}{15}$ (iii) $\frac{3}{5}$ (iv) $\frac{3}{5}$

19. (i) $\frac{1}{6}$ (ii) $\frac{1}{3}$ (iii) $\frac{1}{3}$ (iv) $\frac{1}{6}$

(v) $\frac{5}{12}$

20. (i) $\frac{1}{4}$ (ii) $\frac{1}{2}$

21. Fair

22. (i) 3   (ii) 1   (iii) 5   (iv) $\frac{1}{2}$;

(a) F   (b) could be T   (c) T

24. (i) $\frac{1}{4}$ (ii) $\frac{3}{8}$ (iii) $\frac{1}{4}$ (iv) $\frac{1}{8}$

(v) $\frac{3}{8}$

25. (ii) P(6) $= \frac{1}{2} \Rightarrow$ Estimate of 50

Test yourself 4

1. (i) Impossible   (ii) Likely

(iii) Evens   (iv) Certain

(v) Unlikely

2. (i) A   (ii) B   (iii) E   (iv) G

(v) C   (vi) D   (vii) F

3. 20, 25, 30, 35; Yes

4. (i) $\frac{1}{8}$ (ii) $\frac{1}{4}$ (iii) $\frac{5}{8}$ (iv) $\frac{7}{8}$
   (v) $\frac{3}{4}$

5. (i) 10   (ii) $\frac{1}{2}$ (iii) $\frac{2}{5}$ (iv) $\frac{2}{5}$
   (v) $\frac{1}{5}$ (vi) $\frac{3}{5}$

6. (i) $\frac{3}{20}$ (ii) $\frac{3}{5}$ (iii) $\frac{1}{5}$ (iv) $\frac{4}{5}$

7.

	P	Y	G	P	Y	G
P	PP	PY	PG	PP	PY	PG
Y	YP	YY	YG	YP	YY	YG
G	GP	GY	GG	GP	GY	GG

$= \frac{6}{18} = \frac{1}{3}$

8. (i) $A = \frac{5}{9}, B = \frac{3}{5}, C = \frac{2}{3}$
   (ii) $A = \frac{4}{9}, B = \frac{2}{5}, C = \frac{1}{3}$

9. It doesn't matter; $\frac{3}{5} = \frac{6}{10}$

10. (i) $\frac{2}{11}$ (ii) $\frac{4}{11}$ (iii) $\frac{9}{11}$

11. No. We would expect 30H /30T from 60 tosses and the coin produced 31H/ 29T which is very close.

12.

	1	2	3	4	5	6
1	2	3	4	5	6	7
2	3	4	5	6	7	8
3	4	5	6	7	8	9

, 18 outcomes, $\frac{1}{2}$

Chapter 5: Decimals

Exercise 5.1

1. (i) $\frac{7}{10}$ (ii) $\frac{6}{100}$ (iii) $\frac{2}{10}$ (iv) $\frac{7}{1000}$
   (v) $\frac{7}{100}$ (vi) $\frac{9}{1000}$ (vii) 30   (viii) $\frac{7}{1000}$

2. (i) twenty units   (ii) five tenths
   (iii) six hundredths   (iv) four thousandths

3. (i) 4.3   (ii) 16.07   (iii) 0.17
   (iv) 6.03   (v) 12.028

4. (i) $\frac{1}{10}$ (ii) $\frac{3}{10}$ (iii) $\frac{1}{2}$
   (iv) $\frac{4}{5}$ (v) $\frac{3}{5}$

5. (i) $\frac{1}{4}$ (ii) $\frac{3}{4}$ (iii) $\frac{7}{25}$
   (iv) $\frac{1}{20}$ (v) $\frac{2}{25}$

6. (i) 0.9   (ii) 0.1   (iii) 0.5   (iv) 0.8
   (v) 0.7   (vi) 0.16   (vii) 0.28   (viii) 0.25
   (ix) 0.75   (x) 0.09

7. A = 0.3, B = 0.8, C = 1.8, D = 8.1, E = 9.2, F = 9.7, G = 4.3, H = 4.6, I = 4.9, J = 0.25, K = 0.75, L = 1.5

8. (i) 33.36   (ii) 22.368
   (iii) 28.426   (iv) 5.332

9. (i) 14.6   (ii) 12.43   (iii) 9.28
   (iv) 25.112   (v) 3.16   (vi) 2.026

10. (i) 18.93   (ii) 136.15
   (iii) 46.309   (iv) 49.564

11. (i) 2.57   (ii) 14.7   (iii) 85.4
   (iv) 62.53   (v) 2.146   (vi) 0.014

12. (i) 0.4   (ii) 0.4

13. (i) 0.55   (ii) 3.45   (iii) 4.65
   (iv) 7.8   (v) 2.465   (vi) 0.05

14. (i) 0.08, 0.3, 0.36, 0.4, 0.45, 0.5
   (ii) 1.96, 2.09, 2.17, 2.4, 2.52, 2.73

15. (i) 3   (ii) 8   (iii) 1
   (iv) 2   (v) 7

16. (i) 860.5   (ii) 5.068

17. 7 years

18. (i) 6.85   (ii) 4.35   (iii) 1.75

Exercise 5.2

1. (i) 720   (ii) 1200   (iii) 4000
   (iv) 16   (v) 134   (vi) 1480
   (vii) 2136   (viii) 4850   (ix) 740

2. (i) 17.4   (ii) 1.84   (iii) 0.174
   (iv) 3.87   (v) 0.128   (vi) 0.018
   (vii) 0.387   (viii) 0.0146   (ix) 0.0089

3. (i) 230   (ii) 674   (iii) 0.86
   (iv) 34   (v) 0.0328   (vi) 0.04
   (vii) 4.7   (viii) 1.58

4. (i) 4.8   (ii) 15.5   (iii) 0.96
   (iv) 0.48   (v) 0.66   (vi) 0.69
   (vii) 0.16   (viii) 0.084

5. (i) 36.8   (ii) 49.36   (iii) 20.24
   (iv) 0.72   (v) 11.84   (vi) 76.2
   (vii) 2.55   (viii) 0.336

6. (i) 0.3   (ii) 5   (iii) 0.4
   (iv) 0.4   (v) 0.4   (vi) 0.5

7. (i) 6.4   (ii) 32.1
   (iii) 1.36   (iv) 11.23

8. (i) 4   (ii) 7   (iii) 27.7
   (iv) 15.35   (v) 60   (vi) 510
   (vii) 2.3   (viii) 36

9. (i) (1.2×4) (ii) (0.5×60)
   (iii) (3×0.9) (iv) (1.2×0.2)
   (v) (3×0.2) (vi) (0.8×0.2)
   (vii) (0.5×0.2) (viii) (1.2×0.9)

10. (i) 52.8   (ii) 52.8   (iii) 5.28
   (iv) 0.528   (v) 0.0528

11. (i) 0.98 because $\frac{98}{100} > \frac{89}{100}$
   (ii) 2.750 because $2\frac{750}{1000} > 2\frac{57}{1000}$
   (iii) 104.104 because $104\frac{104}{1000} > 104\frac{40}{1000}$

12. (i) 10, 148.2

    (ii) (a) 10, 14.82   (b) 10, 0.1482   (c) 0.01, 1.482

13. (i) 1.6   (ii) 40

    (iii) 0.9   (iv) 0.06

14. (i) 264 m   (ii) 1320 m   (iii) 3168 m

15. (i) 26   (ii) 26   (iii) 2600

    (iv) 260   (v) 26 000

16. 9.13 kg   **17.** €69.20

18. 32   **19.** 88

20. 54   **21.** B

22. (iv)

23. (i) €64   (ii) €56.65 , €14.16

Exercise 5.3

1. (i) 39   (ii) 12   (iii) 4

    (iv) 16   (v) 24

2. (i) 1.9   (ii) 13.7   (iii) 0.4

    (iv) 3.2   (v) 6.0

3. (i) 8.54   (ii) 0.35   (iii) 0.18

    (iv) 3.01   (v) 9.16

4. (i) 135 km   (ii) 87 km

    (iii) 136 km   (iv) 328 km

5. (i) 1.1   (ii) 0.8   (iii) 12.7

    (iv) 0.1   (v) 1.8

6. (i) CAKE   (ii) CHEESE   (iii) BREAD

7. A & Y, B & X, C & Z

8. (i) 0.5   (ii) 0.25   (iii) 0.75

    (iv) 0.125   (v) 0.375   (vi) 0.625

    (vii) 0.45   (viii) 0.12   (ix) 0.4375

    (x) 0.46875

9. (i) 0.83   (ii) 0.43   (iii) 0.36

    (iv) 0.44   (v) 0.36

10. (i) $\frac{3}{5}$ (ii) $\frac{7}{11}$ (iii) $\frac{7}{12}$ (iv) $\frac{6}{15}$

11. (i) 84   (ii) 12   (iii) 4

    (iv) 7.5   (v) 8   (vi) 24

12. (iv)

13. (i) 31.5, 34.8 (ii) 0.6, 0.6   (iii) 0.1, 0.1

14. (i) €1200 (40 ppl, €30)

    (ii) Bigger; as each number is rounded up

15. C, A, E, B, D   **16.** C: 2.34

Exercise 5.4

1. (i) 0.58, 0.55, A is more likely

    (ii) 0.38, 0.4, D is more likely

2. 0.38

3. (i) 0.23   (ii) 0.35   (iii) 0.35

4. 12 outcomes, 0.25

5. (i) 36

    (ii) (2, 1), (2, 2), (2, 3), (2, 4), (2, 5), (2, 6), (1, 2),

        (3, 2), (4, 2), (5, 2), (6, 2)

    (iii) 0.31

6. (i) 15 outcomes   (ii) 0.27

7. P(girl) $= \frac{7}{16} >$ P(boy) $= \frac{3}{8}\left(\frac{6}{16}\right)$

Test yourself 5

1. (i) 0.3   (ii) 4.7   (iii) 0.15

    (iv) 0.067   (v) 1.03

2. (i) 3.28   (ii) 1.495   (iii) 93.2

    (iv) 0.0328

3. (i) 124   (ii) 1.5   (iii) 12.06

4. (i) 24.6   (ii) 134

    (iii) 1.24   (iv) 4.128

5. (i) 7.53   (ii) 100

    (iii) 0.04563   (iv) 1000

6. $a = 4.2$, $b = 0.24$, $c = 6.375$

7. (i) 726   (ii) 0.726   (iii) 7.26

8. (i) BEAR   (ii) WHALE

    (iii) TIGER   (iv) ELEPHANT

9. (i) 0.72

    (ii) 2; (a) smaller   (b) bigger

10. 4.6125 & 4.61, 4.0613 & 4.06, 4.586 & 4.59,

    4.598 & 4.60, 4.6189 & 4.62

11. (i) $\frac{2}{5}$ (ii) $\frac{1}{4}$ (iii) $\frac{1}{8}$

    (iv) $\frac{2}{25}$ (v) $\frac{4}{25}$

12. €73

13. (i) 9.6   (ii) 4   (iii) 1

14. (i) 0.25 × 0.8 (0.2)   (ii) 0.8 × 1.2 (0.96)

    (iii) 12.6 ÷ 0.25 (50.4)

15. D   **16.** 60 minutes   **17.** 9 outcomes, 1.00

Chapter 6: Sets

Exercise 6.1

1. (i) Y   (ii) Y   (iii) N   (iv) Y

    (v) N   (vi) Y   (vii) N

2. A – days beginning with the letter S

    B – first six natural numbers

    C – summer months

    D – last five letters of the alphabet

    E – counties of Munster

    F – first five even natural numbers

    G – vowels (of the alphabet)

3. A = {a, b, c, d, e}

    B = {3, 5, 7, 9, 11, 13}

    C = {spring, summer, autumn, winter}

    D = {Tuesday, Thursday}

    E = {s, c, i, e, n}

    F = {Cork, Carlow, Cavan, Clare}

    G = {a, e, i}

    H = {red, orange, yellow, green, blue, indigo,

        violet}

4. (i) Assortment of road signs

    (ii) selection of farm animals

Exercise 6.2

1. (i) T   (ii) F   (iii) T
   (iv) F   (v) F
2. (i) $\notin$ (ii) $\in$ (iii) $\in$
   (iv) $\notin$ (v) $\in$ (vi) $\notin$
   (vii) $\in$ (viii) $\notin$
3. (i) T   (ii) F   (iii) T
   (iv) T   (v) T   (vi) T
   (vii) F   (viii) T
4. A = {Mars, Mercury}; B – {a, e, i, o, u};
   C = {2, 4, 6, 8, 10, 12};
   D = {1, 2, 3, 4, 5, 6, 7, 8, 9, 10, 11, 12};
   E = {p, a, r, l, e}; F – {3, 5, 7, 9, 11, 13}
5. (i) {x|x is a whole number between 1 and 8 inclusive}
   (ii) {x|x is a vowel (of the English language)}
   (iii) {x|x is an even number between 1 and 15}
   (iv) {x|x is an EU member state starting with the letter L}
   (v) {x|x is a euro currency coin}
6. (i) Y   (ii) N   (iii) Y   (iv) Y
   (v) N   (vi) Y   (vii) N   (viii) N
   (ix) Y   (x) Y
7. Yes (e.g. 10); No   8. {5, 10, 15, 20, 25}
9. {−4, −3, −2, −1, 0, 1}
10. {12, 15, 20, 24, 30, 40, 60, 120}

Exercise 6.3

1. They contain exactly the same elements
2. A and D, B and C
3. No; they don't contain the same elements
4. X = {T, I, L, E}, Y = {L, I, T, E}; Yes
5. B = {6, 7, 8, 9}; No
6. X = {P,A,R,L,E}, Y = {R, E, P, A, L}; equal
7. (i) {10, 11, 12}   (ii) {2, 4, 6, 8, 10, 12}
   (iii) {1, 3, 5}   (iv) {3, 6, 9, 12}
8. (i) T   (ii) F   (iii) T
   (iv) F   (v) T
9. (i) T   (ii) F   (iii) T
   (iv) F   (v) T   (vi) T
10. (i) {a, b, c, d, e}, $\varnothing$
    (ii) {a}, {a, b}, {b, c, d, e} etc.
11. (i) {1}, {2}, {1, 2}, $\varnothing$
    (ii) {x}, {y}, {z}, {x, y}, {x, z}, {y, z}, {x, y, z}, $\varnothing$
12. C = {5, 7, 9}
13. (i) T   (ii) F   (iii) T
    (iv) T   (v) T   (vi) F
14. B = {a, b, c, d}, C = {a, b, c}, D = {a, b} etc.

Exercise 6.4

1. Venn diagram; A = {1, 3, 4, 6, 8}; #A = 5
2. (i) {3, 4, 6, 8, 9}   (ii) {3, 5, 7, 9, 10}
   (iii) {3, 9}   (iv) {3, 4, 5, 6, 7, 8, 9, 10}

3. (i) A = {1, 2, 3, 7, 8, 9}
   (ii) B = {3, 4, 5, 6, 7}
   (iii) 4 (or 5 or 6)
   (iv) 10 (or 11)
   (v) {3, 7}
4. (i) {3, 6, 7, 8, 9}   (ii) {1, 2, 3, 5, 7, 10}
   (iii) {3, 7}
   (iv) {1, 2, 3, 5, 6, 7, 8, 9, 10}
5. (i) {a, b, c, e}   (ii) {b, d, e, f, g}
   (iii) {b, e}   (iv) {a, b, c, d, e, f, g}
6. (i) T   (ii) T   (iii) F
   (iv) T   (v) T
8. (i) {4, 5, 6}   (ii) {4, 5, 6, 7, 8, 9, 10}
   (iii) {7, 8}   (iv) $\varnothing$
9. (i) {S, C, I, E, N}   (ii) {N, E, A, R}
   (iii) {E, N}   (iv) {S, C, I, E, N, A, R}
10. (i) {1, 2, 3, 4, 7, 8, 9}   (ii) {2, 7, 8}
    (iii) {2, 7, 8}   (iv) {1, 2, 3, 4, 7, 8, 9}
11. (i) {8, 12}
    (ii) {0, 1, 2, 3, 4, 5, 8, 9, 12}
    (iii) {8, 9}
    (iv) {0, 1, 2, 4, 8, 9, 10, 11, 12}
    (v) {1, 3, 5, 8, 9, 10, 11, 12}
    (vi) {1, 8}
12. (i) 7   (ii) 6   (iii) 3   (iv) 10
13. (i) T   (ii) F   (iii) T   (iv) T   (v) F
    (vi) T   (vii) T   (viii) F   (ix) T

Exercise 6.5

1. A′; (i) {1, 3, 4, 5, 6, 7, 9}
   (ii) {1, 3, 4, 7}   (iii) {5, 6, 9}
2. (i) {a, d, e, f}   (ii) {a, d, e, f, g, h, k}
   (iii) {g, h, k}
3. (i) {3, 4, 5, 6}   (ii) {3, 4, 8, 9}
   (iii) {2, 7, 8, 9, 10}   (iv) {2, 5, 6, 7, 10}
   (v) {3, 4, 5, 6, 8, 9}   (vi) {2, 7, 10}
4. (i) {c, f, g, i, j, k}   (ii) {b, c, e, j, k}
   (iii) {a, b, d, e, f, g, i}   (iv) {c, j, k}
   (v) {a, d}   (vi) {b, c, e, f, g, i, j, k}
5. (i) 5   (ii) 6   (iii) 2   (iv) 6   (v) 3
6. (i) {2, 4, 6, 8, 9, 10}   (ii) {1, 2, 7, 8, 9, 10}
   (iii) {1, 3, 4, 5, 6, 7}   (iv) {2, 8, 9,10}
8. (i) T   (ii) T   (iii) F
   (iv) T   (v) F   (vi) T
   (vii) T   (viii) F   (ix) F
9. (i) {1, 4, 5, 7, 8, 10}   (ii) {1, 3, 5, 6, 7, 9}
   (iii) {3, 4, 6, 8, 9, 10}   (iv) {1, 5, 7}
   (v) $\varnothing$
10. (i) B′   (ii) A′
    (iii) (A ∪ B)′   (iv) (A ∩ B)′
11. (i) {1, 4, 6, 8, 9, 10, 12} (ii) {2, 4, 6, 8, 10, 12}
    (iii) {1, 2, 3, 5, 7, 9, 11} (iv) {4, 6, 8, 10, 12}
    (v) {1, 2, 4, 6, 8, 9, 10, 12}; Yes, the same

Exercise 6.6

1. (i) $\frac{1}{4}$ (ii) $\frac{3}{4}$

2. U

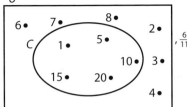

$\frac{6}{11}$

3. (a) U

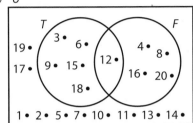

(b) (i) $\frac{3}{10}$ (ii) $\frac{1}{4}$ (iii) $\frac{7}{10}$ (iv) $\frac{3}{4}$

(v) $\frac{1}{20}$ (vi) $\frac{1}{2}$

4. (a) U

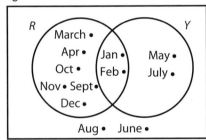

(b) (i) $\frac{5}{6}$ (ii) $\frac{1}{6}$

5. U

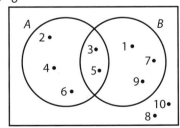

(a) (i) 5   (ii) 5   (iii) 2   (iv) 5

(b) (i) $\frac{1}{2}$ (ii) $\frac{1}{2}$ (iii) $\frac{1}{5}$ (iv) $\frac{1}{2}$

6. {∅, {a}, {b}, {c}, {ab}, {ac}, {bc}, {abc}}

(i) $\frac{1}{2}$ (ii) $\frac{1}{4}$

7. (i) 15   (ii) 9   (iii) 5   (iv) 1

(v) $\frac{3}{5}$ (vi) $\frac{2}{15}$ (vii) $\frac{13}{15}$

Test yourself 6

1. (i) {4, 6, 8, 10}

(ii) {Wicklow, Westmeath, Waterford, Wexford}

(iii) {C, O, M, I, T, E}

(iv) {E, I, O}

(v) {5, 10, 15, 20, 25, 30}

(vi) {1, 2, 3, 4, 5, 6, 7, 8, 9}

2. (i) (a) {a, e, h, m, s, t, x}   (b) {a, m}

(ii) (a) 2   (b) 8

3. (i) {a, b, c, d, e}   (ii) {b, c, e, l, m, n}

(iii) {b, c, e}

4. (i) {1, 3, 5}   (ii) ∅

(iii) {1, 3, 5, 7, 8, 9, 10}

5. (i) {a, e, i, o, u, t}   (ii) {o, p, q, r, s, t, u}

(iii) {o, u, t}   (iv) {a, e, i, o, p, q, r, s, t, u}

6. (i) {3, 4, 5, 7, 9}   (ii) {2, 3, 4, 5, 6, 7, 8, 9}

(iii) {2, 6, 8}

7. (i) {3, 4, 5, 6}   (ii) {3, 4, 8, 9}

(iii) {3, 4}   (iv) {2, 3, 4, 5, 6, 7, 8, 9, 10}

(v) {3, 4, 5, 6, 8, 9}   (vi) {2, 7, 10}

8. (i) $A \cap B$ (ii) $A \cup B$

9. (iii) $A = D$

10. 'A is a subset of B';

(i) ⊂   (ii) ⊂   (iii) ⊄   (iv) ⊄

11. (i) 7   (ii) 6   (iii) 3   (iv) 10

12. (i) T   (ii) F   (iii) T   (iv) F

13. U

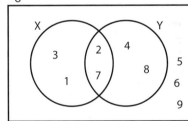

(i) {1, 3, 5, 6, 9}   (ii) {1, 2, 3, 4, 7, 8}

(iii) 3   (iv) 5

14. (i) ∈   (ii) ⊂   (iii) ∉

(iv) ⊂   (v) =/⊂   (vi) ∩

15. (i) 32, 37, 34, 62, 67, 64, 82, 87, 84

(ii) 6   (iii) 3   (iv) $\frac{1}{3}$ (v) $\frac{2}{3}$

16. HHH, HHT, HTH, HTT, THH, THT, TTH, TTT, $\frac{1}{8}$

17. (i) $\frac{13}{24}$ (ii) $\frac{1}{8}$ (iii) $\frac{1}{6}$

Chapter 7: Percentages

Exercise 7.1

1. (i) (a) = 20%   (b) = 35%   (c) = 54%

(ii) (a) = 80%   (b) = 65%   (c) = 46%

(iii) (a) = $\frac{1}{5}$ (b) = $\frac{7}{20}$ (c) = $\frac{27}{50}$

(iv) (a) = 0.2   (b) = 0.35   (c) = 0.54

2. (i) 28% (ii) 54%
  (iii) 15 (iv) $\frac{90}{100} = 90\%$
  (v) $\frac{55}{100} = 55\%$ (vi) $\frac{56}{100} = 56\%$

3. (i) $\frac{1}{5}$ (ii) $\frac{3}{5}$ (iii) $\frac{7}{10}$
  (iv) $\frac{3}{20}$ (v) $\frac{1}{4}$ (vi) $\frac{3}{4}$
  (vii) $\frac{17}{20}$ (viii) $\frac{1}{20}$ (ix) $\frac{1}{50}$
  (x) $\frac{6}{25}$

4. $\frac{15}{200} = \frac{3}{40}$

5. (i) $\frac{1}{3}$ (ii) $\frac{1}{8}$ (iii) $\frac{1}{40}$
  (iv) $\frac{1}{12}$ (v) $\frac{7}{40}$

6. (i) (a) 50% (b) 20% (c) 35%
  (d) 80% (e) 75%
  (ii) (a) 0.2 (b) 0.8 (c) 0.7
  (d) 0.65 (e) 0.95

7. (i) 18% (ii) 47% (iii) 30%
  (iv) 70% (v) 25% (vi) 40%
  (vii) 75% (viii) 85% (ix) 16%
  (x) 38%

8. (i) 0.5 (ii) 0.1 (iii) 0.9
  (iv) 0.35 (v) 0.45 (vi) 0.08
  (vii) 0.125 (viii) 0.24 (ix) 0.01
  (x) 0.245

9. (i) 80% (ii) 40% (iii) 75%
  (iv) 45% (v) 15% (vi) 7%
  (vii) 1% (viii) 12.5% (ix) 34.5%
  (x) 4.5%

10. (i) 36% (ii) 40% (iii) 36%

11. $\left(\frac{4}{5}, 80\%, 0.8\right)$; $\left(\frac{3}{4}, 75\%, 0.75\right)$; $\left(\frac{2}{5}, \frac{4}{10}, 40\%\right)$

12. (i) 20%, $\frac{1}{4}$, 0.3, $\frac{2}{5}$, 50%
  (ii) $\frac{1}{5}$, $\frac{1}{4}$, $\frac{3}{10}$, 0.45, $\frac{1}{2}$, 60%

13. (i) 0.27 (ii) 0.07 (iii) 0.54
  (iv) 0.175 (v) 0.025

14. 25%

15. (i) SATURN (ii) VENUS (iii) URANUS

16. (i) 55% (ii) 32% (iii) 48%

Exercise 7.2

1. (i) 5 (ii) 8 (iii) 12
  (iv) 15 (v) 60 (vi) 48
  (vii) 12 (viii) 66

2. (i) 38 (ii) 272 (iii) 504
  (iv) €63 (v) €63 (vi) €728

3. 24, 12, 84

4. (i) 18 km (ii) €101.25 (iii) 300 kg

5. $17\frac{1}{2}\%$ of €120

6. 58%, 75%, 80%, 68%, 70%, 80%, 58%

7. (i) 25% (ii) 20% (iii) 40%
  (iv) 5% (v) 12% (vi) 15%
  (vii) 30% (viii) 40% (ix) 8%

8. (i) 30 g (ii) 30 g (iii) 96 g
  (iv) 35 g (v) 18 g (vi) 135 g

9. (i) 0.14 (ii) 0.27 (iii) 0.35
  (iv) 0.06 (v) 0.09 (vi) 0.095
  (vii) 0.3 (viii) 0.365 (ix) 0.963
  (x) 0.203

10. (i) 42 (ii) 40.8 (iii) 5.88
  (iv) 182 (v) 207 (vi) 9.75

11. 48% of €55 **12.** €50.15

13. (i) 660 (ii) 198

14. €787.50 **15.** 62%

16. French **17.** 5%

18. 95% **19.** 10%

20. (i) 80 (ii) $41\frac{1}{4}\%$ (iii) $26\frac{1}{4}\%$

21. (i) 15% (ii) 60 g

Exercise 7.3

1. (i) 99 (ii) 72 (iii) 195
  (iv) 36 (v) 96 (vi) 190

2. (i) 160 (ii) 495 (iii) 464
  (iv) 322 (v) 504 (vi) €86.40

3. (i) 0.06 (ii) 0.15 (iii) 0.35
  (iv) 0.7 (v) 0.075

4. (i) 0.38 (ii) 0.6 (iii) 0.13
  (iv) 0.06 (v) 1.2 (vi) 0.125

5. (i) 264 (ii) 210 (iii) €119
  (iv) 210 kg (v) €97.20 (vi) 52 kg

6. (i) 585 g (ii) 825 g (iii) $287\frac{1}{2}$ g

7. 700 **8.** €350

9. €18 500 **10.** €1.62

11. €15.46 **12.** €107.20

13. 40% **14.** €850

15. (i) €20 800 (ii) €17 680

Exercise 7.4

1. €680, €32, €585, €831.25

2. (i) €31.50 (ii) €56

3. €23 375 **4.** €3.20, €320, €320

5. €250

6. (i) €960 (ii) €780
  (iii) €483 (iv) €836

7. €690 **8.** €1020

9. €166.50 **10.** €217.80, €847

11. €576 **12.** €696

13. €5082 **14.** €28

15. €240 **16.** €600

17. €620

Exercise 7.5

1. (i) €24   (ii) €40   (iii) €92
(iv) €54   (v) €6.97   (vi) €135
2. (i) 25% (P)   (ii) 20% (P)   (iii) 5% (P)
(iv) 20% (L)   (v) 30% (P)   (vi) 20% (L)
3. 15%
4. A = S; B = R; C = P; D = Q
5. (i) €8   (ii) €8   (iii) €72
(iv) €24   (v) €750
6. €770   7. 10%
8. €414   9. 25%
10. €1.50, €1.50, €150   11. €110
12. (i) €800   (ii) €920
13. (i) €1008   (ii) 26%
14. (i) €1250   (ii) €26
    (iii) €310   (iv) 24.8%
15. €60
16. (i) €300   (ii) 2%
17. (i) €1200   (ii) $6\frac{2}{3}$%

Test yourself 7

1. (i) 25%   (ii) 40%   (iii) 34%
(iv) 70%   (v) 90%
2. (i) $\frac{1}{5}$ (ii) $\frac{1}{4}$ (iii) $\frac{9}{20}$
(iv) $\frac{1}{20}$ (v) $\frac{7}{8}$
3. (i) 75%   (ii) 20%   (iii) 25%
(iv) 37.5%
4. (i) 70%   (ii) 50%   (iii) 75%
(iv) 40%   (v) 30%
5. (i) 12   (ii) 43   (iii) 9
(iv) 300   (v) 105   (vi) 1080
(vii) $32\frac{1}{2}$ (viii) 6   (ix) 15

6.

$\frac{3}{4}$	0.75	75%
$\frac{3}{5}$	0.6	60%
$\frac{7}{10}$	0.7	70%
$\frac{2}{5}$	0.4	40%
$\frac{9}{10}$	0.9	90%

7. (i) 60%   (ii) 75%   (iii) 48%
8. (i) 120   (ii) 54
9. $87\frac{1}{2}$%, 85%, 80%, 90%, $87\frac{1}{2}$%
10. (i) 10%, 20%, $\frac{1}{4}$, 0.3, $\frac{2}{5}$ (ii) 40%, $\frac{1}{2}$, $\frac{3}{5}$, $\frac{3}{4}$, 0.78
11. (i) LION   (ii) TIGER
12. (i) 240   (ii) 7.5%
13. (i) €632.50   (ii) €148
14. 26%

Chapter 8: Algebra

Exercise 8.1

1. (i) 2   (ii) 9   (iii) 6
(iv) 12   (v) 7   (vi) 11
(vii) 12   (viii) 30
2. (i) 8   (ii) 7   (iii) 10
(iv) 10   (v) 20   (vi) 4
(vii) 5   (viii) 30
3. (10 + 2), (9 + 3), (8 + 4) etc.
4. (15 − 6), (14 − 5), (13 − 4) etc.
5. (i) 11   (ii) 15   (iii) 3
(iv) 10   (v) 15
(vi) 2   (vii) 6   (viii) 11
6. (i) 24   (ii) 15   (iii) 36
(iv) 90   (v) 10   (vi) 54
7. (i) 4   (ii) 8   (iii) 7
(iv) 11   (v) 36   (vi) 12
8. (i) $\triangle + 7$ (ii) $\triangle - 4$ (iii) $2\triangle$
(iv) $\frac{\triangle}{2}$ (v) $\frac{\triangle}{3}$ (vi) $\triangle - 6$
9. (i) 21   (ii) Increase by 6
(iii) 21   (iv) Increase by 5
(v) $\triangledown + 8$ (vi) $\bigcirc + 17$
(vii) 16   (viii) $\square$
(ix) $\triangle - 36$ (x) Decrease by 9
10. (i) 4   (ii) 9   (iii) 9
(iv) 11   (v) 6   (vi) 8
(vii) 6   (viii) 18   (ix) 4
11. (i) $a + 8$ (ii) $b - 7$
(iii) $2c$ (iv) Increase by 9
(v) Decrease by 10   (vi) $5f$
(vii) Multiply by 3   (viii) Increase by k

Exercise 8.2

1. (i) $5a$ (ii) $4b$ (iii) $8x$
(iv) $12y$ (v) $8c$ (vi) $15a$
(vii) ab (viii) $4ab$
2. (i) $8ab$ (ii) $21xy$ (iii) $3ab$
(iv) abc (v) $6xy$ (vi) abc
(vii) $12xyz$ (viii) $10abc$
3. (i) $3x$ (ii) $6x$ (iii) $3a + 7$
(iv) $7b + 6$ (v) $5x + 10$ (vi) $4x + 3y$
4. (i) $3x$ (ii) $2a$ (iii) $17x$
(iv) $2a + 7$ (v) $7b - 6$ (vi) $5a + 2b$
5. (i) $15a + 6b$ (ii) $7x + 5y + 4$
(iii) $7x + 4$ (iv) $4x + 3$
(v) $8a + 3b + 2$ (vi) $6x + 1$
6. (i) $2ab$ (ii) $5ab$ (iii) $2xy$
(iv) $7cd$ (v) ab (vi) $4xy$
7. (i) $3p - q + r$ (ii) $2k + 5$
(iii) $7ab - 3c$ (iv) $4xy + 11z$
(v) $5ab + 5cd$ (vi) $11x - 8xy$

8. (i) $3y + 9$ (ii) $6x + 4$ (iii) $3a + 7$

9. (i) $a + 2b + c$ (ii) $2x + 6y + z$
(iii) $6a + 3$ (iv) $9x$

10. (i) B and E (ii) B and D (iii) C and D
(iv) D and F (v) $5x + 4$

11. (i) x and y (ii) As their values vary
(iii) 3 (iv) -8 (v) No

12. $4c - 3d + 7$

Exercise 8.3

1. (i) 4 (ii) 6 (iii) 12
(iv) 10 (v) 7 (vi) 12
(vii) 6 (viii) 30

2. (i) 8 (ii) 25 (iii) 25
(iv) 8 (v) 7 (vi) 5
(vii) 5 (viii) -6

3. (i) 2 (ii) 30 (iii) 16
(iv) 8 (v) 40 (vi) 8
(vii) 36 (viii) 38

4. (i) 12 (ii) 18 (iii) 12
(iv) 18 (v) 10 (vi) 60

5. (i) 4 (ii) 3 (iii) 33
(iv) 10 (v) 12 (vi) 26

6. (i) 3 (ii) 7 (iii) 15
(iv) 3 (v) 4 (vi) 2

7. (i) 7 (ii) 5 (iii) 1
(iv) 5 (v) $4\frac{1}{2}$ (vi) 6

8. (i) 2 (ii) -4 (iii) 4
(iv) -8 (v) -8 (vi) 4
(vii) 9 (viii) 10

9. $\left(\boxed{p + 5}, \boxed{2}\right)$, $\left(\boxed{2p + 2}, \boxed{-4}\right)$,
$\left(\boxed{6 - p}, \boxed{9}\right)$, $\left(\boxed{3p}, \boxed{-9}\right)$,
$\left(\boxed{3 + 2p}, \boxed{-3}\right)$

10. FRANCE **11.** 49

12. ENGLAND

13. (ii) 47

14. (ii) Yes

Exercise 8.4

1. $4x + 8$ **2.** $3a + 18$
3. $8a + 28$ **4.** $3x + 3y$
5. $10x + 5y$ **6.** $8x + 12y$
7. $12x - 6y$ **8.** $3x + 6y + 3$
9. $12a + 6b + 18$ **10.** $10a + 30$
11. $13x - 2y$ **12.** $9a + 19$
13. $9a + b$ **14.** $2x + 12y$
15. $3a + 7b$ **16.** $9x + y$
17. $-5a + 6$ **18.** $-4b$
19. $-x + 8y$ **20.** $6a - 2$

21. $-3c + 9d$ **22.** $7x + 8y - 3$
23. $6a + 8b + 2$ **24.** $8x - y + 6$
25. $14a - 2b$ **26.** $7x + y$
27. $2a + b$
28. (i) $6x + 10$ (ii) $12h + 20$

Exercise 8.5

1. 5^2 **2.** 4^3
3. a^2 **4.** b^3
5. $2a^2$ **6.** $3x^2$
7. $4b^2$ **8.** a^3
9. x^4 **10.** $4a^3$
11. $6a^2$ **12.** $20x^3$
13. $8x^2 + 23$ **14.** $7x^2 + 18$
15. $3x^2 + 16x$ **16.** $5x^2 + x$
17. $10x^2 - 9x$ **18.** $9a^2 - 13a$
19. $x^2 - 27x$ **20.** $3a^2 - 23a$
21. $-9x$ **22.** $3a^2 + 13a$
23. $5x^2 + 8$ **24.** $14a - 12$
25. (i) 4 (ii) 4 (iii) 8
(iv) 20 (v) 20
26. (i) 13 (ii) 21 (iii) 14
(iv) 22 (v) 35 (vi) 28
(vii) 15 (viii) 22
27. (i) 3 (ii) 15
28. (i) 9 (ii) 16 (iii) 22
(iv) 6 (v) -12 (vi) -24
(vii) 36 (viii) 33
29. 24 sq units
30. (i) C (ii) D (iii) E
(iv) B (v) A

Exercise 8.6

1. $x^2 + 3x + 2$ **2.** $x^2 + 4x + 3$
3. $x^2 + 6x + 8$ **4.** $x^2 + 7x + 10$
5. $x^2 + 7x + 12$ **6.** $2x^2 + 9x + 4$
7. $3x^2 + 20x + 12$ **8.** $2x^2 + 11x + 5$
9. $6x^2 + 11x + 4$ **10.** $x^2 + 2x - 8$
11. $x^2 + 2x - 15$ **12.** $2x^2 - 3x - 2$
13. $3x^2 - 7x - 6$ **14.** $3x^2 + 11x - 4$
15. $5x^2 - 18x - 8$ **16.** $x^2 - 9x + 20$
17. $6x^2 - 7x + 2$ **18.** $8x^2 - 22x + 12$
19. $6x^2 + 7x - 5$ **20.** $20x^2 + 7x - 6$
21. $8x^2 - 8x - 6$ **22.** $6a^2 + 5a - 6$
23. $10a^2 - a - 2$ **24.** $8a^2 - 10a - 3$
25. $ac + ad + bc + bd$ **26.** $xa + xb + ya + yb$
27. $ac + 2ad + 2bc + 4bd$
28. $6ab - 2ad - 9bc + 3cd$
29. $10a^2 - 7ab - 12b^2$ **30.** $x^2 + xy - 6y^2$
31. $x^2 - 4y^2$ **32.** $9x^2 - 4y^2$

33.

	x	2
x	x^2	$2x$
2	$2x$	4

$x^2 + 4x + 4$

34.

	$2x$	y
$2x$	$4x^2$	$2xy$
y	$2xy$	y^2

$4x^2 + 4xy + y^2$

35. $4x^2 + 4xy + y^2$ **36.** $x^2 + 6xy + 9y^2$
37. $4a^2 - 4ab + b^2$ **38.** $9x^2 - 12xy + 4y^2$

Test yourself 8

1. (i) $4x$ (ii) $10x + 2$ (iii) $7x^2 - 7x$
   (iv) $4a + b$ (v) $5p + 2q$ (vi) $6a^2 + 2a$
2. (i) 18   (ii) 12
   (iii) 14   (iv) 17
3. (i) $6p + 13q + 11$ (ii) 54
4. (i) a^2 (ii) b^3
   (iii) a^2b (iv) $4a^3$
5. (i)

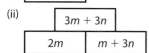

   (ii)

   (iii)

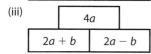

6. (i) $10x - 9$ (ii) $16x^2 - 17x$
7. (i) 4   (ii) -30
   (iii) -13 (iv) -22
8. (i) $x + 4$ (ii) $x - 5$
   (iii) $2x + 4$ (iv) $3x + 6$
9. (i) $4m + 2$ (ii) 3
   (iii) $2m$ (iv) $5m + 4$
10. $x - y + 20$
11. (i) $2x^2 + 11x + 12$ (ii) $6x^2 + 13x - 5$
12. (i) PIG   (ii) GOAT   (iii) HORSE
13. (i)

	$2x$	$+4$
$2x$	$4x^2$	$+8x$
$+4$	$+8x$	$+16$

$4x^2 + 16x + 16$

   (ii)

	y	-4
y	y^2	$-4y$
-4	$-4y$	$+16$

$y^2 - 8y + 16$

Chapter 9: Perimeter and Area

Exercise 9.1

1. (i) cm   (ii) m   (iii) mm
   (iv) m   (v) mm   (vi) m
2. (i) 12 cm 6 mm   (ii) 8 cm 2 mm
4. A = 37 mm, B = 49 mm
5. (i) 50 mm   (ii) 68 mm   (iii) 4 cm
   (iv) 20 cm   (v) 14.5 cm   (vi) 164 mm
6. 3 cm 5 mm
7. (i) 1 m   (ii) 1000 m   (iii) 2500 m
   (iv) 3 m   (v) 8.5 m   (vi) 5500 cm
8. (i) 1.4 m   (ii) 1 m 40 cm
9. (i) 6 m   (ii) 8000 m   (iii) 2800 m
   (iv) 4.8 m   (v) 3280 m
10. (i) 1500 cm   (ii) 280 cm   (iii) 4 cm
   (iv) 12.4 cm   (v) 864 cm
11. (i) 4 km   (ii) 12.8 km   (iii) 0.75 km
   (iv) 3.45 km   (v) 0.09 km
12. (i) 600 m   (ii) 630 m   (iii) 60.9 m
   (iv) 65 m
13. (i) A = 9 cm, B = 11.4 cm, C = 13.8 cm
   (ii) A = 90 mm, B = 114 mm, C = 138 mm
14. (ii)
15. 80 mm, 10.8 cm, 12 cm, 0.8 m, 1.2 m
16. 250 seconds   **17.** 28.8 m
18. No; The 3 units are together 3.05 m wide

Exercise 9.2

1. (i) 29 mm   (ii) 184 cm   (iii) 7.25
   (iv) 67 cm   (v) 85.17 m   (vi) 402 m
2. 27.9 cm   **3.** 2.17 m
4. (i) 50 mm   (ii) 4.5 cm   (iii) 65 mm
   (iv) 28 cm   (v) 85.17 m   (vi) 402 m
5. (i) 33 cm   (ii) 17.5 cm   (iii) 49 cm
7. (i) 12 cm   (ii) 14 cm   (iii) 16 cm
8. (i) 32 cm   (ii) 88 cm   (iii) 41 m
9. (i) 20 cm   (ii) 22 cm   (iii) 21 m
   (iv) 22 cm
10. (i) 36 cm   (ii) 32 cm   (iii) 24 cm
11. (i) 44 cm   (ii) 60 cm   (iii) 34 cm
12. (i) 50 cm   (ii) 56 cm   (iii) 176 m
13. (i) 182 cm
   (ii) (36 cm + 55 cm) × 2 = 182 cm
14. (i) 54 cm   (ii) 44 cm   (iii) 38 cm
15. (i) 46 cm   (ii) 72 cm
16. (i) 6 m   (ii) 7 m
17. (i) 8 cm   (ii) 64 cm

Exercise 9.3

1. (i) 5 cm^2 (ii) 7 cm^2 (iii) 12 cm^2
   (iv) 7 cm^2 (v) 4.5 cm^2 (vi) 9 cm^2
2. 16.8 km^2

3. (i) 63 cm²   (ii) 468 cm²   (iii) 102 m²
4. (i) 112 cm²   (ii) 105 cm²   (iii) 198 cm²
5. (i) 49 m²   (ii) 225 cm²   (iii) 484 mm²
6. (i) 5 m   (ii) 20 m
7. (i) 9 cm   (ii) 12 cm   (iii) 20 m
8. (i) 8 cm   (ii) 20 m   (iii) 12 mm
9. (i) 24 cm   (ii) 22 cm²
10. (i) 124 cm²   (ii) 96 cm²   (iii) 1436 m²
11. (i) 36 m²   (ii) 27 m²
12. (i) 20 cm²   (ii) 15 cm²   (iii) 30 cm²
     (iv) 48 cm²   (v) 156 cm²   (vi) 36 cm²
13. (i) 42 cm²   (ii) 31.5 cm²   (iii) 120 cm²
14. A = 8 cm², B = 9 cm², C = 10 cm², D = 12 cm²
15. (i) 4   (ii) 10   (iii) 6
16. (i) 100 cm²   (ii) 182 cm²   (iii) 270 cm²
17. (i) 4.2 m²   (ii) 4.5 m²
18. 2100 cm²
19. (i) 1050 cm²   (ii) 352 m²
20. 50 cm²
21. (i) 252 cm²   (ii) 264 m²
22. (i) 13.5 m²   (ii) 9 m²
23. 10 m²   **24.** €84   **25.** €780

Exercise 9.4

1. (i) 12 cm³   (ii) 30 cm³   (iii) 63 cm³
2. (i) 32 cm²   (ii) 62 cm²   (iii) 102 cm²
3. (i) (a) 2304 cm³   (b) 1120 cm²
     (ii) (a) 7680 cm³   (b) 2368 cm²
     (iii) (a) 360 cm³   (b) 372 cm²
4. (i) 248 cm²   (ii) 474 cm²   (iii) 750 cm²
5. 84 more cubes
6. (iv) 88 cm²
7. (i) 125 cm³   (ii) 150 cm²
8. (i) 5 cm   (ii) 7 m   (iii) 20 cm
9. (i) 4 cm   (ii) 96 cm²
10. (i) 5 cm   (ii) 125 cm³
11. (i) 15   (ii) 405 cm³
12. (i) 6   (ii) 24
     (iii) 7   (iv) 168
13. (i) 3840 cm³   (ii) 60
14. 60

Exercise 9.5

1. (i) 64 cm³   (ii) 96 cm²
2. (i) 7 cm   (ii) closed   (iii) 672 cm³
     (iv) 472 cm²
3. (i) C   (ii) F   (iii) B
4. (i) C   (ii) B   (iii) F
5. (i) 126 cm³   (ii) 162 cm²
7. (i) 4cm × 9cm   (ii) 2 cm   (iii) 72 cm³
     (iv) 124 cm²

8.

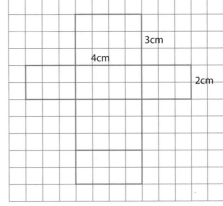

9. (i) Open   (ii) 1 936 cm³   (iii) 836 cm²

Test yourself 9

1. (i) 60 cm   (ii) 72 cm
     (iii) 39 cm   (iv) 92 cm
2. (i) 216 cm²   (ii) 260 cm²
     (iii) 67.5 cm²   (iv) 529 cm²
4. (i) 69 cm²   (ii) 90 m²   (iii) 165 mm²
5. X = 8 cm², Y = 6 cm², Z = 10 cm²
6. (i) 120 cm²   (ii) 196 cm²
     (iii) 300 cm²
7. (i) 106 m²   (ii) 117 m²
8. 5 cm
9. (i) 25 cm   (ii) 32 cm²
10. (ii) It is a square   (iii) 625 m²
11. (i) 576 cm³   (ii) 432 cm²
12. 4.5 cm
13. 125 cm
14. S.A = 150 cm² Vol = 125 cm³
15. (i) 31.6 cm³   (ii) 62.9 cm²
16. (i) 50 cm²   (ii) 15 cm²   (iii) 70%
17. (a) (i) 288 cm²   (ii) 192 cm²   (iii) 96 cm²
     (b) (i) $\frac{1}{2}$ (ii) $\frac{1}{3}$ (iii) $\frac{1}{6}$
18. (a) 50%   (b) (i) $\frac{1}{4}$ (ii) $\frac{1}{4}$
19. (i) 36.54%   (ii) 33.17%,   €975.69

Chapter 10: Geometry 1: Points – Angles – Lines

Exercise 10.1

3. (i) Line AB   (ii) Line segment [AB]
     (iii) Ray [AB   (iv) Ray [BA
5. (i) 4 cm   (ii) 4.5 cm
     (iii) 4.5 cm   (iv) 4.9 cm
6. (i) [AD]   (ii) [CB]   (iii) [AC]
7. (i) 2.85 cm   (ii) 45.6 m

Exercise 10.2

1. ∠ADC, ∠ABC, ∠NLM, ∠NML
2. ∠D, ∠B, ∠L, ∠M   3. River NILE
4. ∠ABC   5. HOW ARE YOU?
6. (i) Acute   (ii) Right
   (iii) Obtuse   (iv) Acute
7. A: acute, B: obtuse, C: acute, D: obtuse,
   E: reflex, F: acute
8. 360°, 180°, 90°, 120°, 60°, 30°
9. (i) $\frac{1}{4}$ (ii) $\frac{1}{2}$ (iii) $\frac{1}{12}$ (iv) $\frac{2}{3}$
10. (i) 90°   (ii) 180°   (iii) 30°   (iv) 240°
11. (i) 120°   (ii) 60°   (iii) 180°   (iv) 90°
    (v) 120°   (vi) 120°   (vii) 210°   (viii) 240°
12. (i) 120°   (ii) 75°   (iii) 135°   (iv) 105°

Exercise 10.3

1. (i) 110°   (ii) 150°   (iii) 80°   (iv) 20°
2. $A = 117°$, $B = 143°$, $C = 73°$, $D = 85°$,
   $E = 112°$, $F = 45°$
3. (i) 14°   (ii) 33°   (iii) 62°
4. $A = 140°$, $B = 130°$, $C = 100°$, $D = 70°$,
   $E = 215°$, $F = 23°$
5. (i) 30°   (ii) 40°   (iii) 18°
6. $A = 70°$, $B = 110°$, $C = 100°$, $D = 80°$,
   $E = 110°$, $F = 70°$
7. $a = 150°$, $b = 30°$, $c = 40°$, $d = 140°$,
   $e = 140°$, $f = 40°$, $g = 140°$
8. (i) 30°   (ii) 65°   (iii) 35°
9. (i) 120°   (ii) 40°   (iii) 30°
10. $A = 58°$, $B = 137°$
12. $A = 71°$, $B = 98°$, $C = 72°$
13. $a = 100°$, $b = 80°$, $c = 80°$, $d = 138°$, $e = 42°$,
    $f = 42°$, $g = 70°$, $h = 110°$, $i = 110°$, $j = 52°$,
    $k = 128°$, $l = 128°$
14. (i) (a) 100°   (b) 80°
    (ii) B is true

Exercise 10.4

1. (i) 5   (ii) 4   (iii) 7
   (iv) 7   (v) 6   (vi) 4
2. $A = 140°$, $B = 50°$, $C = 130°$, $D = 65°$, $E = 65°$
3. (i) 7   (ii) 6   (iii) 4
4. (i) (1, 3), (2, 4), (6, 7), (5, 8)
   (ii) (1, 7), (2, 5) etc.
   (iii) (3, 7), (4, 5)
5. $A = 40°$, $B = 140°$, $C = 60°$, $D = 120°$,
   $E = 120°$, $F = 60°$, $G = 120°$
6. $a = 110°$, $b = 70°$, $c = 50°$, $d = 50°$, $e = 36°$,
   $f = 72°$, $g = 72°$
7. $x = 104°$, $y = 104°$
8. $A = 110°$, $B = 70°$, $C = 50°$, $D = 130°$, $E = 134°$

9. (i) (c) is true
   (ii) angle a must be greater than or equal to 145°
10. (i) d (ii) g (iii) c
    (iv) d (v) f (vi) d
    (vii) e (viii) e (ix) h
    (x) f
11. $V = 58°$, $W = 60°$, $X = 62°$, $Y = 60°$, $Z = 60°$
12. $a = 50°$, $b = 50°$, $c = 42°$, $d = 44°$

Exercise 10.5

1. (i) 90°   (ii) AC
2. (i) PQ   (ii) SP and RQ
   (iii) PS
3. (i) [DC] and [HG]   (ii) [DH] and [CG]
   (iii) 3   (iv) [BC], [FG], [EF] etc
4. (i) T   (ii) F   (iii) T
   (iv) F   (v) T   (vi) T
8. (i) ∠D and ∠C (ii) [DC]   (iii) ∠A
   (iv) ∠E or ∠B   (v) ED ∥ BC
9. (i) River Road   (ii) Church Road
   (iii) Lacken Road and River Road
10. (i) 20°   (ii) 18°   (iii) 30°
11. $x = 90°$, $y = 20°$

Test yourself 10

1. (i) ∠ABC   (ii) ∠FIG
2. $x = 130°$, $y = 60°$, $z = 86°$
3. $a = 110°$, $b = 70°$, $c = 140°$, $d = 55°$, $e = 125°$
4. AB ∥ DE, AD ∥ BE; AD ⊥ AB, DE ⊥ BE etc
5. (a) 60°   (b) 150°   (c) 45°
6. $A = 50°$, $B = 140°$, $C = 50°$, $D = 70°$
7. $a = 40°$, $b = 80°$, $c = 48°$
8. $a = 70°$, $b = 110°$, $c = 70°$, $d = 108°$, $e = 72°$,
   $f = 108°$, $g = 84°$, $h = 96°$, $i = 84°$
9. $A = 125°$, $B = 44°$
11. $a = 40°$, $b = 90°$, $c = 50°$, $d = 40°$, $e = 60°$,
    $f = 60°$, $g = 60°$, $h = 60°$
12. $A = 70°$, $B = 50°$, $C = 60°$
13.

	Pair 1	Pair 2
1 pair of parallel lines	I, m	
2 pairs of alternate angles	G, F	C, P
2 pairs of corresponding angles	E, G	A, K
2 pairs of interior angles	J, G	M, C
2 pairs of supplementary angles	A, E	H, L
2 pairs of vertically opposite angles	A, J	H, I

Chapter 11: Ratio and Proportion

Exercise 11.1

1. (i) $\frac{5}{12}$ (ii) 5 : 7   (iii) 7 : 12
2. (i) 4 : 9   (ii) 1 : 3   (iii) 3 : 10
3. (i) 2   (ii) 8   (iii) 3
   (iv) 9   (v) 8
4. (i) 2 : 1   (ii) 3 : 1   (iii) 1 : 5
   (iv) 1 : 3   (v) 2 : 3
5. (i) 3 : 2   (ii) 5 : 8   (iii) 3 : 7
   (iv) 2 : 5   (v) 5 : 9
6. (i) 15   (ii) 25 ml   (iii) 600 g
   (iv) 600 ml   (v) 15
7. (i) 750 g   (ii) 6 eggs   (iii) 2000 g
   (iv) 10
8. (i) 6   (ii) 6   (iii) 4
   (iv) 21   (v) 1   (vi) 3
9. (i) 1 : 5   (ii) 5 : 14   (iii) 1 : 4
   (iv) 1 : 5   (v) 1 : 3   (vi) 3 : 1
10. (i) 2 : 3   (ii) 3 : 5
11. (i) 1 : 4   (ii) 1 : 6   (iii) 3 : 1
   (iv) 2 : 7
12. (i) 1 : 4   (ii) 2 : 1   (iii) 1 : 3
   (iv) 1 : 2   (v) 1 : 2   (vi) 5 : 8
   (vii) 6 : 7   (viii) 4 : 5
13. (i) 24   (ii) $2\frac{1}{2}$ (iii) 3

Exercise 11.2

1. (i) $\frac{2}{5}$ (ii) $\frac{3}{5}$
   (iii) Anna – €36, Billy – €54
2. Claire – €250, Dara – €150
3. 16
4. Pat – 24; Emer – 12
5. (i) €90, €30   (ii) €306, €408
   (iii) €66, €55   (iv) €74.55, €31.95
   (v) €480, €384   (vi) 81 mins, 9 mins
6. €800, €400, €200   7. 40
8. Beet – 39. barley – 52
9. €231   10. 13
11. 70 cm   12. 288
13. (i) 70   (ii) 90   (iii) 105
14. (i) 40 kg   (ii) 10 kg   (iii) 18
15. 30 home wins and 5 draws
16. €2880
17. (i) 27   (ii) 36
18. (i) 400 g   (ii) 80 g
19. Alan – €3240, Emer – €2160; Alan – €3000, Emer – €2400
20. (i) 5 : 7   (ii) 25 : 49
21. 3 : 1
22. 195

Exercise 11.3

1. (i) 2 : 3   (ii) $\frac{3}{5}$ (iii) 40%
2. (i) $\frac{7}{10}$ (ii) 30%   (iii) 7 : 3
3. (ii) $\frac{3}{4}$ (iii) $\frac{2}{3}$ (iv) $\frac{7}{10}$
   (v) $\frac{4}{7}$ (vi) Boys
4. (i) $\frac{1}{6}$ (ii) $\frac{5}{6}$ (iii) 1 : 5
5. (i) and (iii)
6. (i)

x	5	7	9
y	10	14	18

   (ii)

x	8	9	11
y	24	27	33

   (iii)

x	10	18	30
y	5	9	15

7. €71.10   8. €10.12   9. €54.95
10. €688   11. 250 km   12. 270 g
13. (i) €162   (ii) 23 hours
14. (i) 280 km   (ii) 120 km
15. (i) 625 g   (ii) 10
   (iii) 300 g
16. (i) 75 mins   (ii) 176 km
17. (i) €42   (ii) 250 km
18. (i) 5 m   (ii) 3.5 cm
19. (i) 400   (ii) $4\frac{1}{2}$ mins

Exercise 11.4

1. (i) 37.5 miles   (ii) 50 km
   (a) 65 km/h   (b) 162 km/h
2. (i) 17.5 cm   (ii) 10 in
   (iii) 90 cm   (iv) 32 in
3. (i) 27 l   (ii) $4\frac{1}{2}$ gal   (iii) 81 l
4. (i) €73   (ii) €86   (iii) 325 units
   (iv) 650 units   (v) €20 (Fixed charge)
5. (i) 9 kg   (ii) $4\frac{1}{2}$ kg   (iii) 9 pounds
   (iv) 14 pounds
6. (i) 11 cm   (ii) 17.5 cm   (iii) 31 g
   (iv) 2.5 cm   (v) 53%
7. (i) 86°F   (ii) 10°C   (iii) 113°F
   (iv) 32°C   (v) 65.5°C
8. (i) (a) 2.25 l   (b) 2 l   (c) 0.95 l
   (ii) (a) 5.3 pints   (b) 2.65 pints
   (c) 1.6 pints
   (iii) 8.4 l

Exercise 11.5

1. (i) €1.04   (ii) €0.98   (iii) Value pack
2. 80-bag box
3. (i) €1.28   (ii) €1.20   (iii) Large   (iv) Lighter

4. S: €0.90; M: €0.77; L: €0.82; EL: €0.88; Medium
5. Family size **6.** 1.5 l
7. Large size **8.** 24, 8
9. (i) 18 days (ii) 6 days **10.** 9 days
11. (i) 20 days (ii) 5 days (iii) 8 days
12. 45 **13.** 16 days
14. (i) 6 days (ii) 20 days **15.** (i) 9 days (ii) 12
16. (i) 6 days (ii) 9 **17.** (i) 18 days (ii) 45
18. (i) $\frac{1}{12}$ (ii) $\frac{1}{6}$ (iii) $\frac{1}{4}$ (iv) 4 mins

Test yourself 11

1. (i) 1 : 6 (ii) 2 : 3 (iii) 2 : 3
(iv) 3 : 4 (v) 3 : 2
2. (i) $\frac{7}{9}$ (ii) $\frac{2}{9}$
(iii) Ava – €70, Barry – €20
3. (i) $\frac{4}{9}$ (ii) 4 : 9 (iii) 81 cm^2
4. (i) 500 g (ii) 125 g (iii) 10
5. 45 l **6.** 240 tigers
7. €462 **8.** €83.25
9. (i) L – €2.16, S – €2.28, E – €2.26, T – €3.10
(ii) L, E, S, T
10. Sarah – €150, Jack – €300, Ciara – €450
11. 9
12. (i) 20% (ii) 1 : 4
13. (i) 15 (ii) 7 (iii) 1
14. (i) 75 kg (ii) 20 kg
15. 275 km **16.** 80°, 60°, 40°
17. (i) 231 km (ii) 60 litres
18. 750 g **19.** €5.76
20. (i) Yes, straight line through (0, 0)
(ii) 0.5 A (iii) 1.0 A

Chapter 12: Statistics

Exercise 12.1

1. (i) 15 (ii) 21
2. (i) 13 (ii) 51 (iii) White
3. (i) A = 28, B = 12, C = 23, D = 5, E = 2
(ii) Walk (iii) $\frac{1}{14}$ (iv) Car and Bus
4. (i) N (ii) N (iii) C
(iv) C (v) N
5. (i) C (ii) N
6. (ii) 9 (iii) Red (iv) Blue
7. (i) 10 years (ii) 10
(iii) 11 (iv) 8
8. (i) Saloon car, €20 000, 50 km/h.
(ii) Saloon car (categorical), €20 000
(numerical), 50 km/h (numerical).
9. Numerical [How many times?, how many
children, time to travel]
Categorical [preferred activity]
10. (i) 10 (ii) 6–10 (iii) 17

Exercise 12.3

3. B more suitable **5.** (i) Too personal
10. B is better
11. (i) Too personal
(ii) Leading question
(iii) Not specific enough considering the time-
frame of one week

Test yourself 12

1. (i) C (ii) N (iii) C
(iv) C (v) N (vi) C
2. (i) N (ii) C (iii) N (iv) N
3. Numerical [size / cost]
Categorical [colour / style]
4. (i) P (ii) S (iii) P
(iv) S (v) P
5. $33\frac{1}{3}$% **7.** All leading questions
8. As most of the people there would have driven
due to the location.

Chapter 13: Coordinates

Exercise 13.1

1. A(3, 9), B(9, 5), C(10, 1), D(11, 3)
2. A(2, 1), B(12, 1), C(12, 5), D(9, 8), E(7, 7),
F(5, 3), G(2, 3)
3. A(1, 2), B(2, 8), C(3, 4), D(3, 2), E(6, 1), F(10, 2),
G(8, 4), H(5, 5), I(7, 7), J(10, 7), K(6, 9), L(9, 10)
4. a square
5. (i) (a) DOG (b) HORSE (c) MONKEY
(ii) (a) LIFFEY (b) BOYNE (c) SLANEY
6. (i) (a) (8, 2) (b) (7, 5) (c) (4, 4)
(ii) (a) Caves (b) Pool (c) Pier
(d) Evergreen tree
7. x-axis
8. (0, 1), (0, 4), (0, −3), (0, −7), etc
9. (i) (a) (2, 7) (b) (9, 6) (c) (4, 4) (d) (0, 5)
(ii) Telephone box
(iii) Pub and church
(iv) Bus stop and telephone box
(v) (3, 0), (6, 0), (6, 2), (3, 2)

Exercise 13.2

1. A(2, 2), B(3, 3), C(5, 3), D(5, 1), E(3, 1), F(−2, 3),
G(−4, 2), H(−3, 1), I(−4, −1), J(−2, −1),
K(−3, −2), L(3, −1), M(4, −3), N(1, −2)
3. (i) D(−2, −3) (ii) S(−1, −2)
4. (i) A(5, 2), B(2, 4)
(ii) J(−4, −2), G(−2, −3)
(iii) L(2, −1), H(4, −1)
(iv) F(−3, 0), I(4, 0)
(v) C(0, 1), K(0, −2)

5. A –1st, B– 4th, C – 3rd, D – 3rd

6. (i) *x*-axis   (ii) *y*-axis   (iii) *x*-axis
    (iv) *y*-axis   (v) both axes

7. (ii) (2, 4)

8. (iii) D(−1, 2)

9. (i) (11, 9), (13, 10)
    (ii) (11, 8), (13, 10)
    (iii) (8, −2), (9, −4)
    (iv) (−8, −6), (−10, −9)

10. (i) The *x*-coordinate and *y*-coordinate
      together add up to 8
    (ii) (7, 1), (0, 8), (−2, 10)

11. A(5, −3), B(−3, −3), C(−2, 3), D(3, 0), E(0, −2)

12. A(3, 2), B(7, −3)

13. (2 km WEST, 6 km SOUTH)

14. (i) (6, 4), (9, 6)   (ii) (12, 8)   (iii) (15, 10)

Exercise 13.3

1. (i) A(−4, 3), B(2, 3), C(2, −1), D(−4, −3)
    (ii) (a) (−1, 3)   (b) (2, 1)   (c) (−4, 0)

2. (i) A(−2, 5), B(4, 5), C(4, −3)
    (ii) (a) (1, 5)   (b) (4, 1)
    (iii) D (−2, −3)

3. (i) (4, 3)
    (ii) Add the *x*-values and divide by two and do
      likewise with the *y*-values

4. (i) (3, 2)   (ii) (3, 3)   (iii) (2, 4)
    (iv) (5, 2)   (v) (3, 3)   (vi) (3, 1)

5. (i) $\left(3, \frac{5}{2}\right)$

6. (i) (2, 4)   (ii) (4, 3)   (iii) (2, 1)
    (iv) (2, 5)   (v) (2, 1)   (vi) (3, −3)

7. (1, 0); *x*-axis

8. (i) (4, 0)   (ii) (1, −1)   (iii) $\left(-\frac{1}{2}, -\frac{1}{2}\right)$

9. (i) (−1, 0)   (ii) Yes it is

10. (0, 2)   **11.** (5, 4)

Exercise 13.4

1. *a* – positive, *b* – positive, *c* – negative,
    d – positive, *e* – negative, *f* – negative

2. (i) *b* & *c*   (ii) *a* & *d*

3. (i) $\frac{2}{3}$ (ii) $\frac{3}{2}$ (iii) $2\left(\frac{4}{2}\right)$

4. (i) 3   (ii) 2   (iii) 1

5. Because the line is falling (from left to right);
    $-\frac{3}{2}$

6. $a = -3, b = -2, c = -1$

7. (i) Slope [*AB*] $= -\frac{3}{5}$
    (ii) Slope [*CD*] $= \frac{4}{7}$
    (iii) Slope [*EF*] $= -\frac{1}{7}$

8. (i) 1   (ii) 4   (iii) $\frac{5}{3}$
    (iv) $\frac{1}{2}$ (v) −3   (vi) $-\frac{3}{2}$
    (vii) $\frac{8}{3}$ (viii) $-\frac{7}{3}$ (ix) 3

9. Proof

10. (i) $\frac{1}{20}$ (ii) 6 m

11. 60 m

Test yourself 13

1. (i) A(3, 10), B(11, 10), C(14, 7), D(12, 7),
      E(2, 7), F(0, 7), G(2, 1)
    (ii) (3, 1), (3, 6), (6, 6), (6, 1)

2. (i) (a) (2, 1)   (b) (−2, 1)   (c) (−3, −1)
      (d) (0, −1)
    (ii) Post office, bus station, park

3. a quadrilateral (trapezium)

4. A(2, 4), B(3, 2), C(2, −1), D(−1, 3), E(−4, 2),
    F(−4, −1), G(−2, −3), H(4, −3)

5. (i) A(−3, 4), B(1, 4), C(1, −2)
    (ii) D(−3, −2)
    (iii) (a) (−1, 4)   (b) (1, 1)   (c) (−1, 1)

6. a & $\frac{1}{2}$, b & 1, c & 2.

7. (0, 3), (0, 1), $\left(2, \frac{1}{2}\right)$

8. (i) 3   (ii) −2   (iii) (1, 2)

9. (i) A(4, 1), B(8, 5)   (ii) 1   (iii) −1

Chapter 14: Solving Equations

Exercise 14.1

1. 2   **2.** 7   **3.** 11   **4.** 12

5. 13   **6.** 12   **7.** 12   **8.** 6

9. 6   **10.** 6   **11.** 4   **12.** 35

13. 8   **14.** 24   **15.** 4   **16.** 12 g

17. 8 g   **18.** 9 g   **19.** 8 g   **20.** 5 g

21. 4 g   **22.** 8 g

Exercise 14.2

1. (i) $x + 2$ (ii) $x + 4$ (iii) $x - 3$
    (iv) $x - 10$ (v) $x + 14$ (vi) $2x$
    (vii) $5x$ (viii) $2x + 2$

2. (i) $x + 6 = 12$ (ii) $x - 7 = 10$
    (iii) $2x = 14$ (iv) $2x + 5 = 19$
    (v) $3x - 6 = 15$ (vi) $4(x + 2) = 28$

3. (i) $3n + 7 = 19$ (ii) $4n - 5 = 17$
    (iii) $4(n + 3) = 28$ (iv) $3(n - 2) = 9$

Exercise 14.3

1. (i) 12 g   (ii) 6 g

2. $x = 6$ **3.** $x = 12$ **4.** $x = 5$

5. $x = 8$ **6.** $x = 11$ **7.** $x = 10$

8. $x = 8$ **9.** $x = 11$ **10.** $x = 8$

11. $x = 4$ **12.** $x = 5$ **13.** $x = 3$

14. $x = 5$ **15.** $x = 5$ **16.** $x = 4$
17. $x = 2$ **18.** $x = 5$ **19.** $x = 2$
20. $x = 4$ **21.** $x = 11$ **22.** $x = 7$
23. $x = 4$ **24.** $x = 4$ **25.** $x = 5$
26. $x = 3$ **27.** $x = 2$ **28.** $x = 3$
29. $x = 7$ **30.** $x = 6$ **31.** $x = 4$
32. $x = 1$ **33.** $x = 4$ **34.** $x = 10$
35. 6 **36.** 6 **37.** 6
38. 8 **39.** 3
40. (i) $x = 4$ (ii) $x = 6$ (iii) $x = 8$

Exercise 14.4

1. $7x + 4 = 3x + 20; x = 4$
2. $x = 4$ **3.** $x = 5$ **4.** $x = 6$
5. $x = 3$ **6.** $x = 5$ **7.** $x = 1$
8. $x = 6$ **9.** $x = 5$ **10.** $x = 3$
11. $x = 8$ **12.** $x = 6$ **13.** $x = 7$
14. $x = 7$ **15.** $x = 5$ **16.** $x = 9$
17. (i) 3 (ii) 2
18. 7 cm
19. 180°; (i) 35° (ii) 30° (iii) 50°
20. RABBIT

Exercise 14.5

1. $x = 3$ **2.** $x = 4$ **3.** $x = 2$
4. $x = 3$ **5.** $x = 5$ **6.** $x = 6$
7. $x = 2$ **8.** $x = 5$ **9.** $x = 10$
10. $x = 6$ **11.** $x = 1$ **12.** $x = 10$
13. $x = 10$ **14.** $x = 3$ **15.** $x = 3$
16. $x = 4$ **17.** $x = 5$ **18.** $x = 3$
19. 2 **20.** 5

Exercise 14.6

1. 6 **2.** 7 **3.** 8
4. 3 **5.** 4 **6.** 3
7. 27, 32 **8.** 6 **9.** 7, 12
10. (i) 7 (ii) 5 (iii) $\frac{4}{5}$
11. 4 **12.** 7 **13.** 4, 10
14. Mary = 23, Ann = 28
15. (i) 6 (ii) 12 (iii) 23
16. (i) $x = 44°$ (ii) $x = 29°$
17. 16 years old
18. (i) $3(a + 5) + 3(a + 5) + 4(2a + 1) = 76$
(ii) $a = 3$ (iii) 24 cm
19. (i) $(x - 7)$ years (ii) $(2x - 7)$ years
(iii) 13 years old

Test yourself 14

1. (i) $x = 2$ (ii) $x = 1$ (iii) $x = 2$
2. 12
3. (i) $x = 4$ (ii) $x = 7$

4. (i) $x = 3$ (ii) $x = 6$ (iii) $x = 5$
5. 9 **6.** 4 cm
7. (i) $x = 6$ (ii) $x = 6$ (iii) $x = 3$
8. 10 cm **9.** 14
10. (i) $x = 4$ (ii) $x = 0$
11. 3 **12.** 6
13. (i) 11 (ii) 6 **14.** 3

Chapter 15: Geometry 2 – Triangles

Exercise 15.1

1. (i) 55° (ii) 43° (iii) 82°
(iv) 5 cm (v) 6 cm (vi) 7 cm
2. 32°
4. $A = 30°, B = 56°, C = 19°, D = 49°$
5. $A = 45°, B = 70°, C = 28°, D = 99°, E = 28°,$
$F = 72°, G = 58°, H = 19°$
6. $A = 110°, B = 101°, C = 30°, D = 141°,$
$E = 118°, F = 68°$
7. (i) $a = 55°, b = 100°$
(ii) $a = 100°, b = 55°$
(iii) $a = 70°, b = 110°$
8. $x = 120°, y = 85°$
9. $a = 78°, b = 42°, c = 60°, d = 102°, e = 78°$
10. As a reflex angle is greater than 180°

Exercise 15.2

1. 4 and 5; (i) 5 (ii) 4 (iii) 180°
2. $A = 138°, B = 64°, C = 119°, D = 120°,$
$E = 79°, F = 115°$
3. (i) 70° (ii) 70° (iii) 54°
4. (i) $x = 50°, y = 45°$
(ii) $x = 65°, y = 50°$
(iii) $x = 45°, y = 70°$
5. both 56°
6. $x = 70°, y = 68°$

Exercise 15.3

1. $\triangle$PQT, $\triangle$QRT, $\triangle$TRS
2. (i) Isosceles
(ii) Equilateral
(iii) $\triangle$BEC
3. (i) Isosceles
(ii) Equilateral
(iii) Right-angled
(iv) Right-angled isosceles
(v) Scalene
4. 2 and 3; 5 and 6; 7 and 9; b and c; x and z;
p and r; d and e; m and n
5. $A = 70°, B = 72°, C = 55°, D = 68°, E = 70°,$
$F = 30°, G = 40°, H = 112°, I = 70°, J = 60°,$
$K = 90°, L = 70°$

6. (i) Equilateral   (ii) 60°
(iii) 88°

7. (i) 140°   (ii) 80°
(iii) 60°

8. (i) Isosceles   (ii) 74°
(iii) 60°   (iv) 46°

9. (i) 56°   (ii) 80°   (iii) 62°

10. $c = 64°$, $d = 52°$

Test yourself 15

1. $a = 55°$, $b = 80°$, $c = 37°$, $d = 65°$
2. $A = 50°$, $B = 70°$, $C = 70°$
3. $a = 60°$, $b = 45°$, $c = 105°$, $d = 37.5°$,
$e = 37.5°$
4. $A = 50°$, $B = 115°$
5. 60°; as each angle is 60°
6. (i) F   (ii) T   (iii) F
(iv) F   (v) F

Chapter 16: Presenting Data

Exercise 16.1

1. (i) a football match   (ii) 30
(iii) 6   (iv) 13   (v) 2   (vi) 4
2. (ii) 25   (iii) bus   (iv) 32%
4. (ii) 28   (iii) 11   (iv) 25%

Exercise 16.2

1. (i) 5   (ii) white   (iii) 30
(iv) $\frac{1}{6}$ (v) 20%
2. (i) Dog   (ii) 36   (iii) 25%
(iv) fish   (v) $\frac{1}{12}$
3. (i) 16   (ii) 100   (iii) $\frac{2}{25}$
(iv) 24%   (v) 12
4. (i) 32, 48, 48, 36   (ii) 2nd year
(iii) 4th year   (iv) 1st and 3rd year
(v) 1st year   (vi) $\frac{3}{8}$
5. (i) 7   (ii) History
(iii) 3   (iv) 20%
(v) French and English
7. (i) 60   (ii) 18   (iii) $\frac{1}{5}$
(iv) 40%   (v) 2
8. (i) 5   (ii) 6   (iii) 20%   (iv) 2
9. (i) Swimming   (ii) 74
10. Can't tell
11. (i) Week B   (ii) Week A   (iii) Week C

Exercise 16.3

1. (i) 20   (ii) 93   (iii) 5
(iv) 4   (v) 3

2. (i) 7   (ii) 7   (iii) $\frac{1}{5}$
(iv) 4   (v) 24
3. (i) 26 sec   (ii) 8   (iii) 24
(iv) 39 sec   (v) 68 sec   (vi) 45 sec
(vii) 9
4. (ii) 8   (iii) 10   (iv) 28
5. (ii) 5   (iii) 56   (iv) 25%
6. (ii) 11   (iii) 37   (iv) 8
(v) 36
7. (i) 22.5 sec   (ii) 10   (iii) 8
(iv) 5.2 sec   (v) 20%
8. (ii) 15 years old
(iii) 9   (iv) 34
9. (i) 6   (ii) 26   (iii) 34
10. (ii) 3.9 g   (iii) 10   (iv) 4.6 g
11. (ii) (a) 44   (b) 9
12. (i) Lowest – 0, highest – 35

Test yourself 16

1. (i) 10   (ii) 3   (iii) 4
(iv) $\frac{7}{10}$ (v) 75%
2. (ii) 3
3. (i) Size 5   (ii) 35
(iii) $\frac{2}{7}$ (v) Bar chart
4. (i) Tony   (ii) Darren
(iii) Brian   (iv) Pat
5. (i) 26   (ii) 49
(iii) 8   (iv) 20%

Chapter 17: Transformation Geometry

Exercise 17.1

7. (i) C   (ii) B   (iii) C   (iv) [BC]
8. 3, 2
9. (i) 2   (ii) 3   (iii) 4
11. (i) B   (ii) [BC]   (iii) △BCE   (iv) [BE]
12. (i) F   (ii) [GB]   (iii) △FBE
(iv) [DC]   (v) [BE]

Exercise 17.2

1. (i) and (iii)
2. (i) 4   (ii) 1   (iii) 1
(iv) 2   (v) 1   (vi) 3
3. 1, 1, 1, 1, 1, 0, 0, 2, 0, 0, 0, 0, 1, 2, 0
6. 4
9. (i) All have vertical axis of symmetry
(ii) T, I, V, W, X
10. (i) All have horizontal axis of symmetry
(ii) D, H, I, X, K   (iii) X, H, I

13. (i) H (ii) F (iii) [EF]
    (iv) [EH] (v) [GE]
14. (i) F (ii) [EF] (iii) [FC]
    (iv) [BF] (v) [EC]
15. (i) C (ii) [BC] (iii) [BO]
    (iv) [OD] (v) △BOE (vi) △BOC
    (vii) △DOF (viii) figure EADO
16. 5:05   19. E

Exercise 17.3

6. (i), (iii) and (v)
8. (i) C (ii) B (iii) [CD]
   (iv) [DA] (v) [CO] (vi) △COB
   (vii) △COD (viii) △CDB
9. (i) $Sy(F_1)$ (ii) $Sx(F_2)$ (iii) $Sy(F_3)$
   (iv) $So(F_1)$
10. (i) B (ii) [CB] (iii) [CD]
    (iv) △BAM (v) △CMD (vi) △ACD
11. upside down; (i) No (ii) Yes

12. (i) Axial symmetry (A.S) (ii) A.S.
    (iii) Translation
    (iv) Central symmetry (C.S.)
    (v) Translation (vi) C.S.

Test yourself 17

1. (i) (a) A.S. in the y-axis
       (b) A.S. in the x-axis
       (c) C.S. in the origin
2. (i) Yes, yes, no, yes
   (ii) (a) A(2, 4), B(2, 1), C(7, 1)
       (b) A'(−2, 4), B'(−2, 1), C'(−7, 1)
3. (i) (a) 2 (b) 3 (c) 1
   (ii) (a) C (b) △BOA (c) [DC]
4. (ii) (a) A (b) B (c) C
5. (i) 4
   (ii) (a) $\overrightarrow{YZ}$ (b) Y
       (c) △ZTQ (d) [YX]